BRAIN STORMS

BRAIN STORMS

A STUDY OF HUMAN SPONTANEITY

BY WAYNE BARKER, M.D.

GROVE PRESS, INC.,   NEW YORK

Permission is gratefully acknowledged for quotations as follows:

Doubleday & Company, Inc., Hellen Keller, *The Story of My Life*.
W. W. Norton & Company, Inc., Anthony Burgess, *Tremor of Intent*.
The University of Chicago Press, George Herbert Mead, *Mind, Self, and Society;* C. Judson Herrick, *The Brain of the Tiger Salamander* and *George Ellett Coghill*.
Librairie Ernest Flammarion, Henri Poincaré, *Science et Méthode*.
Harcourt, Brace & World, Inc., William Golding, *The Hot Gates and Other Occasional Pieces*.
The Viking Press, Inc., Franz A. Roedelberger and Vera I. Groschoff, *African Wildlife*.
United Feature Syndicate, Charles M. Schulz, "Peanuts" cartoon from *But We Love You, Charlie Brown*.

DEDICATION

To the memory of two people, each of whom struggled constantly to survive and to grow, each dying in circumstances of great promise and peril, both fighting to the end, which came when this book was going to press:

To Martin Luther King, who saw, taught, and acted upon his belief that what counts is not the duration of life but its quality.

To Catherine Wheeler Davis, who in her three short years was Life, contending against impossible odds, who for a brief while gave to the Spirit of Life "a local habitation and a name."

ACKNOWLEDGMENTS

The University of Chicago, The New York Hospital–Cornell University Medical Center, The Bronx (N.Y.) Veterans Administration Hospital, and the Riverside Hospital of the New York City Department of Hospitals provided me with space and facilities for various aspects of my work and thought. The William H. Wilder and Commonwealth funds furnished fellowships and the Veterans Administration Research Council provided a grant for research. The University of Leeds Medical School and the National Technical Library at Thorpe Arch in England provided facilities for necessary additional library work.

I am indebted to many teachers who shaped the course of my explorations. Some of them, like Drs. George W. Bartelmez and Ralph W. Gerard, encouraged me to formulate my own questions about human brain function and behavior. Others, like Drs. Oskar Diethelm and Harold G. Wolff, confronted me with the desirability of studying brain function in life as well as in the laboratory.

I am grateful especially to Dr. Douglas N. Buchanan, who introduced me to the great intellectual tradition hidden behind the dry visage of clinical neurology. He also taught that "neurology is not a science; it's a sport like trout fishing," and helped me to see that behind the term "fit" played all the fitting-together capacity of the brain, mind, and person.

My family endured when they could not enjoy, and sometimes even encouraged being put aside for "the book." Harold and Maynatalie Rosenberg provided friendly encouragement when it was needed. Other friends, advisers on writing, and research assistants were very helpful and deserve mention, but they are too numerous for more than mere listing—and that would be scant thanks. I thank them all in expressing my gratitude to Dr. Lucian F. Capobianco, who helped me tolerate the psychosomatic accompaniments to crises in writing.

Patsy Southgate has my unreserved appreciation and affection for editorial assistance and support, "without which this book might not have . . ."

—W.B.

CONTENTS

The Relation of "When?" to the How, Why, and
Where of the Transformation of Neuronal Activities Within the Brain into Behaviors and Experiences of the Individual.

PART ONE/THE CONCEPT OF FITS

A Fit of Spelling Combining Obscenity and Wit,
Compliance and Defiance. A Fit or an Act? The
Problem of Spontaneity in Ideas and Actions.

Shifting the Emphasis from Fits as Symptoms of
Medical Disease to Fits as Products of the Brain's
Fitting-Together Capacity. Fits as Modes of "Mind-
ing" Crises.

A Galaxy of Meanings Converge and Diverge at
the Term "Fit" in the Same Way that a Galaxy of
Behaviors Approach and Depart from an Unde-
finable but Theoretically Central "Fit."

An Example of the Fitting Together of Contradictory and Ambiguous—"Dysjunctive"—Elements
in a Crisis.

PART THREE/THE CONCEPTS OF DYSJUNCTIVE SITUATIONS, DYSJUNCTIVE BRAIN FUNCTION, AND DYSJUNCTIVE BEHAVIOR AND EXPERIENCE

and-Now and Not-Here and Not-Now, and of Noetic and Poetic Processes in Fitting Together of
Living.

The Fitting Together of Living by Transformations of Contradictions in Mind-Body Patterns
into Temporal Courses of Minding and Doing.

The Relation of "When?" to the How, Why, and Where
of the Transformation of Neuronal Activities Within the
Brain into Behaviors and Experiences of the Individual.

INTRODUCTION

This book arose from extensive and intensive study of *fits*—epileptic, epileptiform, nonepileptic but symptomatic, and nonsymptomatic paroxysmal attenuations and intensifications of awareness and action ranging from fits of convulsion to fits of creation. In its historical relations, the book is an essay at resolving some of the contradictions between and within the work and thought of Sigmund Freud and John Hughlings Jackson on the sources of episodic nocturnal behaviors and experiences (dreams) and diurnal distortions of action and awareness (fits).

Both Freud and Jackson were concerned with dreams and fits, and with less obvious lapses and excesses of knowing, feeling, and doing. Both devoted some of their most speculative play of the mind to the problem of how covert integrative processes of brain, mind, and person are converted into overt activities. Jackson said, "Find out about dreams, and you will find out about insanity." Later, Freud echoed this view in his statement, "Dreams contain the psychology of the neuroses in a nutshell." Freud thought of the convulsive fit as a device by which energies that could not be managed "psychically" were disposed of. Jackson saw in convulsive actions a condensation of the contention between many incipient movements. All action, he said, begins in dreams.

Freud believed that epileptiform fits, like dreams, symbolized or expressed basic unrecognized emotional conflicts. Jackson held that fits represented a "survival of the fittest" of tendencies contending on a subverbal level of "thinking." But from this essential operational unity, the interests and the terminologies of the great intuitive Viennese philosopher of the mind and the great British pragmatist about the brain seem markedly to diverge. For both were ardent adherents of the doctrine of *psychophysical parallelism,* and took supposedly opposing sides. Indeed, Freud quoted Jackson to the effect that "In all our studies of diseases of the nervous system we must be on our guard against the fallacy that what are physical states in lower centres fine away *into* psychical states in higher centres; that, for example, vibrations of sensory nerves *become* sensations, or that somehow or other an idea produces movement."

Yet despite their oft-repeated assertions of belief in a never-the-twain-shall-meet theory of separateness between the physical and psychical, both understood that mind depends on brain, that cerebration and mentation proceed hand in hand as well as side by side, and that in practical affairs ideas do lead to actions and vice versa. And both began and abandoned work leading perhaps to a psychology of the brain, a physiology of the mind, and eventually to a psychophysiology of the brain-mind-person system.

In 1895, Freud wrote a description of his efforts to prevent the threatened estrangement of psychology from physiology, but did not publish it because, according to his biographer Ernest Jones, he may have concluded that his attempt was wildly premature if not altogether vain. Jackson began but abandoned his projected interpretation of fits (as products of intracerebral fitting together rather than as diagnostically significant *things*) because "I feel that it requires more skill than I possess to make my subject clear to those who have long worked at epilepsy from a totally different point of view."

Conceiving, composing, and communicating hypotheses for resolving the mind-body problem (more accurately, a mind-matter problem) is difficult at any time, and was, perhaps, premature in the late nineteenth century. At any rate, Freud and Jackson each tried to stick to his own side of the street and to work it thoroughly. Jackson held to his view that all psychological explanations of physical events are merely verbal; Freud continued to work from his position that mental events could not be satisfactorily dealt with in terms like "cortical excitation" but must be explained in the language of psychology. Nevertheless, both men were deeply concerned with what went on in the daily lives of their patients, with the relationship between symptoms and the everyday processes from which they arose, and most importantly with episodes which occupied a no man's land between slight symptoms and slight breaks in the continuity of seemingly normal activity. They were both humanly and intellectually interested, that is, in the minor lapses and excesses of normal action and awareness, and the problem of what these "larval," "subclinical," quasi symptoms are symptomatic of.

For in these "thousand shocks the flesh is heir to"—in the

psychopathology of everyday life behavior, the physiopathology of normal brain function—lie the questions if not the answers leading to an understanding of the mind-body problem through close examination of the very slightest discontinuities in the operations of the larger body-brain-mind-person system. And it is in their concern with the little psychopathologies of everyday life and "the slightest departures" from continuity of ordinary knowing, feeling, and doing that the interests of Freud and Jackson converge again, and converge by focusing upon the vagaries of the processes transforming unconscious-neurophysiological happenings into intra- and interpersonal events. Both men believed that close observation and analysis of momentary derangements of bodily and personal functioning would reveal the processes generating both ordinary and extraordinary behavior and experience.

Jackson's views are less well known than Freud's, and it is useful to quote him on his aims:

> The great object I have had in view . . . has been to study the relations of epilepsy or epileptiform seizures to simpler diseases of the nervous system, and *through the latter to normal states* . . . This is just the opposite of the ordinary method. . . . The question commonly put about a case is solely "Is it a case of epilepsy?" . . . Cases are often investigated solely in order to see if the symptoms reach or approach certain Clinical Entities, and not at all as they are signs of *departure* from health. . . . We want positive information as to how a convulsion is a *departure* from health . . . and not how far it *approaches* our idea of the almost metaphysical conception of "genuine" epilepsy . . .

At this point it is essential to grasp that Jackson's "slightest departures" are identical, operationally at least, with Freudian slips of the mind, tongue, and hand—that both are what might be called little fits, and that these little fits are produced by the brain-mind system to preserve and restore the continuity of its operations when that continuity is threatened by a sudden coming together of a momentarily "unthinkable" complex of contending ideas, images, and impulses. For a key, if undeveloped, insight of both Freud and Jackson was that dreams, fits, and lesser distortions of action and awareness were fitted-together in crises in the continuity of integrative activity, and were fitted into incipient gaps in order to restore that continuity.

To Freud, small gaps in or additions to the smooth flow of everyday activity were examples of successful management of momentarily problematical conflicts and tensions. Jackson's "slightest departures," examples of small fits, were to Freud minor examples of wit. They were small models of the situations and processes associated with the production of dreams, unusually witty solutions to problems, psychoneurotic symptoms, and acts of creation.

In his *Interpretation of Dreams* and his *Psychopathology of Every-Day Life* Freud started with the idea that dreams were disguised wish-fulfillment. He concluded, however, that dreaming was a protective maneuver by which crises in the sleeper's awareness were smoothed over. He said, "The whole matter resolves itself into a platitude. Dreams all seek to fulfill *one* wish, which has got transformed into many others. It is the wish to sleep. One dreams so as not to have to wake, because one wants to sleep."

Just who the "one" is that dreams so that another "one" will not have to wake, Freud did not say. But this is the kind of "psychologizing"—personification of a psychophysiological process—that Jackson most objected to. He would hardly have opposed the purposiveness of dreaming; rather he would probably have preferred some formulation such as: Dreaming is the transformation of a contention between numerous faint ideas on the subverbal, subimage level into patterns of action and awareness consistent with persistence of sleep in circumstances otherwise consistent with waking.

The tendency inherent in all of us to explain our troubles in terms of difficulties with things and with other persons instead of deficiencies in the form, content, and relevance of our way of dealing with things and persons no doubt had something to do with the subsequent *reification* of the Freudian Unconscious as a thing-in-itself, and the *personification* of the Unconscious as a distinct and significant personality functioning as a "bad twin." Certainly, because analysis of dreams revealed that the disruptions threatening sleep derived from the sleeper's unrecognized problems of living, emphasis shifted from the protective function of dreams to their usefulness as an indicator of unconscious problems and conflicts. And eventually psychoanalytic tendencies for personification led to Freud's trinity of Id, Ego, and Super-Ego—a trend continued today in Sullivan's Bad Me, Good Me, and Not Me, and in Eric Berne's Child, Adult, and Parent.

Our failure to break out of this anthropocentric ideological prison is understandable. Thinking about thinking is difficult, if not literally impossible. Most of us think in words put together in more or less grammatically and syntactically correct phrases and sentences. Some few carry on this secondary, conscious thinking in visual images, but only a very few use a kind of nonverbal, preimage mode of cerebromentation that may be rather like the primary processes that precede and give rise to conscious thought. Nevertheless, though our failure is understandable, it is also lamentable. Contemporary psychological explanations of behavior, especially of puzzling "senseless" antisocial and violent acts, in terms of subpersonal biological and unconscious drives or suprapersonal environmental stimulation, produce mostly frustration in those who are called upon to judge—to secure punishment or treatment for—persons who plead lack of responsibility because their antisocial actions were impelled by extrapersonal influences. For it is impossible to bring the alleged impersonal forces into court, and the law rightly aims to punish acts, not persons, because we are all guilty of antisocial urges.

A plea of extrapersonal instigation for our disowned actions (the claim of "irresistible impulse" is the only real alternative to demonstrating that one's behavior is continually deranged) harks back to the ideas of possession and inspiration, to conceptions of divine and demoniac control. This atavistic trend is reinforced if one claims the ultimate excuse from responsibility—that the actions for which he is called upon to make amends or restitution were a fit, an epileptic, purposive automatism. The authorities may reject psychoanalytic invocations of unconscious motivation and sociological assertions of environmental determinism by offering their own moralistic explanations, but no one can either affirm or deny with much certainty anything at all about the causes of *idiopathic epilepsy,* whose explanation is by definition unknown, and metaphysically unknowable. Indeed, there is a definite trend in discussions of the senselessness of many recent acts of individual and group violence toward conceiving them as paroxysmal spells, or fits, rather than acts for which the individuals are truly responsible.

When Freud saw that the dream-fantasy-symptom complex was produced in an effort to resolve conflicts carried on outside awareness, he located the site of the struggle in the neglected area of unconscious mental processes, i.e., in subconscious processes. Others, more organic-minded, believe that all behavior, neurotic or otherwise, arises from subconscious and subpersonal organismic, biological, and physiochemical drives. Generally, most students of behavior, whether physiologists, psychologists, or sociologists, tend to assume that behavioral episodes are set off by some kind of internal or external stimulation, and that abnormal behavior results either from abnormal stimulation or abnormal responses to normal stimulation. Most also recognize that conflicts between drives, stimuli, and responses have something to do with abnormal action or inaction.

Freud saw the dynamically significant contention as both within and between conscious and unconscious divisions of the personality and mental life. Jackson saw the contention as within and between faint and strong excitations of sensorimotor centers and other arrangements of nerve cells. Whatever the formulations about the physiological or psychological sites of the contention, of the source and outcome of the conflicts, the terminology of most physiopsychologies and psychophysiologies suggests that underlying them are modern versions of ancient ideas about the struggle between good and evil, between man's animal and spiritual natures, or between some such suprapersonal forces as *yang* and *yin*.

Is it not possible that the source of man's contention and contentiousness is not so much a matter of conflicts in the *content* of his inherent drives and acquired motivations (of which he has plenty) but in the *form* of man himself? In his disjunctive, two-eyed, two-eared, two-limbed, two-faced, twin-natured, bisexual, double-brained structure? Thinking about thinking may be easier if we dramatize the contradictions and crises that give rise to it as struggles between powerful divine or demoniac, interpersonal or interbiological forces. These are all more familiar and safer ground than ideas about congruencies and incongruencies between patterns of nerve-cell discharges. But continual reformulation of ancient myths can take us only so far.

The processes by which interactions between brain cells become interactions within the individual and between persons may be inconceivable in terms accurately applicable to the actual processes; hence all explanations of them may be mythical. Gaps or discontinuities may occur as the progression from neuronal to personal crosses critical interphases when incremental quantitative change in neuronal activities suddenly transforms itself into qualitative change in relations between multicellular networks and circuits. Each of these fissions of quantitative growth into qualitative rearrangements may be recorded and recognized by other nervous structures and processes in terms of similarities and differences between elements of the previous unity. From appraisal of these contradictions and ambiguities meanings may be abstracted and experienced by still other brain centers and circuits. In the end, higher abstractions, broader generalizations, and sharper insights may leap into what we experience as consciousness, and these end products may be products of so many step-wise cogitations (cogitate = *co* + *agitare*, to shake up together) that their final form in no way resembles or recalls their origin.

Indeed, there are sound reasons for believing that two-sided, double-brained man (man's brain has duplicate right and left units in his new, higher primate cerebral hemispheres, and a second old brain below them which is shared with "lower" animals) must "think" by some such alternation of dissolving unities and resolving the resulting contradictions into new ones. It may well be, as suggested in subsequent chapters, that both "I" and the experience of "I" culminate processes of *personation* that momentarily terminate, in turn, a chain of processes of *neuronation, cerebration,* and *mentation.*

If so, "I" and its anxieties, experiences, and actions come into existence by a sudden qualitative transformation of a "me" and "myself" grown too large and diffuse for effective "minding" of the current business of the organism-individual. An "I" so suddenly and recurrently re-created *de novo* can at best have but a dim grasp of its origins and purposes. Nevertheless, once man makes the leap from "Me, Tarzan" to "I am Tarzan," he thereby acquires the inclination and the power to try, if not the skill to succeed at, a formulation of his past and future.

This book illuminates the critical moments in which neuronal interactions are transformed into personal actions. It seeks to do so by examining the differences and similarities between our commonplace *fits* and *acts*, between the processes of *fit* and *wit.* It returns to Freud's ideas about the similarities between the processes involved in epileptic and similar fits, in neurotic and normal behavior, and in acts of witful invention, discovery, and creation. It returns to Jackson's ideas about fits as products of subpsychological contention of neurophysiological operations. In so doing, the word *fit* is stripped of its implications as a "symptom" of epilepticity, and appears, transformed, as a generic term for any significantly structured episode of living. A fit, as an episodic action, is a fitted-together piece of behavior or experience used to overcome a discontinuity in the operations of the organism-individual-person.

But the book also returns to Jackson's emphasis on studying fits, especially small ones, as departures from health. It combines Jackson's notion of small fits as the slightest departures from continuity of interaction with George Herbert Mead's suggestion that the psychical is a temporary phenomenon concomitant with an interruption of organism-environment relations. The very smallest fits, then, are the relatively unnoticed pauses for thought (which are psychical fits of fitting together) in which relatively ordinary episodes of action and awareness are fitted together. The most normal fit, in the symptomatic sense, is the slightest departure from continuity of thinking represented by the brief pause for thought, occasioned by a fleeting crisis involving contradictions between grammatical, syntactical, and other influences upon word selection in the course of verbal thinking.

From this symptomatically normal, and operationally fleeting, fit of paralysis in thinking flow all fits of fitting together in which many contradictory and ambiguous ideas, images, and impulses are sorted out, shuffled about, and condensed, if not actually synthesized, in order to restore the continuity of action and awareness. The fitting-together function that finds the word, which "we" cannot get off the tip of our tongue, goes about its business spontaneously—as free of the will of "I" in ordinary pauses for thought as it is in the fitting together of spontaneous fits of convulsion or acts of creation.

But this statement of the spontaneity of fits of fitting together (which generate all episodes of living) is not *ipso facto* an assertion that all "genuine" or meaningful thinking or doing is and should be spontaneous. For although, as Mead argued, the "I" that comes into our experience as the personified person-who-had-been-trying-to-say-or-do-something does so only after the thing is done, "I" is not merely a passive co-twin born in a short crisis-induced trance-like moment of creation of both thought and thinker, of doer and deed. Once "I" has come into existence through spontaneous generation by the crisis-activated fitting-together capacity, it has, for a while, in its role of abstracted governor of behavior, an illusionary function in shaping the acting-out of the fitted-together resolution of a crisis. "I" for a while behaves (or functions) as if *it* had had the Jacksonian dream of action being carried out, and as if its *intentions* (which are a part of the dream) were shaping the scope, intensity, and direction of immediate living. And, curiously enough, this "as if" functioning of the "I" works "as if" it were "real." The negation of one as if by a second as if operation seems, indeed, to convert "as if" from "it is *as if*" into "it is."

In any case, it is as impossible to distinguish between "as if" and "reality," once "I" is in operation as a supervisor of the unfolding of a fitted-together fit, as it is to distinguish between a fit and an act. Any such distinction, as made in ordinary conversation, has its basis in assumptions about the spontaneity of fits and the volitional intentional quality of acts. But operationally the distinction, if there is any valid one, is a matter of timing. The action that ensues immediately after a brain storm of fitting together begins as a fit, in the sense of maximum spontaneity, and is transformed into an act as time passes—and the apparent impetus for action passes from the spontaneous fit of fitting together to its creature, "I."

But alas, as Valéry said, action sooner or later encounters the indefinable, and as the unrolling of a fit-act-episode proceeds, incipient contradictions previously held together by the creative effects of the fitting together begin to intensify, and they grow sufficiently to threaten once again the continuity of both action and "I." Or upon successful completion of the fit-action, the "I" of that episode finds itself in the ambiguous position of having nothing further to do, and the fitting-together capacity, in its task of minding the long-term business of the organism-individual, has to go into a trance and dream up a new action and a new "I."

The episodes described, analyzed, and discussed in the text, especially in the "Universe of Fits" section, are mostly examples of the extremes of the continuum of fits, i.e., are fits of epilepticity and of creativity. But these extreme examples of episodicity are shown in their dynamic unity with the fits and acts of everyday life by means of linking illustrations and discussions. For the unfathomable quality of the mystery of epileptic convulsions and acts of creation is reduced when they are removed from their isolation as sacred phenomena, and restored to their proper proportionate relation to the small marvels of everyday life. Extraordinary fits of epilepticity and creativity are only quantitatively, not qualitatively, different from any of our own smaller disruptions of unthinkable situations or our modest fittings-together of novel and new patterns of knowing and doing the previously unthinkable.

The intentions of "epileptics," "artists," and "normals" get them into crises, and their crisis-activated capacities for spontaneous fittings-together get them out again. I hope the reader will enjoy contemplating his own patterns of intention and spontaneity—of fitting together—and thus be able to see himself in others, and to facilitate thereby his own living.

PART ONE

THE CONCEPT OF FITS

WHENCE CAME "WHISHIT"?

. . . and has the reader never asked himself what kind of a mental fact is his *intention of saying a thing* before he has said it? It is an absolutely distinct state of consciousness . . . yet how much of it consists of definite sensorial images, either of words or of things? Hardly anything! Linger, and the words and things come into the mind; the anticipatory intention, the divination is there no more. [The intention] has therefore a nature of its own of the most positive sort, and yet what can we say about it without using words that belong to later mental facts that replace it? The intention *to say so and so* is the only name it can receive. One may admit that a good third of our psychic life consists in these rapid premonitory perspective views of schemes of thought not yet articulate.

—WILLIAM JAMES[1]

When we transpose the sound recordings of spontaneous speech into graphic form we are struck by its discontinuous nature. In most cases—and these are utterances of verbally most competent adults—speech is broken up into strings of words which are frequently separated by pauses of varying duration. . . . Some of these pauses occur at clause junctures or ends of sentences but many more are found within the boundaries of syntactical units, and tend to break up the context rather than facilitate communication. . . .

Half our speech time seems to issue in phrases not longer than three words, and three quarters in less than five words at the utmost. An average of 40–50 per cent of utterance time is occupied by pauses. These measurements make it evident that pausing is as much a part of the act of speaking as the vocal utterance of words itself and this suggests that pausing may be essential to the generation of spontaneous speech.

—FRIEDA GOLDMAN-EISLER[2]

Strong and suddenly induced emotion may lead to temporary speechlessness. We suppose that temporary speechlessness with great emotion betokens very numerous and strong nervous discharges, conflicting so as to balance or neutralise one another. . . . The result of numerous sudden, strong and therefore conflicting discharges, would of course be the survival of the fittest, but the survival amidst too numerous and too strong discharges would not be an elaborate and perfect proposition. We suggest that it would be but one word or a jumble of syllables of some words. Of course "fittest" here does not mean "the best," nor the fittest *for the external* circumstances of the time: it is the survival of the fittest under the *internal circumstances*. . . . Such survivals may be little fit or not fit at all to the then external circumstances; they express the emotions and ideas induced well or badly, as well as can be done under the circumstances.

—JOHN HUGHLINGS JACKSON[3]

Once early in the afternoon of a late spring day I sat at my student's desk in a one-room country schoolhouse and watched unfold one of those peculiar dramas of everyday life that are described and discussed in this book as fits, dysjunctive behavior, and brain storms. Because this country-school episode started my wonderings about crises in the continuity of everyday living and their convulsive, conventional, confused, and creative outcomes, it was, in a personal sense, the beginning of this book.

More important, it becomes a suitable beginning because it is a natural example of crises and their fitted-together outcomes. It illustrates the dynamic interplay between endowment, experience, and circumstances culminating in and containing fits, dysjunctive behavior, and brain storms. Its ambiguity—its implications of creativity vs. pathology, of inspiration vs. defeat—illumines the dilemma, the impasse, the crisis in our thinking that is created when we adhere to traditional distinctions between a *fit* and an *act*.

I was at my desk absorbed in my reading but marginally alert to what went on around me. Some of my schoolmates were doing lessons at their desks, others were dawdling or daydreaming. Lined up along the front wall was a class to whom the teacher was giving an exercise in oral spelling. She was passing along the line of pupils giving each a word to spell aloud. Suddenly something about what was going on there at the front of the room broke into our various absorptions and attracted our close attention.

The teacher, a dedicated, stubborn young woman, had come to Marvin, a large and backward boy. Marvin could not reliably spell "cat," or any other word, and was soon to give up forever his struggles with schooling. But our teacher tried persistently to get him to read one full sentence, to complete one arithmetic problem, and to spell at least one word. Each of these occasions was fraught with tension—pressure from teacher meeting resistance from Marvin.

On this occasion the teacher was saying, "Hoo—wich, Marvin, hoo—wich. It begins with double-u." Marvin had been given "which," the easiest word on the day's list but evidently quite beyond him. He stood there mute, red-faced, swaying and shuffling his feet.

"Come on, Marvin, at least try it," the teacher said. He tried: "H . . . w . . ." and stopped. "Not h . . . w, Marvin, w . . . h," she corrected him encouragingly. He tried again: "W . . . h . . . s . . . h . . ." but stopped again as the expectant look on the teacher's face turned to disappointment. He shuffled, shifted his stance, and frowned darkly. Then suddenly, as if galvanized by the teacher's disappointment (I think she was about to give up once more and move on to the next pupil), Marvin straightened up. His face cleared of angry confusion, a peculiar, beatific look came upon him; he began to spell slowly and steadily as if inspired. The letters came at about five-second intervals: "W . . . h . . . i . . .," he paused slightly but continued, spelling now a bit faster, ". . . s . . . h . . . i . . ." and, inevitably, " . . . t . . ." He stopped; his peculiar facial expression vanished; he seemed to believe that he had at last spelled a word; he grinned rather secretively as if pleased with his performance; then he lapsed into his usual scowling slouch.

During Marvin's extraordinary fit of spelling, we were all fascinated. When he finished, we remained too bemused to laugh or giggle. The entranced teacher recovered and passed on to the next pupil as if nothing unusual had happened. Then we began to whisper and exchange notes. We established that Marvin's performance had been spontaneous—no one had been teaching him to spell, nor had anyone, with malice aforethought, been teaching him to spell four-letter words. After school Marvin avoided interrogation. We could only speculate about what had happened and why. That something very unusual had happened was evident in Marvin's sudden change of attitude, his peculiar facial expression, and the measured rhythm of his spelling. When, after a brief pause, he started spelling again with "s . . . h . . . ," most of us had foreseen where he would end unless someone interfered. No one did, perhaps because he appeared to be inspired, possessed. But whether he was inspired to "spell a word," any word—to perform for once as a student should—or whether he was possessed by a need to "spell out" his true feeling about spelling, school, and life (or all three), no one could say.

Nor would I say that my memory of this incident is exact in every detail. But the scene stayed with me, and my remembrance of it was frequently refreshed, in later years, during my studies of epileptic and other fits—of the performances of people in similar crises. It came to serve as a kind of personal prototype, a central example for evaluating the similarities and differences in a vast continuum of convulsions, seizures, paroxysms, spells, attacks, spasms, bouts, episodes, and other fits* of behavior and experience.

The questions raised by Marvin's fit of spelling, his brain storm, recurred in all my encounters with other fits, dysjunctive reactions, and brain storms. They were: What was it? What did it mean? Whatever "possessed" him to do it? Did he know what he was doing? If he didn't know, how could he have done it? Was it a spontaneous fit, a purposeful act, or something of both?

Whatever it was, it was for Marvin as a person, or for his brain as an organ of integration, an extraordinary achievement—a fit-act of creative spelling, from one view. From others, it could be seen as a vulgar protest against spelling and schooling, a deliberate defiance of authority, or a spell of psychomotor confusion engendered by desperate strivings to comply with the multiple demands of the situation. The questions we ask about Marvin's performance are raised by all kinds of episodes, from the mundane to the marvelous. They are, in fact, pertinent to any action or experience, no episode of which is ever absolutely "neurogenic" or "psychogenic," spontaneous or voluntary. The numerous examples in Part Two, and others scattered throughout the text, illustrate the similarities of circumstances that contain, and of the processes that culminate in, fits of wit and creativity, fits of convulsive activity, and fits of relatively conventional behavior and experience.

Common to all these fits and acts, or fit-acts, is a pause produced by a sudden coming together of numerous competing ideas, images, and impulses. This pause—very fleeting in some but outstanding in others—between stimulus-situation and action-reaction is required by the momentary "unthinkability" of the complex of contending and summating information and impulses. Accompanying this transitory or prolonged unmindability there is always, I believe, some kind and degree of uncanny experience. Even momentary shakings of the ongoing integration of one's "self" with its permanent and changing frames of reference are felt as peculiarly unusual activities of body, mind, or person—as, for example, nausea, giddiness, and shivering; intimations of ecstasy or uneasiness; feelings of falling apart or coming together; losing and finding one's self; and so on. The extremes of these abortive or well-developed, awesomely pleasant or unpleasant, subjective experi-

---

* Suggestive speculations about the processes generating fits and acts are made in Chapter 2. The dynamic and descriptive characteristics of fits are discussed in Chapter 3.

ential accompaniments of moments of unthinkability and unmindability are something like Harry Stack Sullivan's "pure" euphoria and "pure" terror. Any term useful for approaching their quality conceptually inevitably suggests not only their intolerability as either pleasant or unpleasant experience but also that the extremes are poles apart.

Yet all extreme uncanny experiences have much in common. The effects of psychedelic drugs and other brain-busting, mind-blowing, self-annihilating agents and influences—of all unthinkable stimuli-situations—are unpredictable, ambiguous, and are often described, as in the case of heroin, as "the most, man, the most!"

Whether one has a "terribly" or "awfully" pleasant or unpleasant experience varies from time to time as well as from person to person. And the rather easy flip-flop from one to the other seems to depend on subtle variations in time, place, and person. The tremulously ambiguous potential of the sources of uncanny experience for both euphoria and terror suggests that the true meaning of *uncanny* has more to do with the literally unthinkable *form* of sudden, intense, contending psychophysiological processes striving for realization in ideas and impulses, awareness and action, than it does with any unthinkably happy or unhappy quality of the psychosocial *content* of its concomitant subjective effects. For, theoretically at least, a state of purely potential "intention to say" or to do can have only *form;* it has no *content* whatsoever. Inexpressible feelings, whether of joy or dejection, arise with unthinkable complexes of ideas and impulses.

If circumstances demand that something be said or done, but the nervous substrate is too contradictory or ambiguous for utterance, pure intention turns into pure tension. This situation, loaded with conflicting inputs, is as intolerable to the brain and its sub-brains as it is to any computer. Computing brains therefore feed signals of "incomputability"* back into the controls of input and output. The brain feeds such signals into its minding circuits, which link inputs and outputs between brain and body with those between brain and environment. There and then elec-

---

* Something useful about these processes and their speed may be conveyed by reporting that when I typed "incomputability," a fleeting crisis arose because of the clash between this word and the more familiar "incompatible." In the typed MS the letters "p" and "u" were both faint. Contention between the habitual tendency to put "a" after "p," as in "incompatible," and the intention to put "u" after "p" reduced the energy of the typing stroke and the "u" was almost ambiguously faint. The faintness of the "p" must have arisen from anticipation and spread of inhibition.

trophysiological tension is transformed into intraorganismic, intraindividual, and intrapersonal tension. This tension is then interpreted as tending toward terror or euphoria, so that the organism-individual-person may "know" what's going on and be "moved" to do something, or nothing, about it.

"Emotion" means being moved out of or from, and its function is literally to move the organism-individual-person system out of a crisis. No appropriate action can be organized from an unthinkable situation, and we are moved to experience the consequences of inaction as unbearable. And our incipient emotion turns into an alleged, peculiar emotion called *anxiety*.

But pure intension-tension, like pure terror or pure euphoria, has no content. None of the three can be experienced as such, only as "something" must happen or "something awe-ful" is about to happen (if the "something" doesn't). Anxiety thus appears as "free energy" when action and actual emotion are blocked. Indeed, all these abstractions come down to the same thing, an energized, empty "most" which is neither good nor bad. It is "the most," the most inexplicable urge and the most unidentifiable feeling, because it is the most in form but at the same time the least in content. It is the experience of the unthinkable as the unknowable, the uncanny.

It is what psychiatrists try to get at with the term "free-floating anxiety," drug addicts mean by "the most," devotees of various things and persons mean by the indefinable "greatest," etc. Discussions of anxiety flounder in trying to provide a content for "free-floating," i.e., for anxiety *qua* anxiety, by treating it as detached, disembodied, free from any specific anchor—an indescribable version of more definable things like fear, apprehension, and so on.

Logically, this version of "the most," as cause, has become the central explanation ("the most" as result) of the most widely divergent and the most important of destructive and constructive human activity, ranging from fits of convulsion to acts of creation.

But because "anxiety" is an experience that accompanies, if it does not cause, paralyzing *inaction*, it is difficult to see how the paralyzing experience of anxiety can serve as a stimulus for any action, for anything other than freezing in immobility or exploding in the unorganized actions of panic. Many theorists, notably Harry Stack Sullivan, recognized that anxiety seems to oppose any action, and, therefore, could not be its stimulus. But these theorists restore anxiety to a causal role by explaining that it is the anticipation, the apprehension and avoidance, of the experience of anxiety that activates our most vigorous, rapid, and subtle accomplishments.

But psychophysiologically, anxiety seems nothing more than something like "the least"—the almost-felt subjective accompaniment of an almost-anything-but-as-yet-nothingness. What we try to get at, to identify (though we cannot experience) by the term "anxiety" does not so much oppose action as Sullivan thought—it *is* inaction but on a neuronal, cerebral, and mental as well as a personal level. It is the "nameless" and content-less concomitant of momentarily unresolvable contradiction, ambiguity, and complexity in the nervous arrangements and processes from which patterns of action and awareness must be made. It is the reflection of a transient derangement of intracerebral models of the courses and configurations of ongoing organism-environment integration which must be corrected, temporarily at least, by some action—any action, however ludicrous or lovely, that will get the brain-mind-person system out of a dysjunctive impasse.

The contention within the brain-mind-person system produced by a sudden coming together of numerous competing ideas, images, and impulses gives rise to a brain storm of integrative fitting-together activity aimed at resolving contradictions and ambiguities if *the* most apt solution cannot be organized. These brain storms are themselves fits, or subfits, of intracerebral activity in which logical and paralogical processes and ideas and impulses are all "shaken up together."

The pauses, in which all this stormy "turning of the wheels" of cerebration occurs, are periods in which complicated interconnections matching out-put to in-put can be made. They are the same as delays in stimulus-response experiments when complexes of conflicting emotion and motivations are aroused. They are discussed at length in Part Four in terms of *still reactions, pregnant intervals,* and *integrative trances.*

That such pauses are in fact pauses for thought, pregnant intervals for the spontaneous generation of awareness and action, is evident from many observations, as, for example, Frieda Goldman-Eisler's finding that pausing is more frequent and noticeable when the speaker is discussing the meaning of events than when he is simply narrating the course of events.[4] These pauses, in the sense of James's "intention to say," are also momentary suspensions of knowing, feeling, and doing and, *ipso facto*, the operational bases for unthinkable anxiety, euphoria, and uneasiness. They are also—grammatically, syntactically, and psychophysiologically—crises in the continuity and flow of living.

In everyday activity, pauses and the fits they give rise to may notably disrupt the flow of events, but they may also be masked by "natural" breaks between episodes, the second of which may be a disguised fit. The pause and its outcome—both of which comprise the whole fit—may be very brief or very protracted.

Pauses preceding the rapid responses of very witty people may be barely perceptible. Dorothy Parker, one of the ready wits of the fabulous Hotel Algonquin Round Table, was known for her quick reactions. Once, for example, she and another woman arrived together at the exit door of a restaurant. The other woman stepped aside, saying to Miss Parker as she did so, "Age before beauty, my dear." With no notable pause, Miss Parker graciously accepted the deference, swept past through the door, calling back over her shoulder as she did so, "And pearls before swine."

This may not be the wittiest remark ever made by Miss Parker, but it does illustrate a central characteristic of the processes generating both *wit* and *fit*, i.e., the coupling of contradictory elements according to their similar differences and their different similarities. The juxtaposition of elements having both divergent and convergent tendencies gives a situation a *dysjunctive* quality. Formulating a more or less unifying response that both preserves and resolves such contradictions is what I mean by dysjunctive brain function and behavior.

Just as dysjunctive situations elicit dysjunctive reactions from some people—who may be sensitive to such things, and in addition have a disposition to react dysjunctively—so, in turn, one person's dysjunctive behavior may be a stimulus producing a dysjunctive effect in an observer. Dysjunctive effects are, I believe, responsible for the mysterious hair-raising, spine-tingling, tear-and-laughter-provoking experiences which we have at more or less uncanny moments of encounter with crises and their resolutions in life and art.*

The impact of dysjunctive situations and effects arises from the suddenness, the spontaneity, of our confrontations with contradictions and crises. It has two components: anticipatory tension from sudden recognition of the paralyzing possibilities of an unthinkable situation, and retrospective, rebound relief upon resolution of the crisis, at having escaped from paralysis. All unexpected contradictions are momentarily unthinkable, and being unable to

---

* Dysjunctive situations, effects, and behavior are discussed in detail in Chapter 4, and in Part Three specifically. Pauses preceding reactions combining wit and fit are discussed especially in Part Two.

think terrorizes us even more than being unable to act. We seem convinced that movement in time-space, real or imagined, is synonymous with living, and that to stop is to die. Thus, however a crisis is resolved—whether in an outburst of tears or laughter, a flash of comprehending insight, a paroxysm of convulsive or disordered behavior, or a fit of creation—we quiver and quake in anticipation and shiver in relief. Any significant crisis involves some reorganization of our ego or self; crises, and the fits of fitting together of patterns of action and awareness to resolve them, require, in a sense, the death and rebirth of "I."

In our play, our jokes, riddles, puzzles, and art—in all of our life—we rehearse, sharpen, and shift our styles and strategies for dealing with crises. For upon our management, our "minding," of the frequent small crises of daily life depends our ability to handle large ones. Quantitatively or qualitatively important crises may require long periods of fitting-together activity—trial-and-error, logical deduction, and intuitive guessing are all brought into play. The furor of crisis-induced fitting together may be obvious; it may, however, be concealed by ostensible absorption in conventional or substitutive activities. In one such episode of extended sequential fitting together, the mathematician Poincaré spent several days working out, by a series of painstaking steps and inspired intuitions, the solution of a problem which had stumped him.

Suddenness of onset and termination is a characteristic by which we recognize fits, from fits of convulsion to fits of creation. Duration, too, is a common criterion for recognizing fits, because only when a fit is relatively brief can we see the connection between its onset and its termination, and identify the fit as a discontinuity. But neither speed nor duration is an essential ingredient in the processes that culminate convulsively or creatively. The quantity and quality of the contending elements in a dysjunctive situation, together with the individual's inherent or acquired capacity for minding contentious contradictions, are the heart of the matter.

For all our data on the structure and function of the brain and on the origin and development of the personality, we know very little about the minding of crises—about the fitting together of momentary and enduring solutions of contradiction and ambiguities, the balancing of dangers and opportunities. Indeed, we are not at all sure whether minding is a function of the brain, the person (the "I"), or some independent agency called "mind."

Marvin's fit of spelling-obscenity is a good example of the problem of locating and defining the minding that resolves a crisis. Was it a spontaneous performance of his brain, his "unconscious mind," or a willful activity of the person? In traditional terms, was it a *fit* or an *act*? But this question cannot be answered; it poses but does not resolve the crisis in our thinking about such matters. What is required is to deepen our understanding and broaden our comprehension of human behaviors and experiences which have the dual characteristics of what we have called fits and acts. Any episode of awareness and action begins, develops, and ends according to the inherent and acquired characteristics of the individual's brain as an organ integrating knowing, feeling, and doing, and according to the inherent and acquired style of the person who is the knower, feeler, and doer.

Out of this contentious contradiction between, and about, person and brain has arisen the concept of *mind*. Of late, this concept relieves the person of responsibility and punishment but saddles the brain, as the organ of mind, with the risk of chemical, surgical, and electrical manipulations by therapeutic brain-ticklers. Current concepts of mind and mental illness are too contradictory and ambiguous for much use. They have been vigorously criticized, particularly in the United States by Dr. Thomas Szasz.

The crisis in our neurological-psychiatric thinking, reflected in the controversy between philosophies of "organic" and "psychogenic" causation of behavior, viewed as medical symptoms, has produced a kind of paralysis. Effort to ameliorate the crisis by shifting attention from "mind" as a *thing* to "minding" as a *process* is one of the few steps in the right direction. But the problem remains: Who or what does the minding?

And behind this question lurk even larger ones. Is the minding that produces what we call fits the same as that producing acts? Is there any essential difference between the genesis of fits and other symptoms and the genesis of conventional and creative acts? Is there an abnormal as well as a normal psychology?

Marvin's fit, as a fringe case having the aspects of both a fit and an act—as a performance touched with both criminal and creative coloration—is a good beginning for a consideration of the contradiction between brain and body on the one hand and person and mind on the other. It is a perfect example in that its imperfections serve well to introduce this study of fits, dysjunctive behavior, and brain storms, their nature as products of the brain's fitting-together capacity, their role in the fitted-together continuity of everyday living, and their significance for understanding the fitting-togetherness of the body-mind-person system.

Notes

1. William James, *The Principles of Psychology*. Henry Holt, New York, 1890, Vol. I, p. 253.
2. Frieda Goldman-Eisler, "Hesitation, Information, and Levels of Speech Production," in *Disorders of Language*. J. A. Churchill, London, 1964, pp. 97–98.
3. John Hughlings Jackson, *Selected Writings*, edited by James Taylor. Hodder & Stoughton, London, 1931; Basic Books, New York, 1958, Vol II, p. 195.
4. Goldman-Eisler, *op. cit.*, p. 103.

WHAT IS A FIT?

A fit, even the grossest major convulsive fit of epilepsy, is many things happening at once. Fits are patterns of awareness and action, combinations of knowing, feeling, and doing. They are episodes of behavior and experience put together by the brain during crises in the continuity of living. Such crises are characterized by a sudden coming together of a complex of conflicting and disparate ideas, images, and impulses; fits are syntheses of such complexes that both resolve and represent their otherwise unthinkable contradictions and ambiguities. By providing more or less fitting resolutions of crises, fits serve to maintain or restore the crisis-disrupted continuity of transactions between organism and environment.

Fits are punctuations of living—discontinuities in the form of ongoing activity that enhance the continuity of meaning. A fit is both a dis-junction and a con-junction in the flow of thought, feeling, and action. Just as a poem exerts its effect because its words convey both sound and sense, so a fit exerts a dual effect, in both form and content—a dys-junctive effect produced by the tension between its dis-junctive and con-junctive elements.

Fits occur when the specific and general fitting-together capacities of our brain are activated by a momentarily unmindable impasse in ongoing activity. Fit-producing crises occur on any level of organization of the body, brain, and person. Fit-behaviors and fit-experiences range from *grand mal* convulsive seizures through fleeting arrests of thought and action to a *grande crise créatrice*, a major fit of creation.

Fit-producing crises are really quite common in everyday life. All of us, every day, are confronted with problem situations that momentarily stump us for an answer or action. Like Marvin, we are caught in a crisis of continuity. The ensuing fit depends upon our endowment, experience, and interpretation of the circumstances.

We may "stop to think" but find that we can't. Then we experience the tension that goes with having something "on the tip of the tongue"—the peculiar distress of an urgent intention that cannot, for the moment, be realized in thought, word, or action. The longer a solution escapes us, the more intense the frustration of intention becomes. Our tension mounts toward excitement, embarrassment, anxiety, panic, etc. Our intention is absorbed into our tension. We may then react "reflexively" with a ready-made, conventional maneuver designed to reduce tension and obscure the crisis. Accompanying these quick adjustments with little discharges of accumulated tension, we are apt to belch, blush, laugh, cough, sneeze, yawn, or in some way substitute a subpersonal, bodily activity for a more pertinent action. Sometimes we are stuck with the critical situation and can only caricature problem-solving activity. Our posture and performance then mimic "thinking hard." We frown, grimace, scratch our scalps, and otherwise indicate that we are "using our heads." We may attempt to deal with our distress by various manifestations of fight-flight, offense-defense, or approach-avoidance reactions.

On the other hand, if we can endure confrontation with the unthinkable, we may be able to fit together new patterns of awareness and action. We might, that is, have a fit of insight, inspiration, invention, or creation. The propensity for finding the answer—the lure of creating or discovering the new—no doubt has much to do with some people's ability to endure tension until something new emerges from the contradictory and ambiguous situation. Some people seem to have an affinity for unthinkable situations but lack the ability to resolve them. Their tolerance may be strained to the limit in particularly crucial circumstances. Then, according to their endowment and experience, they will somehow disrupt the situation and start all over again. Among these people are those whose heredity, history, and current life situation produce epileptic disruptions.

All the diverse convulsive, caricatured, conventional, and creative outcomes of crises in the continuity of living can be thought of as fits. This suggestion may seem rather startling. For it implies that a large part of our everyday living is made up of fits. And the term *fit* suggests loss of control and convulsive illness even though the formulation includes fits of creation as well as fits of convulsion. The basis for this formulation may be seen more clearly by considering the question "What is a fit?" from another point of view.

The concept of *fits* is rooted in everyday experience and thought.

References to fits are common in ordinary conversation. People discuss, for example, fits of colic, fits of sneezing, fits of temper, fits of laughing, fits of shivering, and fits of fear and ecstasy, as well as fits of convulsions or fits of creativity. A tendency to distinguish between a fit and some other episode is widespread, but it is exceedingly difficult to identify the criteria by which fits are recognized. It evidently is like recognizing a friend at a distance or a familiar face in a photograph of a sea of faces—it is easy to do but hard to explain. There is great difficulty in defining a fit because the process is intuitive rather than deductive: there is no single specific element or set of them for diagnosing fits. In some instances, however, as in the major convulsive fit, there are practical criteria. In the *grand mal* seizure it is the pattern of convulsive behavior itself. In others, the fit-behavior in itself may be quite ordinary but is irrelevant, inappropriate, or absurd under the circumstances. In still other examples, fits are reactions to stimulus-events known to have fit-provoking potency; in these cases the fit quality resides in the cause rather than the fit-behavior itself. Thus, combinations of flickering light and drugs produce fits of one kind or another in many people; whatever the nature of an individual's reaction, if it is repeatedly set off by flickering light, it is a fit. Finally, there are people who have recurring episodes that are linked with personal characteristics—fits of temper, for example, are likely to occur in people who "have a temper."

Evidently signs of a fit can be both specific and general and can be found in either the nature of the circumstances, the characteristics of the person, or the pattern of behavior; the several criteria of "fitness" overlap and intermingle. Certain potent odors, for instance, seem to set off fits of creation as well as fits of convulsion. Shifts from waking to sleep or from sleep to waking also set off fits of all kinds. A single stimulus-event may give rise to a great diversity of fits or, conversely, a single kind of fit may be produced by a wide variety of stimuli-events.

John Hughlings Jackson, the great nineteenth-century student of epileptic and other fits, once said, "Anything from fright to flatulence can cause a fit." I would add, "Anything from flatulence to fright can *be* a fit." It is clear that any simple definition of fits will elude us. That the nature of "a fit" (as an abstract concept representing the whole class of fits) is indeterminate could be expected from consideration of the large number of synonyms for "fit." We speak not only of fits but also of seizures, spells, paroxysms, attacks, bouts, spasms, sieges, outbursts, and so on. None of these is exactly equivalent to another and all have slightly different centers and overtones of meaning. Of all these, the concept of *fits* seems to me to contain the most meaning—to be the most "supple, mobile, and almost fluid representation, always ready to adapt itself on the fleeting forms of intuition"—even though its very adaptability stems from imprecision.

Lack of precision in specifying how we recognize a fit flows from approaching the task diagnostically—from thinking of the fit as a thing. If, however, we think of the fit as an instance of the fitting-together processes of the brain, we can begin to see a fit in a quite different light. We can see not only the possibilities of precision in defining *fit* as the product of a particular process, but also the similarities in process, however different they seem in content, of fits of convulsion and fits of creation—a similarity long puzzled about in the relationship between epilepsy and genius. A brief account of how I came to shift my conception of fits from one of things to one of processes follows.

Some twenty-five years ago, I set out to study just one kind of fit—the so-called epileptic fit. I spent many years trying to find in the work of others or to formulate by my own efforts a satisfying definition of an epileptic fit. But there is no one, single kind of epileptic fit. Then, as now, these fits were divided into three main kinds: *grand mal* convulsions characterized by loss of consciousness, rhythmic contractions and relaxations of all body muscles, followed by profound coma; *psychomotor* (or "psychic") *seizures* ranging from brief uncanny feelings (of uneasiness or ecstasy) through protracted "fugues" mixing confused action and awareness, to elaborate, coordinated, seemingly purposeful acts of the whole person; *petit mal* attacks consisting of brief arrests of awareness and action beginning and ending suddenly. These three supposedly different epileptic fits* grade into each other by imperceptible degrees, so that there is a continuum of almost innumerable epileptic fits reaching from dramatic convulsive disruptions of ongoing activity to seemingly insignificant pauses for thought. *Grand mal, psychomotor seizure*, and *petit mal* are not three kinds of fit, or illness, they are zones in a spectrum.

This spectrum of fits is said to be symptomatic of a mysterious disease, "epilepsy." I could not then find nor formulate a statisfying definition of epilepsy as a disease that was both meaningfully comprehensive and precise. The problem of locating "epilepticity" as

---

* Many patients have all three; many patients have both "epileptic" fits and attacks of psychosomatic and psychiatric symptoms; nor are geniuses who have had epilepsy extremely rare.

well as "fit-ness" in either the circumstances, the fit-behavior, or the person was insoluble. No one has ever been able to formulate an acceptable definition of epilepsy, the "sacred disease," nor to demonstrate a specific pathology for epileptic fits. "Epilepsy," derived centuries ago from the Greek *epi* and *lambanein,* simply means "seized upon" or "seized from above." The term implies that *anyone* offending the gods sufficiently could be "seized upon from above" and thrown into a fit. And, indeed, the central, most typical symptom, the major convulsion, can easily be produced in anyone, as the widespread use of shock therapy has shown.

The capacity to convulse is inherent in the normal brain (like sneezing) and cannot be a symptom of any particular disease. The parts of the brain, body, and person behaving "epileptically" in an epileptic fit work quite normally in periods between fits and could not, therefore, be diseased in any ordinary sense of the word. There is no such disease as "epilepsy" nor can there be any such disease. The problems of epilepsy, then, are those of psychophysiology rather than of pathology—problems of process in work rather than structure in disease.

Epileptic fits, I discovered, merge by ill-defined degrees into a much larger group of fits of disturbed action and awareness ambiguously related to epilepsy. These "epileptoid" and "epileptiform" fits include the symptoms of migraine, narcolepsy, cataplexy, abdominal migraine–epilepsy, hysteroepilepsy, sleep paralysis, hypnogogic hallucinations, and so on.

In turn, this larger class of epileptiform fits blends into a broader spectrum of paroxysmal disturbances of bodily and personal function ordinarily thought of as symptoms of various medical, psychosomatic, and psychiatric conditions. Just as it is impossible to distinguish absolutely between epileptic and nonepileptic fits, so too it is impossible to differentiate between symptomatic and nonsymptomatic episodes. Combinations of action and awareness traditionally held to be symptomatic of a disease grade imperceptibly into structurally similar episodes presumably symptomatic only of a transitory functional derangement of minding, and on into episodes indistinguishable from normal actions and experiences.

Thus trying to define an *epileptic* fit transformed itself into trying to define a *fit* in general. And, as we have seen, the difficulties in defining a fit, whether convulsive or creative, arise from the shifting, indeterminate location of fit-ness—the elusive fit-quality produced somewhere in the dynamic interplay of circumstances, behavior, and person.

Another side of the difficulty is seen when we try to specify what a fit is not. For in defining an episode as not-a-fit, we are led into trying to define an *act,* the apparent logical-legal opposite of fit. The operational opposite of a fit, as an episode, would be something like smoothly continuous, unchanging behavior or experience. But knowing, feeling, and doing do not long remain static except in the pauses that punctuate living. An enduring period of unchanging action or awareness would be a fit rather than its opposite; it would be inaction, not action; it would not be what we ordinarily mean by an act. Both fits and acts are instances of episodicity.

In the absence of distinguishing criteria based on description and duration, we fall back upon criteria of cause. We may, with easy confidence, assert that acts are things done under "conscious control of the person," whereas fits are "involuntary," subpersonal responses of the "unconscious mind," brain, and reflex nerve-circuits. But, paradoxically, our greatest, most genuinely personal acts are spontaneous; they occur as sudden involuntary resolutions of mounting tension that ensues when a conventional voluntary intention has been inadequate or blocked. The transformation of intention to tension when a familiar form for the intended is unavailable or undesirable may be relieved by spontaneous eruption of a cliché, a clumsy caricature of the familiar, or a moderately witful new response. But it may also produce a truly creative performance. We cannot, therefore, distinguish between "voluntary acts" and "involuntary fits" on the basis of spontaneity.

Ideas of voluntariness—of volition, will, and will power—depend upon an assumed distinction between consciously planned action and unconscious reflex response. But confusion arises, and contradiction slides into ambiguity, when "consciously intended action"—like acts of courtesy and sociability—grades imperceptibly into culturally conditioned "reflex" performances. In laughter, for example, our most genuine personal laughter is that which is least forced, least contrived. In laughter and in other responsive behavior, we impress others as most genuinely ourselves when we are most spontaneous, when we exert the minimum of conscious intention. On the basis of spontaneity, of involuntariness, then, we are most convincing when we least intend it. Our most genuine laughter occurs when suddenly something strikes us as funny, i.e., when something serves as a fit-stimulus for a "fit of laughing." We are held to be most genuinely courteous when our graciousness is most automatic, is an unbidden response that has become "second nature." Is a fit, then, a kind of *super*-act, a supremely spontaneous action by which we reveal our real selves and exercise our true nature?

Our greatest achievements are acts of invention, discovery, and creation. In these, spontaneity, involuntariness, and "accident" are outstanding. Discussions of these superlative acts by scientists and artists themselves, and by students of imagination and creativity, reveal remarkable parallels between the dynamic and descriptive characteristics of "acts" of invention, discovery, and creation and "fits" of epilepsy, hysteria, psychosomatic disturbances, and other episodes of crisis-induced behavior. Artists and scientists talk about their creative activities; sportsmen and artisans discuss their exceptionally skilled performances; and medical patients recount the onset and development of their symptoms in similar terms that justify the use of "fits" for all these episodes and suggest that these fits are all produced by similar dynamic processes.

Differences between the social value of a fit of convulsion and a fit of creation should not be allowed to obscure the dynamic similarities of their form and development. A product of the fitting-together capacity may be lamentable or lovely, but the fitting-together process is much the same in all fits, whether these are creative or convulsive, major or minor, effective or ineffective solutions for the crisis at hand.

At this point it would be easy to get lost in elaborate pursuit of those aspects of fits and acts suggested by the terms consciousness, unconsciousness, voluntary, involuntary, will, purpose, intention, and spontaneity. These terminological pitfalls in the path of understanding brain function and behavior can be avoided, for the time being at least, by defining a fit as any episode of behavior or experience having a more or less definite beginning, middle, and end, which is preceded by a crisis in the continuity of ongoing activity, and which is followed by diminution or resolution of the crisis. The validity and usefulness of this conception will be seen in examination of the etymology of the word *fit*.

But before turning to this aspect of fits, it may be helpful to point out that Sigmund Freud derived much of his theory by interpreting dreams as disruptions of sleep which served to preserve its continuity, i.e., as punctuations of sleep. My interpretation of fits is based upon conceiving them as playing such a role in waking, everyday activity. Transformations of fits of dreaming into fits of convulsing, and conversion of fits of convulsing into fits of dreaming do occur. Transformations from one kind of "epileptic" fit to another, and from "epileptic" to "nonepileptic" occur frequently enough to suggest that all are produced by a multi-potent fitting-together capacity of the brain.

The suggested dependency of convulsive fits, fits of dreaming, fits of creating—and, indeed, all fits—upon a common fitting-together capacity will be further strengthened by considering the origin and development of the concept of *fits* in the history of our language. Most people think in words. By struggling to put thought into words, they energize and direct the transformation of inter-neuronal into intrapersonal and on into interpersonal processes. At critical moments, pauses in thought give rein to the putting-together capacity that organizes and executes all fits. Attention to the words we use and have used concerning fits and fitting together should illuminate the problems of crises in thinking and of thinking in a crisis.

THE ETYMOLOGY AND MEANING OF "FIT" 3

The word "fit," like the behavior to which it has been applied, derives from several sources and has a variety of meanings and diverse functions. It can serve as a noun, verb, or adjective. It can designate an episode of sudden activity or inactivity, an attack of illness, a paralysis of function, a transitory state, a mood, a violent onslaught of laughter or rage, etc. It is the key to a whole series of concepts and behaviors like paroxysm, attack, spell, outburst, etc. It also implies: suited for a purpose, good enough for something, in harmony with, of right measure, conflict, juncture, meeting, matching, fitting, and so on.

Fit comes from the Old English noun *fitt,* meaning conflict or point of danger and hardship. The Middle English verb *fitte* signified a marshaling of forces and also had connotations of junctures, meetings, arrangements, and matchings. *Fytte,* an archaic form of Old Saxon *fittia,* latinized as *vittea,* designated a part of a poem or song, and carries implications of arrangements designed to convey meaning by both form and content. As to structure and form, *fittiz* suggests Old High German *fizza,* list of cloth, German *fitze,* skein of yarn and the mark at the end of a day's work. Icelandic *fitja* means to knit and Dutch *vitten* to accommodate.

In the galaxy of meanings surrounding the word *fit,* there are strong suggestions of marshaling, arranging, and fitting together.* That the "fitting" involves not only matching similar pieces but also matching them with dissimilar, conflicting elements is evident from the cluster of meanings. Hence *fit* implies both paroxysmal excited disruptions and inhibitory interruptions; fitting together

---

* The Oxford Dictionary of English Etymology (Clarendon Press, Oxford, 1966) says, "The chronology of the evidence is inadequate for the determination of the relation between this set of words," i.e., of the various "fits." The meanings of *fit,* that is, must be marshaled and fitted together.

also, therefore, involves fitting the fit into its context of on-flowing behavior and experience.

Ideas of arranging, adjusting, accommodating, and matching lead into the ideas of putting something into proper condition or suiting it to the circumstances. In some cases harmony is produced. But *fit* also involves being "fitted out" or made ready for something, and this begins a chain of meanings that leads away from those of harmony. That is, one can be "fit to be tied" or even "fit" for murder. Fitting together can resolve a crisis or it can prepare an explosion, depending on the elements brought together. In soapmaking, the mixture of components is "fit" when the fluid soap is ready to separate into two layers. And Shakespeare in his Sonnet CXIX says, "How have mine eyes out of their spheres been fitted, / In the distraction of this madding fever!"

Thus exploring dictionaries for the meanings of *fit* reveals shifting foci of meanings and frames of reference. Interminglings of cause and effect, ambiguities in the essence of "fit-ness," and contradictions in weaving together of similarities and differences are as characteristic of the etymology of *fit* as of analysis of fit-behavior. Both the word and the behavior are dysjunctive mixtures of disparate, ambiguous, and contradictory elements.

As a juncture of conflict, a point of danger, *fit* is closely related to *crisis*, which means turning point, point of decision. "Fits" and "crises," as events, do in fact occur together in everyday life. The relationship is forthright in my French-English dictionary, which contains this definition: "*crise* (n-f) crisis, conjuncture, decisive moment; fit, convulsion." Elaboration of thought and communication, for example, is punctuated by crises during which the most fitting word must be selected and fitted into the given pattern of sound and sense—of meaning, logic, and grammar. The course of everyday living is, in fact, a pattern of fits and starts, a succession of crises requiring decisions between and about disparate, contradictory, and ambiguous elements.

Crises and fits occur not only in actions pertaining to our immediate purposes and circumstances, they also occur when it is necessary to adjust our immediate activity to larger circumstances and purposes. We repeatedly reorganize the direction, scope, and intensity of our activity. We must take account of and assess discrepancies between the actual here-and-now and other not-heres, not-nows, and adjust our activity accordingly. Crises requiring decisions and fittings-together also arise outside our own activity. Events may intrude by signaling imminent danger or opportunity, bringing activity to a halt and requiring sudden evaluation and action. It is etymologically relevant here that the Chinese ideograph for *crisis* combines two separate ideographs: one for danger, the other for opportunity. It is pertinent, too, that many people are very confused between the dangers of "making fools of themselves" and the opportunities for "putting their best foot forward."

This exploration of the concept of fits allows us to move from the impossible task of describing what a fit *is* to examining what *goes on* in a fit and to the question of how the fitting-together of a fit is carried out. What leads up to a fit and what goes on in one can be suggested by reverting to an analogy between the confluence of disparate etymological elements into our present concept of fits and the confluence of diverse dynamic elements brought into contention in fit-producing life situations, and blended more or less fittingly in the resulting fit. Because analysis of fit-producing, or fit-containing, life situations revealed a complex of elements that shared both similarities and differences—that were both disjunctive and con-junctive—I began to think of fit-contexts as being *dys-junctive*, i.e., momentarily ill-fitting complexes of ideas, images, and impulses. Analysis of fit behavior revealed that condensation, compression, and symbolization had shaped the form and content of fit behavior much as in wit and dreaming. Thus, fits can be thought of as dysjunctive reactions. And the processes producing fits, dreams, and wit can be thought of as brain storms.

Many of the elements providing the basis for these concepts are easily visible in Marvin's fit of spelling. A brief analysis of this particular episode is now in order.

ANALYSIS OF THE "WHISHIT" FIT 4

Sigmund Freud once said, "Find out what's going on and the treatment will take care of itself." Psychiatrists will testify that finding out *exactly* what's going on is not always easy. Trying to ascertain what goes on during fits is particularly difficult.

The course of events culminating in fits is often very complex, involving contention within and between several different features. "Why?" and "how?" involve both specific stimuli and general pattern. And just as fit-producing situations are characterized by conflict, confusion, and complexity, so, too, is fit behavior. Marvin's fit, for example, is a mixture of conventional, caricatured, convulsive, and creative elements. And it is impossible to determine with certainty whether his performance was an *act* planned and executed consciously by him or whether it was a *seizure* organized and carried out not by "him" but by some subpersonal capacity of the brain using "him" more or less as its instrument.

What did happen during Marvin's fit of spelling? The simplest statement is that the teacher asked Marvin to spell a word and that he did so. In form, Marvin did "spell a word," but he did not spell the word "which" correctly. Many generalizations about fits, like the simple statement above, are half-truths. In analysis of fits, it is essential to describe the fit-behavior in detail. What Marvin did do was to spell out "w . . . h . . . i . . . [pause] . . . s . . . h . . . i . . . t."

Was his "whishit" a single, one-piece performance? If so, was it simply a misspelling of "which," an error due to his well-known inability to spell? Usually Marvin did not completely spell out words even incorrectly. He would start, but his efforts would trail off after a few letters. Ordinarily both the teacher and Marvin would have given up after he had tried with "h . . . w . . . ." But this time the teacher was unusually urgent and Marvin unusually responsive. He spelled out "whishit" as if there were such a word, and as if he were suddenly inspired to spell it. One can say that he seemed to be trying to spell "which"; he certainly acted as if he were spelling something. But this account fails to contain all the relevant elements in the situation and in the boy's performance. Just as a major convulsion is only the central part of a complex major convulsive fit sequence, so Marvin's "whishit" was only the central element in a larger complex.

First of all, Marvin gave up his usual pattern of "trying to spell." He first tried "h . . . w . . . ," and then, after the teacher's prompting ("Not h . . . w . . . , Marvin, w . . . h . . ."), he tried again and got further than usual with his "w . . . h . . . s . . . h . . ." before he stopped again. Then the teacher's gesture of resignation produced a crisis and activated him to exceptional activity. When he began his final performance, his whole attitude changed notably and his spelling was measured and steady. He produced an approximate version of "which." In that part of the United States at that time, the word "which" was sometimes pronounced as if it were spelled "whicht," and Marvin's "whishit" may be considered a kind of caricature both of this local pronunciation and of the correct spelling of "which." Many fits are compromises between alternative resolutions of crises—caricatures of genuine syntheses.

Second, though the interaction between boy and teacher was more intense and effective than usual, Marvin's final response was not directly to her encouragement and prompting. He began his final spelling only after she was about to break off their interaction. His response was to her disappointment and resigned movement away from him to the next pupil in line. His fit was, in that sense, a "rebound reaction" to the termination of their engagement. Such rebound effects are common in the genesis of fits, particularly at the end of intense involvements.

Was Marvin's performance a two-piece combination of "conscious" effort and "unconscious" automatic activity? If so, where was the dividing line? Was it when he paused for breath after "w . . . h . . . i . . . ," and started off again with "s . . . h . . ."? Most of the other children to whom I talked seemed to have known at that point what the outcome would be. But they saw the outcome as a deliberate act. They ignored the pre-pause "w . . . h . . . i . . ." and Marvin's abrupt change of posture and facial expression. His beatific look and the measured rhythm with which he spelled out "whishit" were, for them, signs of conscious determination. To them, Marvin "deliberately" spelled out a vulgar, four-letter word. They were not concerned with whether Marvin had done it consciously or unconsciously or with whether he was unwittingly expressing his deep feelings about spelling, school, or life. To them, this was an act in defiance of authority. The school board apparently agreed, for Marvin was soon expelled.

If Marvin's fit, however, began with the abrupt transformation of his manner from that of an angry, confused boy to that of an inspired speller, then his "w . . . h . . . i . . . [pause] . . . s . . . h . . . i . . . t" was a single, complex piece of behavior. This seven-letter utterance combined diverse elements. It was a confluence of: the teacher's demand, the pressure of being on the spot before the whole school, his need to perform for once as a student, and his need to express his feelings. And in this last regard, it was both a compliance with, and defiance of, demands for behavior beyond his capacity. It was many things in one.

In the same way, "whishit" combines the teacher's word "which," a four-letter vulgarism, and the regionalism of "whicht." Conflicting elements in both the fit-context and the person's responsive capacity are characteristically combined in fits.

Upon analysis, fits of epilepsy, fits of neurotic behavior, and fits of conventional activity, as well as fits of insight and creation, are compressed fittings-together of the contending elements with which the person and his brain have been struggling. All fits, in short, seem to be products of the synthesizing processes seen in wit, humor, jokes, dreams, discovery, creation, and epileptic and other fittings-together. These are not separate processes but only different manifestations of a central fitting-together capacity of the brain. They intermingle and overlap. Fits may be creative syntheses that render thinkable the previously unthinkable. They may be witty solutions that allow us at least to contemplate the unimaginable. They may be dreamlike actions or fantasies that portray the problem and caricature its solution. Some fits, of course, avoid the problem or disrupt it convulsively. Frequently, as in Marvin's fit, there are traces of all these processes at work. Fits are, as we say today, "happenings." The answer to "What happened?" depends on how comprehensive or precise one is able to be.

We must keep in mind that fit-producing crises are crises in the continuity of action and awareness. These crises occur when what is going on at the moment suddenly becomes unmanageable. They do not necessarily involve "important" problems such as those of sex and aggression. In Marvin's situation, as in many fit-contexts, the contradictions are not merely simple conflicts between an urge and inhibition, between competing drives or contending persons. There are conflicts within individuals and circumstances as well as between them. When Marvin began with "h . . . w . . . ," for example, the teacher prompted him encouragingly. But it was her earlier "hoo—wich," no doubt, that suggested "h . . . w" to Marvin. (We were taught at that time that "w" was sometimes a vowel, as in Welsh, and equivalent to "oo.") Teacher's "Not h . . . w, Marvin, w . . . h" contradicts her initial prompting and could have been confusing. The structure of her contradicting encouragement resembles the so-called double-bind maneuver* by which some parents are said to throw their children into schizophrenic confusion. "Yes but no" instructions confuse anyone and are common in the genesis of fits.

One other quality of fit-contexts in general, and of the circumstances of Marvin's fit in particular, deserves mention—the problem of a single stimulus versus the cumulative effect of a progression of several events. It can be seen by reviewing events discussed above from another point of view. Marvin was under pressure to spell and spell he did, in a fit of spelling, while holding the class and teacher spellbound. His fit can be viewed as a stimulus-response reaction with the teacher's resigned turning away from him as the triggering stimulus. On the other hand, the interaction between boy and teacher can be seen as a progressive series of interactions culminating with a "last straw." Many fit-contexts contain one overwhelming stimulus which dominates the context; others are characterized by a rhythmic, incantatory, hypnoidal progression of events. In everyday life most fit-contexts have both qualities.

Finally, in Marvin's case, for most of his schoolmates (as in more important and well-publicized cases, for most people) the great question was "How could he have done it?" They meant "Why did he do it?" and were concerned with the problem of motivation. But if his action is viewed as combining diverse situational pressures and several individual reactive tendencies into a single complex of compliance and defiance (and his "w . . . h . . . i . . . [pause] . . . s . . . h . . . i . . . t" is seen in its many-things-in-oneness), the question really is "How did he do it?" And this involves, not motivation as such, but processes of psychophysiology.

The question "How could he [or she or they] have done it?" was much discussed during the 1960s in connection with assassinations, multiple killings, and other "senseless" crimes. "How," "Why," and "What" were intermingled. Motivation was mixed up with method. At the heart of these discussions was a debate about

---

* A "double-bind maneuver" both welcomes and repels, as when a mother tells her child, "Come and sit on my lap, but don't wrinkle my dress."

whether the individual committing "senseless" crimes was to be punished as a criminal or treated as a sick person. The old question of whether a person is "out of his mind" or "in his right mind" was posed as a problem of location—whether someone is "in" or "out"—and as a conception of two minds, one "right" and one "wrong."

There is no meaningful answer to such questions, because people are not in or out of wrong or right minds. People have brains whose task it is to mind their affairs. "Mind" is not a *thing;* it is a process of minding. And it is the brain that does the minding. The problem is not one of persons and minds so much as it is of how the brain, which *personifies* and *minds,* goes about these activities.

The psychoneurophysiological question, the problem of "How," is: Did the person use "his" brain to formulate and execute a plan of action? Or did the brain somehow short-circuit and by-pass its own creation, the personified person, and organize and carry out the action independently, using the individual more or less as a tool? Can mixtures of personal purposive and subpersonal unintended action be produced by the brain? If so, how? And when?

In terms of Marvin, was he a student trying to spell "which"? Or was he no longer acting as a student but rather as a frustrated, angry, and rebellious boy? Did he respond to the crisis by some sort of yanking on his intellectual bootstraps so that he rose, inspired, above himself and produced the one performance which solved everyone's problems? Was *he* "possessed" momentarily by *his* "unconscious," which produced a crude sort of joke? Or was his brain thrown into some kind of psychomotor epileptic fit? All these problems and questions can be reduced to one: Whence came "whishit"?

Marvin's "whishit" had several personal and situational sources, each of which contributed to the final complex combining all of them. These individual elements were compressed and fitted together by the crisis-activated fitting-together capacity of his brain. The guiding principle—the aim—of this fitting-together capacity is seen in the effects of Marvin's fit of spelling. The short-range effects were to restore the continuity of the spelling exercise, to get Marvin and the teacher off the spot, and to relieve the tension all of us had built up. Marvin spelled a word; the teacher had her triumph; the class resumed spelling; and the rest of us went back to our work and loafing. Marvin's fit created and filled a gap in *time.* But the long-range effect was to produce a discontinuity, a permanent one, to put an end to Marvin's distressing and humiliating experiences in school and to the teacher's problem with him. With Marvin out of school, things went much more smoothly there, and one hopes his life was smoother too.

Thus Marvin's fit demonstrates another dysjunctive aspect of fits in that it served ambiguously as both a continuity and a discontinuity in his living. It must have been produced by some kind of capacity for managing the continuity of configurations in space and courses in time. It involved the brain's ability to get from the here-and-now to a different not-here, not-now. These transitions in time-place require the use of time-traveling foresight, hindsight, and insight. Something like imagination, some unusual capacity to "see" is necessary. Hughlings Jackson held that all actions must be preceded by dreams formulated by the brain as models which guide action to its proper completion. Some kind of dream is required for a fit-action as well as any other. In this sense, Marvin's "whishit" was the product of a dream and a good example of how the brain "dreams up" the fits with which it maintains or restores continuity in moments of crisis.

THE INDETERMINATE NATURE AND
LOCATION OF EPILEPTICITY

To "Anything from fright to flatulence can cause a fit," we have added: "Anything from flatulence to fright can be a fit." The picture thus completed is sufficiently comprehensive for grasping fits-as-a-whole, but it is too broad to be useful for precise purposes. It is presented here, however, for exactly that reason—to convey the vast, polymorphous quantity and quality of fits, and to indicate that fitting together is involved in all behavior and experience. The concepts of fit, fits, and fitting together require play on words and much play of the mind.

Discussing the difficulty of catching the quality of fits in words, Jackson said, ". . . it is very difficult to show that such different lines of thought harmonize. Evidently in writing the earlier chapters of this book I must anticipate conclusions to be reached in later ones. I have endeavoured to render my method less difficult to the reader by a free use of footnotes. Such a way of handling a subject is, however, not favourable for clearness of exposition. . . . I have therefore for several years delayed execution of this work. . . ."[1] And Jackson was trying to deal only with epileptic and epileptiform fits. My solution for the impossible task of writing a simple exposition on the subject of fits will be to return repeatedly to one area of interest and to reconsider it from different points of view.

Jackson thought of fits as ranging in a continuum "from the greatest to slightest departures from health." And one can conceive of a straight-line spectrum of fits, with one end in pathology and the other in normal behavior, which reaches from the dramatic "mindless" violence of a major convulsion to seemingly insignificant breaks in thought. But if one tries to plot all the fits on such a continuum, the chain develops too many side branches. Fits sharing important similarities also have significant differences. Any plot of the universe of fits would be a complex, multigalactic structure more or less congruent with the universe of all behavior. Several kinds of fits are commonly recognized in everyday speech, fits of all sorts of knowings, feelings, and doings including fits of epilepsy and of madness. These popular classifications offer certain suggestive clues concerning the nature of fits and of fit-provoking circumstances, but neither they nor professional medical classifications do more than suggest the elusive, essential fit quality that makes an episode a fit. To get at this essential quality, it is necessary to read between the lines, as it were, or even, in Peter Viereck's phraseology, to read "between the betweens."[2] To get at the betweens, it is helpful to give some thought to classifications of fits.

The great difficulty in any effort to classify fits is the problem of pinpointing fit quality. It may seem to reside in the environment, in the behavior seen in the fit, or in the person having the fit. Epileptic fits are a case in point. The indeterminacy of locating epilepticity was a problem even in ancient times. The Romans, for example, attributed fits occurring at moments of tension in senatorial debates to the circumstances and named these fits *morbus comitialis*. On the other hand, fits characterized by falling unconscious were assigned to a *morbus caducus*, a "falling sickness," on a descriptive basis. Another classification of fits directed attention to the "seized" or "possessed" state of the person and was called *morbus sacer*, the sacred disease.[3] In contemporary popular usage, there is a similar shifting of focus. Thus a "fit of temper" hints primarily at personal attributes—people who have fits of temper are likely to have a temper. A fit of laughter directs attention mostly to the laughter itself, to the seeming contradiction between fit and laughter. A fit of disgust seems most heavily laden with innuendoes regarding what might have set it off. Fits of sneezing and fits of hiccups direct attention mostly to what to do about them. All classifications of fits overlap and conflict because fits brought together on one basis differ on another. Furthermore, a fit is actually a sequence of events, and it is difficult to evaluate separately the contribution of situation, behavior, and personal attributes.

Epileptic fits are, again, a case in point. The definition of these fits has been a problem for medicine since Hippocrates wrote the first book about them some 2,400 years ago. Hughlings Jackson could find no absolute distinction between epileptic, epileptiform, and nonepileptic seizures and tried to locate the source of epilepticity in a discharging process of brain cells. Abandoning the effort to define epilepsy or the epileptic fit, he defined instead a physiological process, "an epilepsy" linking all fits. He said, "An epilepsy is a sudden, excessive, and rapid discharge of some part of the brain; this discharge occurs in all degrees; it occurs in all sorts of conditions and under innumerable circumstances."

Such a process could account for any kind of fit. The nerve-cell discharge directly into motor, secretory, and other effector structures could result in the stereotyped, rhythmic patterns of ordinary epileptic fits; or discharge into other nerve centers could activate or inhibit them and their effect upon bodily and personal activities, and produce patterns of action and awareness not at all epileptic. The concept of "an epilepsy" extends the concept of epileptic fit far beyond the confines of clinical epilepsy. All fits, in this light, are epileptic. This means, however, only that epilepticity has something to do with suddenness of onset and termination, stereotyped form and content, and self-limited duration. For epilepticity may be located in the brain but not necessarily in any abnormality thereof, because, as pointed out earlier, the most typical epileptic fit, the major convulsion, can easily be produced from any brain.

To say "all fits are epileptic" is, really, to repeat oneself. Epilepsy means "seized upon" or "seized from above"—in contemporary slang, "all shook up in the head"—hence "all fits are epileptic" means only "all fits are fits." The general term, fit, is all that is actually needed for any seizure from major convulsions to flights of fancy. But if the distinction between epileptic and nonepileptic vanishes, and the dividing lines between other kinds of fits are equally insubstantial, what criteria can we use for our reading between the betweens—for abstracting the essential qualities of "fit-ness"? Jackson's definition of an epilepsy must be replaced by a definition of a fit suitable for illuminating the common qualities of all fits. Such a definition was provided in Chapter 2 as a postulate to analysis of Marvin's fit, from the etymology of the word and from other considerations. It can be restated here: A fit is an episode of behavior or experience put together during a crisis in the continuity of ongoing living to restore that continuity. Crises result from suddenly insoluble conflicts in living, from intrusions of significant danger or opportunity which arrest ongoing activity, and from sudden phase changes in the relations between person and circumstances. Fits are put together by the brain during a trance-like moment of "dreaming up."

The validity of this hypothesis will now be checked by scrutinizing a sampling of the vast variety of fits. Selecting a representative sampling of fits would be easy enough if there were reliable classifications of fits. But *any* classification treats fits as "things" and, as we have seen, a fit is a process. A fit can be anything from a brief muscle twitch, a stab of sensation, or a flicker of feeling to an elaborate act. There are literally thousands of kinds of fits. A fit is a sequence of crisis and resolution, and fits are a recurring part of daily living. We live, in fact, through a succession of crises and resolutions. Thus our sampling of fits must provide examples not only of fit classifications but also of the various mundane and marvelous crises and resolutions that punctuate the living of both ordinary and extraordinary people.

Notes

1. John Hughlings Jackson, *Selected Writings,* edited by James Taylor. Hodder & Stoughton, London, 1931; Basic Books, New York, 1958, Vol. I, pp. 175–176.
2. Peter Viereck, "Russia's Conspiracy of Feelings." *Mount Holyoke Alumnae Quarterly,* XLIX (fall 1965).
3. Oswei Temkin, *The Falling Sickness.* Johns Hopkins Press, 1945, pp. 7, 83.

PART TWO

FITS, DYSJUNCTIVE BEHAVIOR, AND BRAIN STORMS: VARIATIONS ON A CENTRAL THEME— THE UNIVERSE OF FITS

INTRODUCTION TO THE UNIVERSE OF FITS 6

Like the astronomic universe, the universe of fits seems at first glance to be made up of single elements, systems of related elements, and galactic groupings of different "things." But even in the astronomic universe, evidence suggests that there is a steplike progression from hot stars to cold planets, that all parts of the universe were generated by a common process, and that their unity is as significant as their separation. In the same way that artificial distinctions between kinds of fits fall apart with recognition and study of in-between, ambiguous fringe cases, so arbitrary distinctions in the sidereal universe have begun to vanish. Astronomers by observation and study of ambiguous elements like quasars have had to turn from describing their infinitely large universe to studying nuclear processes in the infinitely small. Analysis and explanation of the astronomic universe may begin at any one point, but must inevitably include it all because all points are linked inextricably by common processes—the interactions of atomic particles. So too, when we examine the universe of fits, dysjunctive reactions, and brain storms we find that superficially different elements share common formal features and a common dynamic process—that all are linked as products of the fitting-together capacity of the brain. Each fit proves to be a variation on a central theme.

So, as Hughlings Jackson turned from classifying epileptic fits to defining an epilepsy as a single discharging process producing all epileptic fits, we must define the fit-process as well as the fit-pattern of behavior. To identify this fit-process, we must examine the dynamic characteristics of the *fitting-together process* and the structural features of *fitted-together fit sequences*. Information for this task, however, can be gotten only by comparing and contrasting a significant number and variety of fits, dysjunctive reactions, and brain storms. Yet by even the simplest of classifications—as into long and short, normal and abnormal, epileptic and non-epileptic, or convulsive and creative—merely listing the members of each class would take pages. Indeed, a thorough account of any one fit can require extended discussion, as we have seen in the case of Marvin's fit of spelling. Any systematic effort to deal with the main divisions of the universe of fits would take volumes even if each example were described sketchily and its significance were only outlined. Furthermore, selecting perfect examples of different kinds of fits would necessarily emphasize differences. On the other hand, selecting perfect examples of in-between cases would emphasize similarities and increase confusion. Hence it was desirable to choose examples revealing the interrelations of fits and fit-processes, instances combining similarities and differences. Each example had to contribute something to understanding of the general pattern of the universe of fits and illumine some aspect of the fitted-together quality of everyday living.

The data about fits are full of contradiction and ambiguity. Examination of a single fit stimulates diverse lines of thought leading to entirely different subjects; it is essential to keep in mind that *"plus ça change, plus c'est la même chose"*—the more it changes the more it remains the same thing. As with almost no other subject, pursuing the mystery of fits produces many moments of perplexity and bafflement; in the midst of a puzzle, one is apt to feel puzzled. The dysjunctive quality, especially notable in major fits of epilepsy and creation, has kept many wise men from writing about fits and many interested students from reading extensively what has been written. Readers have been trained to expect, as Marshall McLuhan pointed out in *The Gutenberg Galaxy*, a linear organization of thought—one thing leading to another in logical sequence.[1] And it is difficult to organize an extended linearly logical discussion of fits; things tend to go shooting off in several directions at once. Thinking along several lines at once is difficult; comprehending numerous things simultaneously, and especially contradictory things, requires a nonlinear, all-at-once fitting together; situations that tend to activate our all-at-once fitting-together capacity also tend to activate apprehension that the resulting fit may be one of stunned stupidity rather than a flash of insight.

A discussion of fits and brain storms must necessarily have a dysjunctive quality; it must provoke some intellectual discomfort. A certain play of the mind is necessary to grasp the interplay between diverse aspects of the subject. Dealing with the dysjunctive is the *sine qua non* for trying to comprehend the complexity

of fits in particular, and the episodicity of human behavior in general. However, some people (young-minded readers, perhaps) are freeing themselves from the linear, logical, perceptive activity of the detached observer and are acquiring an ability to comprehend complex situations all-at-once and from inside as participants.[2] Such capacities are very useful in comprehending the universe of fits and in understanding the trancelike processes of fitting together.

Making sense out of dysjunctive data may be facilitated by a preliminary sketch of the general lines of relatedness between fits and an outline of the temporal sequence in different kinds of fits. It may be helpful to think of *fits* as describing the temporal sequence of events, to think of *dysjunctive* as referring to the contentious qualities of situations and reactions, and to think of *brain storm* as designating the whirlwind of intracerebral activity by which dysjunctive complexes are fitted together into fit-behavior.

For a physician, the logical starting point for a survey of the universe of fits would be the greatest, the seemingly most pathological —the *grand mal* major convulsion. From it one could proceed along several lines of decreasing epilepticity toward what Jackson called "the slightest departures from health." Around the major convulsion, for example, are clustered closely related major seizures: migraine and fits of headache; narcolepsy and fits of sleep and motor paralysis; psychomotor seizures and fits of "purposive automatism"; hysteria and fits of disordered awareness and action, etc. From each of these the discussion could then progress to fits of painful reaction to internal and external stress, fits of boredom and physical weakness, fits of compulsive and confused behavior, fits of momentary mental derangement, and so on. In theory, the discussion could go on to the relatively normal dysjunctive reactions of everyday life, but in practice, long before that one would have at least one full volume already.

We could also arrange the material from a medical-symptomatic point of view by discussing the various spectra of epileptic fits as if they began at the littlest-fit end of the epileptic continuum, the brief *petit mal* attack. From these minor, and often hardly noticeable fits—which resemble exaggerated pauses for thought, and which are in many ways the opposite of major convulsions—we could work outward along lines of increasing severity and active involvement of all the functions, to all the major fits of convulsion, frenzy, and catatonic inaction. But both these procedures would deal with fits primarily as symptoms of medical disorder; they would also more than fill the rest of this book. A lot of information can be acquired by considering fits as symptomatic "things," but there is more nourishment for understanding in dealing with them as outcomes of a general process. And using examples primarily to illumine this process is the only way one can show, within manageable time and space, the innumerable possibilities of its expression in fits.

The familiar "pause for thought" is also the natural starting place for all those medically nonsymptomatic fits that make up the other half of an abnormal-normal scheme. On this side of the crisis-pause in thinking, the greatest normal departure from the ordinary is the major act of creation. Between this most successful fit, through increasingly less successful ones, and diverse fits symbolizing and disrupting failing fitting-together activities, is a large area which could be filled in with various arrangements of normal psychomotor and psychosomatic fits. For from the everyday standstills in action and awareness, through those associated with grimaces, gestures, shifts in posture, coughs, swallowings, bursts of thought and feeling, etc., radiate several linear spectra of crises-and-outcomes, along lines of increasing complexity and intensity, to all sorts of marvelous performances.

And around the "major fit of creation," a *grande crise créatrice*, in a fashion analogous to the pattern of satellites around the major convulsion, are grouped all those important performances called acts of skill and mastery, of insight, invention, inspiration, and discovery. And these extremes on the creative side of fits have, we must note, many elements and overtones suggestive of psychological and physiological pathology in their occasional compelled quality, their sometimes explosive spontaneity, their often odd irrelevance to the situations in which they occur, and their coming, unsummoned, out of nowhere. These extraordinary performances, which are as much fits as acts, evoke ideas about inspiration and possession, about the involvement of subpersonal and suprapersonal influences in fits. With such ideas we come once again to the problem of connections between epilepsy and genius, between both of these and mental illness, and between all fits and acts.

Our thoughts also turn from fits of creation to fits of mental illness and epilepsy because many acts of discovery, invention, and creation seem quite crazy in their own time. They appear, from descriptions provided by their authors, to have been produced by something quite like a psychomotor automatism. Only years later, sometimes, are fits of discovery recognized as products of creative, rather than of foolish, fancy—and only then if the cultural context that gives them meaning has changed significantly. Once the idea is accepted that fits of convulsion, of mental illness, and of creation are produced by a similar fitting-together process, it is easy enough to see also that they develop by a similar temporal pattern of elaboration.

There are, then, three conceptual centers, starting points for an exploration of the universe of fits: the dysjunctive situation, the fitting-together process, and the fitted-together dysjunctive reaction —a crisis, a brain storm, and a fit.

The dysjunctive situation is a crisis in the continuity of ongoing activity produced by the sudden coming together of dys-congruous elements. The fitting-together process is a trancelike state of trans-normal "seeing." The dysjunctive fit-sequence reveals the development of discontinuity and its resolution. The nature of the trance-like fitting-together process will be dealt with in Part Four; a brief discussion is necessary here on the general pattern of the fitted-together fit-sequence. On this basis, it will then be possible to consider the universe of fits by means of a relatively small number of examples chosen to illustrate one or more of these three main characteristics: situation, process, and sequence.

In the simplest way, the fit-pattern begins with a transition from prefit events into the performance constituting the fit itself; it ends with another transition, that from fit to postfit activity—a switch-on, switch-off sequence. Often enough, however, anticipatory and rebound reactions occur so that the general form of fits has several phases. These fit-segments will be discussed as separate processes, but in life they flow into each other, and in any one fit some phases may be omitted or condensed. At the heart of the fit and fit-sequence is the trancelike fitting together of the dream from which the fit unfolds. Indeed, many fits consist, as far as one can see, of this trancelike dream alone—as in a fit of inspiration producing a conventional idea of action as if it were a revelation.

Generally speaking, major fits of convulsion or creation are preceded by some kind of *prodrome*—a period of incubation and "cooking-up." Signs that something unusual is going on, and in the making, are visible in evidence of mounting tension, and in its in-creasingly frequent manifestation. The individual may be elated or depressed periodically or continually, and may exhibit one or another disturbance of bodily and personal function. At the end of the pro-dromal period and at the beginning of the fit proper, there are often immediate warning signs. Conflicts and problems, unresolved during the prodromal period, intensify; a crisis is precipitated. The individual clearly indicates to the observant eye that something is now about to happen. The "aura" preceding some epileptic fits, the hallucinations preceding many migraine headaches, uncanny feeling, anxiety, and other such signals mark a crisis in continuity and the transition from personal to depersonalized minding of it.

The fit begins. It may consist solely of the trancelike dissolution of "I," which occurs as the brain takes over from the person the task of fitting together a solution for the unthinkable. Feelings of "something terrible (or beautiful) is happening" may herald the beginning of an extended fit or constitute the content of a brief one.

A postdromal phase of transition and recovery follows the fit and sometimes may be, as in automatisms following *petit mal,* the most notable part of the fit sequence. The recovery phase may be very brief or very prolonged. It is followed, in turn, by the final transition to postfit activity which may have the character of a rebound reaction.

In experiments involving laboratory models of life-situation fits, five phases can sometimes be distinguished by means of significant reactions of brain waves at the transitions between one phase and another. I call these the anticipatory reaction, the "on" reaction, the middle phase of fit activity, the "off" reaction, and the rebound reaction. These reactions, some of which are illustrated in Figure 1, are mentioned here only to underline the fact that fits are sequential structures in time.* Presumably, then, they are produced by that part of the brain that controls the configuration and course of the organism's operations in space-time.

In summary, even an epileptic fit is a fitted-together sequence of epileptic and nonepileptic elements. Fit and fit-sequence are not necessarily synonymous. The fitting-together process takes place in a trancelike moment. There are then two main ideas to be comprehended from a scrutiny of the samples of the universe of fits; the fit as a *fitted-together structure* of behavior and experience, and the fit as a *fitting-together process* within the brain. The latter is the dream and the former is the acting out of that dream.

The fits presented in this section were selected primarily to illustrate the dimensions of the universe of fits, brain storms, and dysjunctive behaviors. The fits, or groups of fits, in each of the chapters were chosen also to show some of the most important kinds of fits and the most significant dynamic characteristics of crises and their outcomes. Space requires omission of many different kinds of fits (narcoleptic fits of sleep, for example), but since those eliminated occur in the same kinds of situations as those

---

* This is one example of Jacksonian "anticipating conclusions to be reached in later chapters."

Figure 1. Some aspects of the concept of trajectory illustrated by events during an experiment with the effect of pain upon brain, body, and person. The experiment as a whole comprises one larger trajectory made up of shorter subtrajectories of reaction to each of the pain stimuli.

In line 1, an epileptic patient reacts to application of moderately severe pain to his little finger much as most of us do to the pain, say, of dental drilling. There is tensing up during the pain, in this instance accompanied by swallowing and wincing, and a slight movement of rebound readjustment when the pain stops.

In line 2, the patient tries to adjust to the experience of pain. He was instructed before the experiment to remain motionless and as relaxed as possible in order to prevent obscuring the brain-wave pattern by muscle-movement electrical potentials such as those that occurred in line 1. In this instance he manages to suppress almost all reaction to pain.

In line 3, he manifests no bodily reaction—there is no muscle tension —but when the pain stimulus ceases, his brain produces a burst of spike-and-dome brain waves typical of a small intracerebral epileptic fit. No visible signs of bodily or personal reaction accompanied this electrical brain storm. In the simplest way, this purely intracerebral, electrical epileptic fit can be seen as a rebound reaction to cessation of pain, and as a discharge of energy, accumulated during the experience of pain, which had not been discharged in bodily tension or movement. It could also be viewed, physiologically, as a product of summation of the effects of three pain stimuli, each of which in itself was just below the threshold for producing an epileptic brain reaction. It also suggests that action energy that cannot be discharged by the brain into muscular activities may, however, somehow evade total inhibition and dissipation and be transformed into pure nerve cell discharges. That is, epileptic fits, intracerebral or extracerebral, might be viewed as dysjunctive combinations of both inhibition and excitation.

In line 4, the patient returns to a relatively normal response to pain— a somewhat reduced version of his initial reaction. A cycle, or subtrajectory, has been more or less completed. His reaction is in between those of lines 1 and 2.

In line 5, when he showed no visible reaction to the pain, he was asked, "That hurt?" just as the pain stimulus ceased. He replied, "Yes, it hurts!" and as he said this his brain reacted with a modified spike-and-dome outburst. The interesting point here is the suggestion that when the patient could respond verbally, and emotionally, the brain-wave paroxysm was much less typically epileptic than that of line 3.

A six-part trajectory

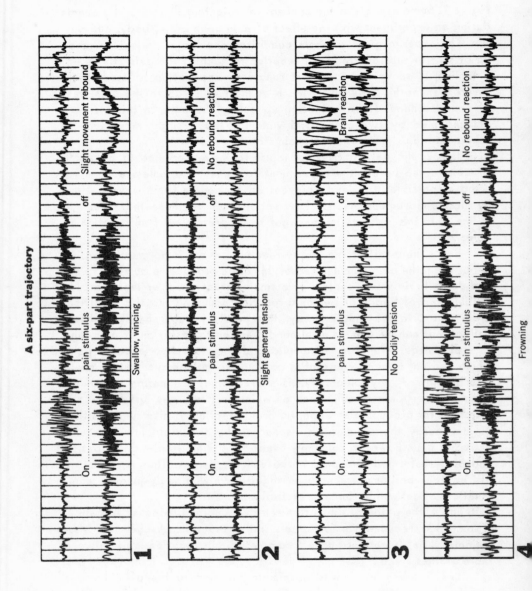

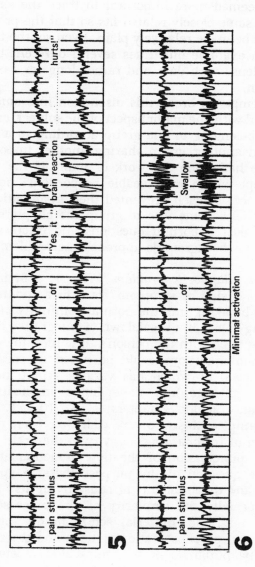

In line 6,
the swallowing reaction upon cessation of pain can be taken as a rebound reaction to the sixth pain stimulus itself or to the end of the experiment. In other experiments, as in this one, a reaction (swallowing, in this case) seen at the start of an experimental trajectory is often seen at the end as a rebound reaction. Later, in repetitions of the experiment, the same reaction may be seen as an anticipatory reaction just before the experiment begins.

presented it seemed more important to trace the similarities and differences of some closely related fits so that the processes underlying all could be made relatively plain. Even so, the final selection, in which each example illustrates several different things, is *ipso facto* rather dense with data and rather long for easy, immediate comprehension.

Several attempts to break this discussion into smaller sections, each concerned with one major aspect of the subject, came to naught because a fit belonging to one group according to a given feature was needed in another group sharing another important feature. Each example had to do the work of many if the whole sample was to be kept within manageable proportions; hence the multiple significances of each prevented their systematic organization into groups. One scheme was to group the chapters according to seven of the most important questions and interests with which people of various backgrounds approach the problem of fits. These are:

1. *The basic diagnostic problem.* What is a fit in terms of its significance as a sign or symptom? Is a fit a spontaneous, irrelevant eruption breaking into the normal continuity of whatever the person is doing? Or is it a breakdown of integrative continuity that has something to do with the person's "intention to do"? These and similar pertinent questions could be posed by means of several fringe cases, each of which has various symptomatic and nonsymptomatic, epileptic and nonepileptic implications. Such a grouping would include Chapters 7, 8, 10, 11, 15, 19, and 25. These examples illustrate very well that what may appear to be the product of "discharging" activity in the brain also serves as a meaningful punctuation of the flow of action and awareness; they raise the question of the purposiveness of spontaneity and automaticity, and the ambiguity of causality in fits. These chapters also raise especially the similarity of the processes behind the symptoms of migraine, hysteria, schizophrenia, epilepsy, homosexual panic, and psychosomatic reactions and the signs of neuronal epilepticity, outbursts of wit, miraculous events, and bodily reactions to creative artistic experiences.

2. *The problem of consciousness and unconsciousness in fits; intention and spontaneity as aspects of motivation and of consciousness.* Fit-behavior may appear descriptively to be genuinely epileptic, i.e., that of an "unconscious" person and therefore quite unintended and accidental, but the appearance of the fit as occurrence, i.e., the circumstances in which it occurred and its relevance to them, may suggest that it is purposive in dynamics. Can a "typi-

cally epileptic" fit (i.e., behavior presumably beyond a person's intention and control, and therefore spontaneous) descriptively be simulated? Chapters 9, 16, 17, 18, 21, and 30 illustrate significant aspects of the relation between fits and intentions, between intentions and consciousness.

3. *The question of importance; the practical importance of "big" fits, and the theoretical importance of little ones.* "Slightest departures" are more frequent, more people have them, and they are more available for study. With "greatest departures" for comparison, we could examine the extremes of the fit continuum for light on the structure and operational significance of all. Chapters 10, 12, 15, 16, 18, 22, 24, and 26 could have been grouped for this purpose, and subgroups concerned with such things as fits associated with "thoughts crowding into my mind" could be made, for example, from Chapters 7, 8, 9, 15, 17, 27, and 28.

4. *The problem of the temporal structure of fits.* This can be posed in terms of when a fit begins and ends. The importance of the transition into and out of a fit, especially when the fit-behavior is purposive in form and not irrelevant to the circumstances, might be studied as one group in Chapters 8, 10, 11, 14, 17, 18, 24, 28, and 31. In this group, one can see the importance of temporal structure, of visible signs that a fit is about to occur, is occurring, or has occurred, particularly in uncanny and horrifying fits, and in cases of murderous, absurd, or illegal behavior.

5. *The question of the interrelation between incremental tension and sudden, spontaneous resolutions of problems.* This question, and other aspects of the temporal organization of fits, can be examined in a group made up of Chapters 22, 26, 29, 30, and 31. All these bear on the question, Is there a *status creativus,* analogous to *status epilepticus,* in which repeated fits make one extended, complex episode (see Chapter 31)? In this chapter, too, one can see that a prodromal period of distressing tension can precede a fit of creation as well as a fit of convulsion.

6. *What is the significance of the fact that convulsive, psychomotor, and fits of purposive behavior are observed in animals other than man?* This and other important questions pertaining to the biology of fits might well be examined in a separate group comparing animal and human fits, as in Chapters 11, 12, 13, 14, 15, 20, and 25. In this group the problems of consciousness, intention, and the social significance of fits could be studied by comparing human and animal "purposive automatisms" which also shed light upon direct, empathic, interorganism communication, and the role of fits in promoting survival and growth.

7. *Questions concerning the magical, mysterious, and uncanny aspects of fits.* These are formulated and studied in Chapters 8, 17, 18, 19, 20, 24, 25, 28, 29, 30, 31, and 32, which could be grouped together and discussed in terms of the metapsychology of fits. In Chapters 28, 29, 30, and 31, for example, an "intention to see" generates ordinary and extraordinary instances of fitting together by "see-ing."

There are, of course, many other legitimate questions, problems, and interests in the subject of fits, especially in this conception of them as encompassing all kinds of episodic behaviors and experiences. The reader will find familiar ones, and many new ones, popping into mind which are not at the moment immediately dealt with. For example, the question of epileptic brain waves accompanying a fit occurs early in this section and is discussed several times later on. A separate discussion could be devoted to this question and to other intriguing and important ones. But there simply is no feasible way to deal with all the most important questions systematically by devoting a section, made up of several examples, to each—too many examples, or too many repetitions and cross references to the same example, would be needed.

The model of the universe of fits presented, therefore, consists of a series of examples beginning with those dominated by convulsive activity and ending with those characterized by the processes of creativity. In between are examples of mixtures of these processes and activities and manifestations of slightest and greatest expressions. At one time or another, and often several times, most of the fundamental questions about fits are dealt with. Occasionally it is necessary, as Jackson said, to anticipate conclusions to be reached in later discussion. If one is trying to understand epilepsy, hysteria, mental illness, mystic experiences, and creative performances—episodic behavior and experience—through the study of fits, one has to deal with fringe examples illustrating several things and characterized exactly by deep ambiguity (even "multiguity"), otherwise one is likely to end up understanding only one kind of behavior, or none, but not all, from the study of perfect, and perfectly isolated, instances of typical kinds.

When the reader finds questions raised for him that are not immediately dealt with he will, I hope, keep the questions in mind until they are dealt with. Or reference to the index may help him find more quickly what satisfaction there is for a particular question. Indeed, this section is really more a series of reference points than an in-line straightforward analysis of a problem which cannot be dealt with by linear logic, and the reader may do well to pursue an erratic course through it.

As astronomers need patience, so explorers of the universe of fits need tolerance for the unbearable type of tension that comes from confrontations with contradiction and ambiguity, for only by "waiting to see" can come a creative resolution of these minor crises in thinking—that is the nature of thinking in a crisis; it is, in fact, the point of the chapters in this section, and of the book.

Each example was selected to provide a somewhat different aspect of the nature of crises, the variations in form and content of their resolutions, and the relations between crises-cum-outcomes to the situations in which they occur. Grasping these three things at once will sometimes stretch the reader's fitting-together capacity, but this stretching has its rewards as a useful instance of mind-expanding.

Notes

1. Marshall McLuhan, *The Gutenberg Galaxy*. Routledge & Kegan Paul, London, 1962; University of Toronto Press, 1962.
2. Charles Davy, *Words in the Mind*. Chatto & Windus, London, 1965; Harvard University Press, 1965.

"ALL OF A SUDDEN IT COMES IN MY MIND I'M A QUEER . . ."

7

Occasionally we pause for thought to break up living into segments of manageable proportions—to bite off no more at any one time than we can chew. In our speech we pause frequently while our brain-mind system arranges thought and communication into appropriate grammatical forms and meaningful verbal content. The pause for thought, the processes that go on during it, and the patterns of knowing, feeling, and doing that arise from it are three aspects of a fit. Most of our living is made up of these fitted-together episodic behaviors and experiences, and an explanation—a psychology—of the spontaneous, nonpersonal, nonrational genesis of so much of our living properly begins with the "pause for thought" during which dreams are dreamed, fits are fitted, fancies fantasied, and actions plotted.

When some people pause, they do so because their thinking confronts an impasse whose resolution is, at the moment, beyond their intellectual and emotional capacity. Patients often block when dangerous or forbidden ideas, images, or impulses cannot be transformed into awareness and communicative action. That such events are threatening is evidenced in various defensive and protective maneuvers (in addition to or concomitant with the blocking of thought). An epileptic patient* (diagnosed by others as having convulsions and psychomotor attacks) was discussing with me a spell of blankness he had had earlier in the day on the hospital ward. "I had a spell this morning in the room . . . a fellow was fooling around with his belt. That's the last thing I saw before the spell." I asked him, "And what did that bring into your mind? What comes to mind about it now?" He answered, "When I find myself watching a guy fool around with his pants, I just begin to

---

* Identity-revealing detail and circumstances have, in all examples, been altered as necessary to conceal identity but retain essential accuracy.

think I'm something like a . . . I can't say it . . . I don't know!" He was tense, red-faced, and seemed both angry and confused. Then he burst out, "I know I'm not a queer!"

The form of his reaction has much in common with other fits, in which an explosive, spontaneous utterance of the previously unutterable follows a blocking delay. This young man, like many another, suspected that he might have had something like homosexual tendencies (whatever they are), but he knew that he was not, in practice, "queer." Terms such as "homosexual tendencies" and "latent homosexuality" were not in his vocabulary, and he could not use them to clothe his thoughts in words. Anyone, illiterate or erudite, will block when suitable verbal forms for realizing subverbal cerebrations are not immediately available.

The person who "can't quite say it"—who can almost but not quite complete an utterance or an action (whether this be verbalizing a thought, bringing about an orgasm, or some other completion)—is in exquisite distress. A breakdown or explosion threatens; ancient devices for preserving the continuity of living activity are activated. The results of their activation is seen in the bodily reactions displayed. Blocking can be produced experimentally by tongue-twisting and brain-twisting tasks, and characteristic reactions can be also obtained in this way from psychosomatic and epileptic patients. The simplest way of producing blocking reactions for experimental observation is to get the person engaged in conversation about significant life problems and wait for dysjunctive impasses to occur spontaneously. Blocking is often quite obvious in protracted pauses for thought, and in the gestures, changes of facial expression, and shifts in posture that accompany them. Minor reactions may signal the occurrence of disturbing thoughts, feelings, and memories. Inquiry into what was going on just before will often uncover significant personal problems.

During my studies of epileptic fits I carried out one series of experiments designed to ascertain what subjective events, if any, were associated with significant changes in brain waves recorded during conversations or while the patient was resting quietly.[1] In one such session, the young man mentioned above was lying quietly while his brain waves were being recorded. The pattern of waves, which had been quite normal, suddenly showed a burst of large, slow brain waves. Runs of brain waves larger and slower than usual are not specifically epileptic but do indicate the sudden activity of some unusual discharging process. (Brain cells isolated from the rest of the brain by chemicals or surgery do tend to beat in unison as if, relieved of their integrative functions, they could harmonize their purely physiological cellular rhythms.) Though this burst of large, slow waves did not specifically signify epilepsy, it did indicate that some kind of epileptic discharging process had been triggered; hence the course of thought and feeling immediately preceding this paroxysm of abnormal waves was explored as follows:

"What was going through your mind just then?"

"Nothing."

"Your mind was absolutely blank?"

"Yes. I wasn't thinking about anything."

"What was the last thing you remember thinking about?"

"Well, I guess about bowling the other day."

"What about it?"

"It was just a regular game. . . . I had a spell there."

"What do you remember about it?"

"I had just had my turn. . . . I was watching the others. The spell just came on . . . there wasn't anything to remember."

"Were you thinking about anything in particular?"

"No. Well . . . I had just got a spare. I was feeling good."

"What did you actually do? Did you speak to anyone?"

"Oh, yeah! I was joking with one of the guys. He got up for his turn and was looking over the balls trying to pick one. I said, 'You won't find any green ones, they're all black.' He didn't say anything. I felt funny . . . afraid people would think I was funny. The joke fell flat. I felt peculiar."

"Did you talk to anyone else? Did anyone else say anything?"

"Oh, yeah! I just remembered! That's what I was thinking about a while ago when you asked me. When I said that about the balls, the guy next to me said, 'You're a character.' That made me feel funny."

"You felt funny?"

"Sort of peculiar . . . like a character."

"What kind of character?"

"A peculiar guy. I thought maybe the guy thought . . . I was sort of . . . well, like a queer. My mind got fuzzy like it does. All of a sudden it comes in my mind I'm a queer. That's when my mind goes blank."

But shocking intrusions of thoughts, ideas, and images toward and into awareness may initiate creative activities as well as cellular discharging reactions. The circumstances facilitating the popping into mind of the ideas and images that trigger composition of poems and music, or which start the solution of scientific problems, are quite similar to those which trigger fits of epilepsy. The processes that elaborate into a creative heightening of man's awareness and improvement of his action, and those which degenerate into abolition of consciousness and convulsive discharge of neuromuscular energy in meaningless patterns both begin, very frequently, in moments of blocking produced by confrontation with the unthinkable and unimaginable.

Notes

1. Wayne Barker, Susan Burgwin, and Donald J. Simons, "The Significance of 'Spontaneous' Abnormalities in Brain Wave Patterns as Observed During Interviews with Epileptic Patients." *Journal of Nervous and Mental Disease, 112*: 187, 1950. See also Wayne Barker and Susan Barker, "Experimental Production of Human Convulsive Brain Potentials by Stress-Induced Effects Upon Neural Integrative Function: Dynamics of the Convulsive Reaction to Stress." *Proceedings of the Association for Research in Nervous and Mental Disease,* XXIX, 90, 1950.

"I'M ALMOST FINISHED" . . . "SO AM I!" 8

In his fits of blocking, the patient's mind went blank and some of his brain cells fell into a pattern of synchronous discharging visible as a burst of large, slow waves rather like those of the sleeping brain. His brain cells, as it were, went to sleep instead of thinking about being queer. His brain seemed to withdraw from the problem; or perhaps it was prevented from dealing further with it by some kind of epileptic short-circuiting process.

Sometimes, instead of blankness, one sees a complex sequence combining both problem-solving and problem-avoiding gestures. All fits combine diverse elements, but in most of them it is possible to identify one outstanding element and to name the fit accordingly. Occasionally, however, a fit-sequence is so complex that it is difficult to give it a particular name. One day in the brain-wave laboratory, I had done a long series of experiments designed to elicit the effect of various stimulus-maneuvers upon the brain waves of one of my most cooperative patients, a young man who had both major and minor convulsive seizures and whose EEG occasionally broke into the three-per-second spike-and-dome pattern said to be characteristic of epilepsy. Noticing that he was becoming somewhat restless and tense, I said, "I'm almost finished." He said nothing at first, but swallowed once, and then his brain waves flattened out briefly in an activation-alertness response, as if he had been stimulated by an unvoiced thought. He said, "So am I." Immediately thereafter a brief outburst of spike-and-dome waves appeared. I was surprised that he said anything at all, because he was usually so compulsively cooperative that he would speak only to answer questions. But we had gotten to know each other during several days of experiments and he evidently felt secure enough to complain jokingly of the weariness and strain he was beginning to feel. Even so, his humorous protest was preceded by a psychosomatic swallowing reaction (as if he were trying to dispose of his irritation by swallowing it) and followed by an epileptic one.

Similar sequences of events are described and illustrated in Part Three. Without brain-wave recording, the epileptic component would have been missed, and "So am I" would have seemed only a simple joke. The humor, swallowing, and epileptic brain waves constituted one complex effort to deal with situational tensions. It must be borne in mind that although spike-and-dome brain waves accompany characteristic attacks of *petit mal*, they can occur without any typical external epileptic manifestations; conversely, *petit mal* attacks are seen sometimes without any accompanying spike-and-dome brain-wave pattern. These most typically epileptic waves can be produced by nonepileptic brains affected by various chemical and physical agents, and they also accompany symptoms other than *petit mal*.

The full-blown *petit mal* attacks that completely disrupt awareness and communication are replaced at other times by punctuative activities which are not at all epileptic in appearance. These *petit mal* equivalents may or may not be accompanied by brief outbursts of spike-and-dome. Here it is important to notice that the epilepticity of brief distortions of action and awareness is not a black-and-white proposition but a matter of gradations from epileptic to nonepileptic.

In Figure 2, for example, during a series of repeated brief hyperventilations (taking a few rapid deep breaths), an epileptic patient was told, "Let's try that again." He swallowed, took four deep breaths, said to himself, "What do you mean, 'try'?" and swallowed again. A brief burst of spike-and-dome waves appeared in his EEG just as he swallowed the second time.

The most important implication of these examples is that sequences of psychosomatic, humorous, and other supposedly nonepileptic reactions, together with epileptic reactions, can be produced by a single fitting-together capacity in one complex reaction. It is as if there were a "running-through" in sequence of a small repertory of responses. Brain storms do not always produce simple outcomes, whether the storms are convulsive, nonconvulsive, or creative. The fitted-together dysjunctive reaction is often a complex sequence, and it may combine all kinds and degrees of fit.

A small fit of humor, swallowing, and spike-and-dome

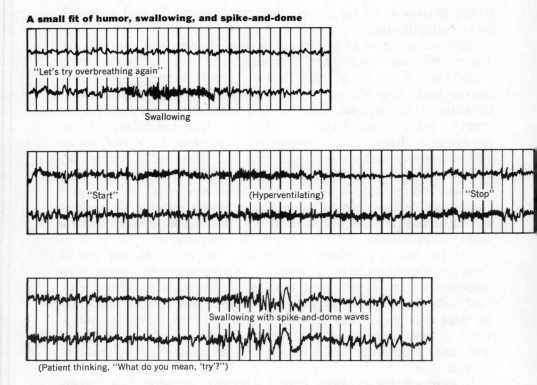

Figure 2. A sequence of events in the laboratory which reproduces the impure complexity of dysjunctive situations and reactions that occur during interviews, and in the course of daily events, in "experiments arranged by life."

The patient, an epileptic, and I had been engaged in a long series of experiments, in part testing the effect upon brain waves of brief hyperventilation, i.e., taking four to six deep breaths in as many seconds. The pattern of response during the series was something like that illustrated in Figure I. That is, the epilepticity and bodily-and-personal reactivity varied rather inversely (i.e., when "he" reacted, his brain did not, and vice versa). In addition, reaction of brain, body, and person tended to wax and wane.

After a period of relative unresponsiveness before, during, and after overbreathing, and of rest, I decided to put him through the brief hyperventilation maneuver once more, and said, as indicated in line I, "Let's try that again." He swallowed, in a stimulus-response reaction to that command, and this response can be interpreted variously: (I) as a conditioned response, because in previous brief hyperventilations, the command to begin overbreathing was often followed by swallowing, bursts of spike-and-dome brain waves, or other transitional phase-change dysjunctive reactions; (2) as a psychosomatic maneuver for disposing of accumulated resentment and tension associated with the experiment and previous hyperventilations; (3) as an anticipatory reaction in adjustment to the overbreathing about to begin, and so on.

He took four deep breaths, and as he completed them, he thought of saying to me, "What do you mean, 'try'? I don't have to 'try,' I'm an expert now. You may be trying to give me a fit." With the completion of this thought, and of hyperventilation, he swallowed a second time, and a brief burst of spike-and-dome waves was seen mixed in with the muscle potential spikes produced by the swallowing. (The effects of thought, feeling, and hyperventilating cannot be separated.)

This simultaneous combination of swallowing with spike-and-dome is one version of "minor epileptic-dysjunctive reaction" in which there are mixtures and sequences of reactions of brain, body, and person. These combinations and sequences are, in fact, minor fits. In Figure 14 (page 184), for example, swallowing is followed in about one second by a brief spike-and-dome reaction; these sequences of events are analogous to the sequential relation between a "motor aura" (at the start of a major convulsive fit) and the subsequent convulsion (accompanied by abnormal brain waves, often of the spike-and-dome variety). Combinations of swallowing and spike-and-dome in minor fits differ only in degree from major seizures combining atypical, nonconvulsive bodily activities with convulsions and epileptic brain waves.

". . . AND THEN I HAD A SPELL"

A dysjunctive confluence of humor, aggression, and epilepticity like that seen in the preceding example is also found in the genesis of some full-blown *petit mal* attacks. A young married woman who, because of her fits, had been consulting me for some months told me during an interview about a pain in one of her legs which had been present when she awoke that morning. The pain was in the thigh muscles used to hold the legs together. As I listened to her description, I thought she was more concerned with telling me about her pain than with getting relief for it. Earlier she had complained of her husband's lustful behavior during the previous evening. Up till then he had for weeks avoided marital relations despite overtures on her part. It seemed she was trying to start a discussion of this problem, so I asked, "Did you ever feel leg muscle pain after intercourse?" She started to reply, "Well, yes . . ." but her speech was interrupted by a *petit mal* attack consisting of absolute immobility of face and body, ending abruptly after about six seconds. Then she continued, "Yes, but not that one specifically," and broke into laughter.

In other conversations during this period, *petit mal* attacks often occurred instead of answers to probing questions or as disruptions of answering. Sometimes attacks were accompanied by humorous reactions, but at other times they were associated with outbursts of anger. Wit and aggression are intimately related, according to psychoanalytic theory,[1] and humorous accompaniments of *petit mal* attacks during psychiatric interviews are not entirely free of aggression. Conversely, outbursts of irritation often have their humorous aspects. To say, therefore, that "wit," "fit," and "twit" are different aspects of a common process is more than a crude play on words.

Petit mal attacks during psychiatric interviews are also accompanied by psychosomatic bodily reactions as well as by overt emotional responses. Swallowing, belching, coughing, shivering, weeping, etc., play their part in sequences of epileptic and nonepileptic dysjunctive reactions. Psychosomatic dysjunctive reactions were interpreted by Dr. Harold G. Wolff and his research group as partial mobilization of biological protective patterns of offense and defense against situational threats.[2] Negativistic, defensive, and protective reactions are logical responses to the efforts of others to force patients to understand too much too soon. Otto Fenichel, one of the great teachers of psychoanalytic technique, stressed the need for tact in making interpretations timely and useful. Harry Stack Sullivan counseled the psychiatrist to clear his throat or make some gesture signifying "get ready," whenever he was about to change the subject or present the patient with something new and perhaps startling.

A schoolgirl patient was telling me about trying to get her mother to admit that the patient needed new dresses and accessories less girlish than she had been wearing. This patient had *petit mal* lapses of awareness and action two or three times in a day at least once each week. She was discussing the circumstances in which she had had one of her spells as follows: "I was lying down thinking about whether to buy a new dress for my girl friend's Sweet Sixteen party when I had a spell." She went on to elaborate: "I was wondering whether the halter dress I had was appropriate. I had decided that it was okay since Mother wasn't anxious about getting another dress to hang in the closet. . . . I have several summer dresses there, but they are all too young for me now. Mother found one, though, that could be fixed up with a new belt. But, you know, the new belt would cost almost as much as a new summer dress. Later, we spoke about it sensibly and I decided not to get a new dress." I asked, "And who was so sensible, you or your mother?" Whereupon she had a *petit mal* attack.

In discussing with me the effect of my question upon her, the patient pointed out that a part of her complex reaction was annoyance that I would twit her about trying to be sensible with her mother when I had earlier helped her to see that contention with her strong-minded mother was unproductive.

Notes

1. Martin Grotjahn, *Beyond Laughter*. McGraw-Hill, New York, 1957.
2. Harold G. Wolff, "Protective Reaction Patterns and Disease." *Annals of Internal Medicine*, 27: 944, 1947.

"MY HALF-SISTER IS CUTE . . ."

When the fitting-together capacity manages, despite repeated difficulties, to get on with the job, one sees a discontinuous pattern of integrative activity interrupted by a series of dysjunctive reactions. Each of the dysjunctive disruptions is a sign of momentary difficulty which may intensify or diminish. The fits of belching and one-sided spasm discussed below will give some idea of this process as well as illustrate the repetition of one kind of fit during troublesome communication. During psychiatric interviews, minor fits call attention to the patient's difficulty in formulating what he has to say and/or to his difficulty in communicating it. The first example in this chapter will illustrate the first kind; the second will deal with the latter.

One of my patients, during early history-taking interviews, had spasms of stiffness and twisting contractions in her right arm and leg whenever she tried to tell me how she had felt as a child about her stepmother, her sisters, and a younger half-sister. The same kind of spasm also affected her arm and leg at the onset of the major convulsions for which she was being treated. Eventually, when she could talk more freely about her problems, these spastic contractions were replaced by fits of air-swallowing and belching. The timing of her air-swallowing and belching is best illustrated by a fragment from one of her speeches.

My half-sister is cute [belch], but she is terribly spoiled. I think Father actually loves her more than any of us. We were too much of a problem [belch]. I am always the goat for my sisters too. After Father was married, we would all of us go over to my aunt's without permission. But I was the one that got the blame [belch] because I was the oldest. I didn't tell them what to do [belch]. If they wanted to come along [belch] that's not my fault. My stepmother told Father I made too much trouble [belch], and he seemed to believe her. He told me to stay out of trouble with her and not to make trouble, but I think he thought *I* was the trouble [belch, belch]. . . .

At this point her arm and leg began to contract and twist about. She then seized the twisting right wrist with her left hand and, as if by an act of will, managed to bring the spasm to an end. Then, tears coming to her eyes, she burst out, "I guess the trouble was that I thought he hated me. I've never been able to say it before, but that's the way I felt!"

Her sudden utterance of the previously unspeakable was a great relief to her. It recalls the case of the young man who could not bring himself to say "all of a sudden it comes in my mind I'm a queer." Patients do punctuate dysjunctively the stream of thought and feeling while formulating it and sometimes repeated punctuations culminate in explosive, disruptive outbursts.

Other patients, or the same ones at other times, have their difficulties primarily in communicating. Some of these react when the physician tries to advance understanding by contributing to a dialogue. One of my patients would take a short gasping breath and hold it briefly whenever she opposed some statement I had made, or if I showed any skepticism or disagreement while she was speaking. I called her attention to these "gasps of astonishment at opposition" and asked her about them. She said, "When you raise an eyebrow or frown, I know what you're thinking and I disagree. I feel like saying, 'Oh, no!' Catching my breath means that I disagree. When I do it, I am summoning up all the forces at my command to resist."

She had been raised by a mother who was a psychologist and "very skillful at handling children." This turned out to mean that mother often gave her long analyses of her behavior and required silence until she had finished the lecture, no matter how much the girl might wish to speak up in self-defense. By the time mother finished, she would have anticipated and demolished any arguments the daughter might have offered in opposition. There would be little left for the girl to say. So she had taken to holding her breath as a means of suppressing her desire to speak up. It was some weeks before she could stop holding her breath when she thought *I* was about to speak up and question her line of reasoning.

A TREMOR OF INTENT

"Psychiatry," Harry Stack Sullivan used to say, "is the study of living in order to facilitate it." To the study of living the psychiatrist should bring not only his medical training but also information and technique from many other fields. Psychiatrists have drawn heavily upon literature and biology for useful analogies and insights. Fits, especially, require ideas and information from all possible sources for their fullest comprehension. In this chapter, examples of dysjunctive, interpersonal encounters will be taken from a novel; in the next, examples of fits will be borrowed from accounts of animal behavior.

In novels, characters develop through their encounters with trials and triumphs of living. In creating one fictional person, the novelist sometimes illuminates the general quality of human life. Quite often, because writers usually are concerned with all aspects of humanity, medical and psychological processes are depicted intuitively. For example, in his *Tremor of Intent*, Anthony Burgess describes a fit of psychosomatic reaction in portraying the outcome of a clash between two of his characters. The scene is a dormitory in a Catholic boarding school for boys in northern England; the protagonists are Roper, a fifteen-year-old boy who is to become an outstanding scientist, and the rather incompetent chemistry master, Father Beauchamp.

> . . . I remember one fifth-form chemistry lesson in which Father Beauchamp, an English convert, had been dully revising [reviewing] the combining of elements into compounds. Roper suddenly asked, "But why should sodium and chlorine *want* to combine to produce salt?"
>
> The class laughed with pleasure at hope of a diversion. Father Beauchamp grinned sourly, saying, "There can't be any question of *wanting*, Roper. Only animate things *want*."
>
> "I don't see that," Roper said. "Inanimate things must have

wanted to become animate, otherwise life wouldn't have started on the earth. There must be a kind of free will in atoms."

"*Must* there, Roper?" said Father Beauchamp. "Aren't you rather tending to leave God out of the picture?"

"Oh, sir," cried Roper impatiently, "we ought not to bring God into a chemistry lesson."

Father Beauchamp chewed that for two seconds, then swallowed it. [Italics added.]

Tamely, he said, "You asked the question. See if you can answer it."

. . . What Roper said, I remember, was that the sodium atom had only one electron on its outer shell (nobody had ever taught us about outer shells) but that the chlorine atom had seven. A good stable number, he said, was eight and very popular with the constituents of matter. The two atoms, he said, deliberately came together to form a new substance with eight electrons on the outer shell. Then he said:

"They talk about holy numbers and whatnot—three and seven and nine and so on—but it looks as though eight is the really big number. What I mean is this: if you're going to bring God into chemistry, as you want to do, then eight must mean a lot to God. Take water, for instance, the substance that God made first, at least the Bible says about the spirit of God moving on the face of the waters. Well, you've got six outer electrons in the oxygen atom and only one in the hydrogen atom, and so you need two of those to one of oxygen and you get water. God must have known all this, and yet you don't find eight being blown up as a big important number in the teachings of the Church. It's always the Holy Trinity and the Seven Deadly Sins and the Ten Commandments. Eight comes nowhere."

"There are," said Father Beauchamp, "the Eight Beatitudes." *Then he had a brief session of lip-biting,* not sure whether he ought to send Roper to the Rector for blasphemous talk. Anyway, he let Roper alone, and the rest of us for that matter, bidding us read up on the stuff in our books. *A twitch started in his right eye and he couldn't stop it.* It was Father Byrne in the dormitory all over again. [Italics added.]

Earlier, Roper had thrown Father Byrne into a fit of hiccups by disputing his interpretation of the clash between good and evil. Roper's Socratic questioning of Father Byrne ends with the latter ordering all the boys to prayer. Roper offers to help Father Byrne, who smells of whiskey.

"If somebody were to thump you on the back," Roper kindly said, "or nine sips of water, sir." [The priest ignores this offer.]

"Almighty God," began Father Byrne, "Who knowest the secret

thoughts of, hic, these boys' hearts. . . ." And then he became aware of a certain element of unwilled irreverence, the hiccups breaking in like that. "Pray on your own," he cried. "Get on with it." And he hiccupped his way out.[1]

Some people seem to have a talent for generating dysjunctive, fit-producing situations. Often, like Roper, they are intolerant of, and intolerable to, any but the smoothest working, genuine authority. In a quiet way they throw authoritarian, nonexpert persons into a fit. Others, like the chronic martyr, provoke those who try to engage in any kind of meaningful dialogue with them by a kind of psychological jujitsu. These people all work, in one way or another, by mobilizing other people's inner conflicts or by seducing others into controversies beyond the capacity of even the wisest philosophers. Very frequently, again like Roper, they then offer solace for the difficulties they have provoked. An important aspect of this example is the sequence of events. Father Beauchamp ignores the warning signs—he "chewed that for two seconds, then swallowed it"—and suppresses his misgivings. He then is led into a situation full of conflicts and confusion and accompanies his final indecision with lip-biting. The dysjunctive situation is broken off when he develops an uncontrollable bodily reaction, the twitching of his eye. Like Father Byrne, he is driven to flight.

Dysjunctive situations and dysjunctive reactions often develop progressively in an extended sequence. The interaction of the protagonists, and of situation and reaction, has some of the formal characteristics of ritualized combat between animals. In these rituals, often the issue is decided long before the end of the interaction. Brain storms, like meteorological storms, are structured in time, and are usually more than a single lightning flash.

Notes

1. Anthony Burgess, *Tremor of Intent*. W. W. Norton, New York, 1966, pp. 8–10.

". . . HE WILL GIVE THE ALARM BY VIOLENT SNEEZING AND IMMEDIATELY FLEE BACK TO THE RIVER"

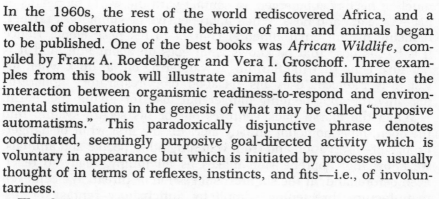

In the 1960s, the rest of the world rediscovered Africa, and a wealth of observations on the behavior of man and animals began to be published. One of the best books was *African Wildlife*, compiled by Franz A. Roedelberger and Vera I. Groschoff. Three examples from this book will illustrate animal fits and illuminate the interaction between organismic readiness-to-respond and environmental stimulation in the genesis of what may be called "purposive automatisms." This paradoxically disjunctive phrase denotes coordinated, seemingly purposive goal-directed activity which is voluntary in appearance but which is initiated by processes usually thought of in terms of reflexes, instincts, and fits—i.e., of involuntariness.

The first example, dealt with in this chapter, depicts sneezing as an alarm reaction when an apprehensive animal reacts to very weak environmental stimuli. The second example, described in the next chapter, describes actual and ritualized combat between male hippopotamuses, and provides some light on how differences in internal chemistry and environmental situation modify instinctive reactions. The third, discussed in Chapter 14, concerns collective defecation as one aspect of the synchronized group behavior of weaver birds; it raises the question of the role of weak stimulation in empathic brain-to-brain communication and touches upon the uncanny element in the epidemicity and contagion of group behavior.

Roedelberger and Groschoff give the following account of the marsh buck's apprehensive sneezing.

> Along the great rivers from the Senegal to the Zambesi the shy Situtunga move through dense reeds, for these three-foot-high swamp antelopes love moisture. Once they have chosen a certain region they defend it jealously against all rivals. During the day

they stand for hours in the river, singly or in pairs, with only their heads, or even just their muzzles, showing above the water. At dusk they begin moving about to feed on the juicy water plants. . . . On their nocturnal excursions they always follow the same tracks which wind like tunnels through the rushes and papyrus, bamboo, and palm forests. Rarely will a Situtunga buck wander out into the savannah, and the moment danger threatens he will give the alarm by violent sneezing and immediately flee back to the river.[1]

What sets off the alarm? Almost any threat or hint of danger. The shy Situtunga finds security in a swamp by hiding in the water and sticking to familiar tunnels through the vegetation which provide both food and shelter. Why sneezing? Note that he spends much of his day submerged, in contact with the world by means of his eyes, ears, and nose. When apprehensive he submerges farther, reducing distant environmental contact to his nose alone. Hence it is by his nose that he knows what goes on about him, and it is not surprising that the Situtunga, wandering out at dusk when his vision is reduced, uses his nasal-olfactory-respiratory apparatus not only for apprehending danger but also for giving the alarm.

When the marsh buck ventures out of his secure swamp into the open, he is no doubt already alert for the first whiff of danger. From self-observation and from watching other people and animals, we know that apprehension makes us all jumpy, ready to react, even beforehand, at the slightest suggestion of threat. We can even manufacture threatening stimuli by anticipatory fantasy or distortion of neutral events; we often jump before we need to.

Thus the Situtunga's sneezing can be set off by very slight, weak stimuli, and these may actually arise from the environment or be hallucinated, as it were, from self-generated excitement. Apprehension is one name for the subjective accompaniment of confrontation with unthinkable complexes such as the many different, competing, and ambiguous odors assailing the marsh buck's nose. The apprehensive organism is vulnerable to weak stimuli, even fantasied ones, which may trigger unresolved and mounting tension into sudden flight reactions. The apprehensive individual reaches out for any excuse for action. Weak and self-generated stimuli, therefore, may set off many instances of seemingly spontaneous fits.

In many motion picture comedies (particularly of the Chaplin, Keaton, Lloyd, and Laurel and Hardy era) people often betrayed themselves in moments of danger by sneezing, and scenes in which the person struggled to suppress sneezing were milked for comic effect. Thus observations of naturalists are supported by perceptions of artists.

"Sneezing," according to Hughlings Jackson, "is a healthy epilepsy." Jackson expressed in this way his conclusion that explosive discharge of motor brain cells was not uniquely epileptic, and that epileptic fit-behavior was produced largely by the same processes of brain, body, and person as normal behavior. In his view, an epileptic discharge was a relatively weak burst of nerve impulses from within the brain which substituted for and acted through the same channels as an ordinary extracerebral stimulus from the body or the environment. When an apprehensive Situtunga, poised for action, erupts into sneezing and flight, the origin of the triggering stimulus may well be indeterminate.

In humans, fits of sneezing, like fits of classically epileptic behavior, can be fired off by any of a wide variety of stimulus-events ranging from sudden bright light[2] to sexual excitement, from irritating odors to feelings of irritation. The interchangeable causes reduce to a common dynamic quality lying between irritation and excitement and a quantitative characteristic which might be thought of as "overload." The quantitative element, of course, varies with the individual's readiness-to-respond, and in an already excited organism may be relatively insignificant. Whatever the proportion of fit-provoking stimulation and receptivity, the brain's fitting-together capacity is activated and appropriately prepared performances are triggered into action. The nature of the action depends upon the organism's endowment, experience, and interpretation of the circumstances. Fits of sneezing, like other fits, seem to have inherited, acquired, and situational characteristics.

The act of sneezing is not a simple reflex. Any sneeze is a complex performance coordinating several sensorimotor components. A sneeze is "reflex" in that it works without conscious, voluntary control. But sneezing can easily be suspended, at least for a while, by volition. It can be modified by intention (pressing upward on the bottom of one's nose) and by the activity of others when they make us self-conscious. Generally, sneezing serves as a device for explosive blowing and washing away of actual or symbolic irritations.

These operational qualities are characteristic of all fits of purposive automatism, even of those in which the purposive aspects are obscure. Among the less obvious purposive effects of automatisms is the self-limitation of behavior. When the Situtunga wanders to the edges of its accustomed watery habitat and confronts the unknown dangers of the open grasslands, its apprehensive sneezing may alarm only itself. Its fit of sneezing and flight may, indeed, serve as a self-induced, self-controlling device for driving it back into familiar territory. The Situtunga lives, as it were, in a self-limited area bounded by its own anxiety and sneezing.

These ideas call to mind stories that horses led from burning barns will, in their moment of panic, try to return to the familiar sanctuary within the barn. They also remind us that studies of human animals over long periods show that fits of epileptic, psychosomatic, and psychiatric symptoms often serve to drive people back into accustomed, though basically unsatisfactory, situations, offering a more or less certain, if spurious, security.

Social interaction also limits the territory of animals' movement. They fight when one crosses into another's domain. The style and intensity of the fighting vary according to several factors. Actual combat over mates and territory is often replaced by relatively automatic ritualized combat which settles disputes without much damage. An examination of one such set of purposive automatisms will further our exploration of this area of the universe of fits.

Notes

1. Franz A. Roedelberger and Vera I. Groschoff, *African Wildlife*, translated by Nieter O'Leary and Pamela Paulet. Constable & Co., London, 1964, p. 88; Viking Press, New York, 1965.
2. Henry C. Everett, "Sneezing in Response to Light." *Neurology, 14:* 483, 1964.

". . . PROPELLING THEIR TAILS TO SHOWER DUNG OVER THEIR RIVALS"

When battling for supremacy hippopotami bulls, who are usually placid, become furious monsters. If a stray bull invades the territory of another out of the mating season, the dispute can be settled by a ritual in which the opponents "shoot" with bowel ammunition, propelling their tails to shower dung over their rival and spread a veritable cloud of odour. During the mating season, however, such skirmishing is but the prelude to a terrible battle which is accompanied by snorting, neighing, and roaring that can be heard for miles around. After some hours of embittered struggle the deeply wounded loser drags himself away from the victor's domain.

—FRANZ A. ROEDELBERGER and VERA I. GROSCHOFF[1]

In this example, the opening phase, the prelude portion, of the full-blown mating-season combat sequence is ritually reenacted at other times as a substitute, or equivalent, for destructive combat. This substitution of a part for the whole, of a ritual for the "real," is analogous to the substitution of an equivalent part for the whole major convulsive fit sequence that one sees in the long-term pattern of symptoms in cases of epilepsy. The briefer and milder equivalent fits occur in circumstances in which a major convulsion usually appears (as, for example, before menstrual periods, after excessive consumption of alcohol, during quarrels, etc.), but apparently the fit-provoking circumstances or the fit-susceptibilities of the patient are somehow diminished at these times.

For hippopotamus bulls, mating season is the crucial influence that turns ritualized equivalent into full-scale combat. The precipitating event is an encounter between two bulls, neither of which promptly makes a gesture of submission. In mating season the presence of receptive females provides "releaser" stimulus-cues for secretions and internal changes that then "energize" fighting. Without releasers and energizers, many purposive automatisms have little steam and become ritualized, stereotyped fit-behaviors. Fortunately, many disputes between animals are settled by ritualized combat, and in many species actual, destructive fighting is the exception.

Occasionally, for no apparent reason, a solitary animal will suddenly go into fighting, mating, or nesting rituals even though no prospective opponent, mate, or material for nesting is at hand. These brief bursts of "vacuum behavior" (so called because it is grossly out of context) have much in common dynamically and descriptively with human psychomotor fits. It is possible that some weak environmental stimulus—an effective releaser unnoticed by human observers—sets them off, or that they are triggered by a spontaneous intracerebral discharge of accumulated tension which has the same effect as a stimulus-induced discharge.

Survival and strengthening of a species may be served by contests of strength during mating season which ensure that the most potent males will breed with the most attractive, stimulating females. However, survival is even better served by preseasonal ritualized contests which preestablish dominance so that destructive combat during mating season is avoided or shortened. And, in fact, as noted earlier, many species do utilize ritualized trials of strength to reduce injury during the contentions necessary for the establishment of rank and dominance.

Ritualized decision-making implies that considerable communicative sharing of appraisals goes on between the contestants. And intensive studies, as by high-speed slow-motion photography, show that both ritual and "real" combat have elements of a duet between partners as well as of a duel between antagonists. The pattern of interaction is not simply an alternating exchange of blows and counterblows, of tit for tat. Anticipation of each other's actions goes together with evidence that both animals come to foresee the same probable outcome. Who is to win and who to lose seems clearly to be established at a moment of decision and agreement well before the end of the engagement. A kind of mutual validation of shared appraisals of the course of the combat, and of each other's styles, seems to take place at these points of decision and change. Action is then broken off through a series of gestures, or suddenly ends with a duet in which the roles of winner and loser are acted out.

My own observations of fighting between semiwild pony stallions of the New Forest in England confirm that even in mating season struggles for supremacy and choice of mates is often carried on by largely ritualized and nondestructive duet-duels. In these rituals, defecation and sniffing of the opponent's feces seems to play a significant, if poorly understood, part. Odors are potent activators of automatisms—from fits of convulsing through fits of remembering to fits of creating.

Recent explorations of the function of the so-called olfactory brain in integrating "instinctive," "involuntary" biological activities with "voluntary" ones provide a basis for the ancient association between odor and coordinated automatisms. It is quite likely that odors are the unrecognized releasers, the weak environmental stimuli, that set off many episodes of human "vacuum behavior." Elephants are thought to activate and energize themselves by sniffing their own odor-producing glands.

In Western culture particularly, a large and prosperous industry thrives on first deodorizing, by means of soaps and chemicals, and then reodorizing, by means of lotions and perfumes, an increasingly larger number of men and children as well as women. All this because we have been taught that the natural odors we and others produce are *offensive.* Even so, as Kinsey pointed out, the individual, activated into biological preparation for offense, is at the same time more than halfway activated for sexual activity. Patterns of physiological preparation for fighting and mating share many common elements. The seeming contradiction between these somewhat disparate activities is resolved when it is recognized that both are distance-diminishing and contact-promoting. We may be aware only of our conditioned feelings of repulsion, but our bodies may react with disturbingly lustful responses to the unrecognized effects of certain odors. In years past, dancehall sharpies bent on seduction believed, not without reason, that "perfuming" their breast-pocket handkerchiefs by keeping them for a while in their armpits aided their efforts to excite chosen females.

It may be that the increased freedom for "four-letter" thinking gained during the 1960s will in time allow us to think more freely about aspects of behavior previously censored wittingly or unwittingly. We may then be better able to understand and resolve some of the contradictions between our "nature" and "culture" and to work better with them.

The role of odors, gestures, visual patterns, and other weak environmental stimuli and their interaction with organismic states of readiness-to-respond will be dealt with further in the following and later chapters. It is sufficient here simply to suggest that human fits of convulsing or creating may be set off by organism-environment interactions like those activating the sneezing marsh buck or the feces-throwing hippopotamus.

Notes

1. Franz A. Roedelberger and Vera I. Groschoff, *African Wildlife,* translated by Nieter O'Leary and Pamela Paulet. Constable & Co., London, 1964, p. 49; Viking Press, New York, 1965.

". . . FROM NEARLY EVERY NEST A WHITE RAIN FALLS AS BY COMMAND"

In this third example from *African Wildlife*, we come to the role of weak stimuli and the problem of empathic, direct brain-to-brain communication in group activities. Weaver birds live in colonies; their individual nests are built close together in trees which look as if they were loaded with coconuts; the birds move about in swarms, and the collectiveness of their living extends into communal defecation during sleep. What happens at night is described by Roedelberger and Groschoff:

> After a day of common activity when they have all sung together, set out in search of food together, and flown to the watering places, the whole industrious swarm slips into their spherical nests for the night. But even during sleep their community spirit brings about exemplary collective hygiene. Thrice nightly a quiet whispering comes from the tree, and from nearly every nest a white rain falls as by command.[1]

Who gives the command? What is its nature? How is it transmitted? Or is the synchrony of defecation merely the result of sameness of diet, simultaneity of feeding time, and identity of the weaver birds' digestive processes, so that simultaneity of emptying the bowel follows upon simultaneity of feeding? If so, there must be little individual variation from bird to bird; so great an identity and interchangeability of individuals would be even more marvelous than the fact of collective defecation.

Are the birds conditioned by their group living so that the sound of the droppings coming spontaneously from the first few birds triggers off defecatory reflexes in the others? Is the thrice-nightly bowel emptying a matter of synchronized cycles of sleeping, waking, dreaming, etc.? Could there be such an empathy between these communal birds that the activity of one brain affects others?

No one knows exactly how the thrice-nightly "exemplary collective hygiene" comes about. But I believe that there is a direct, empathic (brain-to-brain or mind-to-mind) communication of uncanny stimuli and meanings in fits of epilepsy, schizophrenia, and creation. Much of the aversion to epileptics results, I think, from unrecognized empathic apprehension of the patient's distressing involvement with the uncanny aspects of the fit-situation and of revulsion against the uncanny overtones of fit-behavior.

Most people react adversely to the slightest whiff of the uncanny, and even in the form of awe-inspiring, ecstatic, transcendental experiences, the uncanny makes people's "hair stand on end," and gives them shivers and gooseflesh. The effects of poetry, as artists know, depend upon communication of meanings achieved by the juxtaposition of contending elements, so that one perceives not only what is between the lines but also "between the betweens." Such subverbal, or interverbal, meanings are *ipso facto* in the area of the uncanny.

Epidemics of fits—whether of defecation in sleeping weaver birds, of hysterical and convulsive behavior among excited adolescents, of fads in fashion-minded women, or of war hysteria in grown men—do spread by a kind of contagion, and do respond to measures for controlling epidemics of infections. Contagion of fits is an ancient problem in the history of epilepsy and of medical psychology. In this process something called "imitation" is as important as what is called "infection." Imitation came into question, historically, in cases of epilepsy in which the first fit followed shortly after the patient-to-be witnessed another person having a convulsion. In a broad clinical experience today, one sees enough instances of this kind not to dismiss the ideas of contagion and imitation solely as old wives' tales.[2]

Direct and lasting influence-through-seeing also occurs in the "imprinting" process by which young animals, ducks and geese for example, acquire behavior patterns from whatever animal they happen to be watching during sensitive periods in their early development. Imprinting and imitation are involuntary, unavoidable. They stand in relation to ordinary learning-by-observation in the same way as hypnotic suggestion does to logical persuasion. More ordinary modes of learning by observation can also spread through a group by a kind of contagious mimicry. Japanese behavioral scientists studying tribes of wild monkeys, for example, observe that significant skills invented by one enterprising monkey spread rapidly through the group in an epidemic of learning by seeing and doing. Animal automatisms have sources in inheritance, imprinting, imitation, invention, and social learning.

Some of the performances of police and citizens during the ghetto riots in American cities during the 1960s showed many characteristics of automatisms generated by apprehensive readiness-to-react triggered by weak or even nonexistent environmental stimuli, and spread by epidemic contagion. Failure to recognize and comprehend the uncanny element in these situations leaves a vacuum filled by explanations solely in terms of organized "police brutality" and of "outside agitators." A parallel between some aspects of these riots and combat between hippopotamuses is not merely fanciful; it is revealed by the sameness of pattern and duration from one riot to another, whatever the competence, tactics, and intentions of the leaders of the city administrations and black communities. These contests have elements of both ritual and real combat, but most importantly they are decision-making interactions; they will very likely not subside until some more suitable means of posing the issues and reaching decisions is developed by a fitting-together process that arranges the contention effectively.

Notes

1. Franz A. Roedelberger and Vera I. Groschoff, *African Wildlife*, translated by Nieter O'Leary and Pamela Paulet. Constable & Co., London, 1964, p. 91; Viking Press, New York, 1965.
2. Oswei Temkin, *The Falling Sickness*. Johns Hopkins Press, 1945, pp. 113–114, 213, 215–216.

"THE EGGPLANT GOES HERE!"

Fits commonly occur, in life and in psychiatric interviews, as immediate responses to questions or during formulation of answers. A relationship between the origin of fits and the formulation of awareness and communication may have something to do with the relative taciturnity of epileptics and the avoidance by physicians of pursuing, in conversations with patients, the possibilities of significant connections between convulsive fits and the circumstances in which they occur. It certainly has something to do with the precipitation of fits and with what goes on during them.

In his book *How Children Fail*, a compendium of misadventures between schoolchildren and teachers, John Holt explored with one class how they felt when their teacher asked a question they could not answer. Most of the children, Holt observed, went into a kind of shock. They were "stunned" for a moment and then got busy with various maneuvers for avoiding the appearance of stupidity. Though they were "stopped" by unanswerable questions, the children tried to keep going in one way or another and to conceal the block.[1]

In my own experience, in conversations with patients I have often unwittingly provoked major fits and sometimes wittingly precipitated minor ones by sharp and probing questioning. Also I have observed that fits often occur while the patient is trying to formulate answers. Schoolchildren who have *petit mal* attacks (and keep diary notes of the circumstances in which these occur) report that many of their fits during school come on just as they are about to answer questions, especially in written examinations. These "intention-to-answer" fits are closely related to many other fits that occur as an intention is about to be "real-ized." I recently saw a boy who has right-sided tonic paralysis whenever he starts, "without thinking," to get up from a chair. This kind of fit, in turn, blends into others exemplified in the following:

A nineteen-year-old youth had psychomotor epileptic fits, usually at home, sometimes at school, but rarely when hanging around with his gang. Whatever the circumstances, fits occurred when he was in some way put "on the spot." When he was with friends, he used his considerable wit to get "off the spot" and seldom had fits. According to his family, the boy's fits consisted of brief episodes of confusion during which he mumbled Latin prayers. With parental approval, he was considering becoming a priest. He was the youngest of five sons. He told me that he was babied by his parents, bossed by his brothers, and patronized by his teachers. When he resisted domination by his brothers and argued with one of them at home, his mother would stand behind the patient making signs at the brother not to aggravate him lest he have a fit. Various such interfamily processes interfered with his efforts to break out of junior status.

During an interview with him and his father I probed rather insistently into the circumstances surrounding a fit he had had two days earlier. The father reported that in this fit the patient mumbled prayers and looked "peculiar"; it had taken place while he and the boy were planting in the family garden. I asked the patient for his version of the event. He remembered only that he and his father were "discussing" what they would plant and where. I asked about the details of each step in their activity and what they had said. I got some details about their talk and work interspersed with reassurances from both that there had been no dissension, that nothing unusual had happened. The boy's fit came out of the blue, as it were. They "maybe" had "argued a little" about where the eggplant was to go, but all was otherwise smooth. So I said, rather sharply, "Well, something must have been going on! These things don't usually come out of the blue, especially in your case."

At this the boy started to answer but stopped; his face went blank, then red, then became fixed in a frowning, frozen expression. He looked around the office as if seeking something. Then he took some paper from my desk and tore it methodically into small squares. These he proceeded to lay on the floor in lines and rough patterns, mumbling rather incoherently as he did so. Among his mumblings were a few Latin words, but mostly there emerged distinct phrases such as, "Eggplant . . . that's eggplant . . . carrots here . . . tomatoes . . . damn fool . . . tomatoes there . . . damn fool could see. . . ." He emphasized some placements with vigorous pointing and nodding. From time to time he looked contemptuously at me as if he were instructing a stubborn but idiotic pupil. Suddenly his face and manner returned to normal; he looked at me and asked, "What did you say?" His father saw this fit as typical.

Later, with the father out of the room, the boy talked about this fit and the one of two days earlier. He spoke of difficulty in reconciling his desire always to behave respectfully toward his father with his growing contempt for certain of his father's performances. Two days earlier, before his fit, he had tried to criticize his father's scheme for the garden and to put forward what he felt was a better one. He was "irked," he said, when his father would not even accept his ideas about where the eggplant was to go. It was in the garden at the peak of annoyance with his father that he had his fit. In the office, with his father present, he had felt trapped, unable to talk freely about his life problems because his father was there. He was angry with me for thus putting him "on the spot." He was angry with his father because he felt generally oppressed by him. My comment, "Well, something must have been going on. . . ," triggered a complex reaction. He resented my having his father present. He felt that I was as blind as his father to his need for recognition as an independent individual. Thus his fit combined "telling me" about relations with his father and "telling me off" for my own transgressions against his self-esteem.

Both the "telling" and the "telling off" were embodied in a caricature or mimicry of gardening. There was only the slightest hint of Latin prayers. Many psychomotor fits are performances dramatizing in a half-revealed, half-concealed fashion ideas, feelings, and activities that the person cannot quite clearly recognize, communicate, or perform. Difficulties in formulating these ideas, images, and impulses into coherent patterns of action and awareness arise not only from conflicts between content and conscience, between individual and environment, but also from conflicts within the ideas, images, and impulses themselves.

The half-revealing, half-concealing quality of behavior in such fits suggests the processes of repression, displacement, and disguised expression by which hysterical symptoms are said to be generated. These processes involve a shift from "conscious" to "unconscious" control. But discussing such performances in terms of mimicry suggests a shift from the personal to the biological. It directs attention to such things as "playing 'possum," "ritualized territorial combat," and other biological protective activities. These maneuvers in offense and defense, fight and flight, or approach and avoidance are derivatives of a basic "still reaction," a state of intense immobility produced when danger arrests ongoing animal activity. The still reaction is a precursor for any and all the activities of which the organism is capable.[2] It is therefore a condition of relative omniscience and omnipotence for the individual organism. In this and other respects the still reaction is a hypnoidal state induced by crises, for bringing the total capacity of the organism to bear for resolution of a crisis.

But mimicry also has its overtones of "putting on"—of pretense, purpose, and intention. These shift attention back to the level of "conscious" and "unconscious" personal operations. So both psychomotor fits and "playing 'possum" involve contradiction between personal and organismic elements—interactions and interminglings of "mind" and "brain."

In the trancelike condition of psychomotor fits, both human and nonhuman animals are in some ways responsive and in other ways unresponsive. During his fit the patient ran out of paper, took some more from me when I offered it, and went on with his arranging. Thus, though psychomotor fits do unroll more or less automatically, they are modifiable by the circumstances in which they occur. Clearly, the "person" may be "unconscious," but some part of "his" integrative capacity is aware and capable of varying behavior accordingly.

The sustained red-faced frowning of this patient (and similar circulatory, respiratory, and secretory reactions of other patients) suggests that biological centers controlling involuntary bodily processes are activated during psychomotor fits. But some of the activities seen in such fits, however stereotyped or caricatured they may be, are of the personal, voluntary type. The brain centers controlling the fit are able to override prefit behavior and substitute both involuntary and voluntary behavior. Some sort of brain-within-a-brain seems to take possession and produce a combination of organismic and personal action and awareness aimed at dramatizing, if not resolving, the crisis.

Very few people are acquainted sufficiently with the neurological works and workings of the brain to speculate about the nature and location of the "highest centers" or "center of centers" which could integrate organismic and personal activities in such moments of crisis. But most of us are familiar enough with our own and other people's behavior to recognize that we all have fits and that some center for fitting together these episodes must exist. This center is seen at work when someone is momentarily stumped for an answer, and we can almost see the wheels turning as he tries to organize his answer.

Lots of people are "touchy" about something and "throw a fit" of one kind or another at the mere mention of the topic to which they are vulnerable. For some it is a person; for others it is politics, religion, young people's activities, etc. Some people "clam up" and "freeze"; others get "purple in the face" or "hot under the collar." Often these fits are quite stereotyped, but they are not simple reflexes; they result from very complex causes and are expressions of complex meanings.

Notes

1. John Holt, *How Children Fail.* Pitman, New York, 1964.
2. J. Grandson Byrne, *Studies on the Physiology of the Eye: Still Reaction, Sleep, Dreams, Hibernation, Repression, Hypnosis, Narcosis, Coma, and Allied Conditions.* H. K. Lewis & Co., London, 1942.

"WHAT DOES 'MINCOPERT' SPELL?" 16

In his classroom studies of "games" teachers and students occasionally play, John Holt describes the combined set of reactions children experience when the teacher is fond of occasionally "throwing them a bit of a curve to keep them on their toes." These reactions reproduce in a small way the universe of fits. Among the behaviors observed are caricatures of the correct answer seemingly produced by processes similar to those behind Marvin's "Whishit."

On one occasion, a child stumped by the task of spelling "microscope" finally, in desperation, produced "mincopert." Holt found, when he presented this misspelling to another class, that two children guessed that "mincopert" was an effort to spell "microscope."[1] I have tried this problem of recognition on a number of people, and it is surprising that quite a few of them could identify "mincopert" as a garbled version—a halfway deciphered form—of "microscope."

It is well known that some people are better than others at decoding garbled communications. Some schizophrenics, for example, can accurately interpret, it is said, the significance of behavior whose meaning escapes experienced psychiatrists. In these processes, both recognition and interpretation are probably involved in the reshuffling of clues and in the closure of Gestalts leading to comprehension.

But exactly how we know what another person means by a word or a gesture constitutes a very real problem in recognition, interpretation, and comprehension. And how we know what another person means by a seriously misspelled word is also rather mysterious. In games such as charades and Twenty Questions, some people can make remarkable leaps from very slight clues in getting the correct answers. It is quite possible that some kind of direct empathic transfer of meaning—like that observed in weaver birds, in the conversation of gestures of ritual courting and combat, and in paralinguistic communication via weak stimuli or faintly perceived general pattern—is responsible for one's recognizing what is spelled by "mincopert."

Notes

1. John Holt, *How Children Fail*. Pitman, New York, 1964, pp. 38–39.

"IT'S GETTING MIGHTY HOT IN HERE!"

Epilepticity, in the form of the occasionally abrupt episodicity
of everyday behavior—our numerous "fits and starts"—is no
stranger to any of us. Nor is creativity, in the guise of the "great
ideas" and brain storms that come to us all at one time or
another.

The idea that epilepticity and creativity share a common process,
episodicity, has very important consequences. It provides a link
between fits of creation and convulsion, and also a bond between
ordinary "us" and extraordinary "others" who are epileptic or
creative. It raises interesting questions: What, for example, is the
common psychophysiological link between creative people who
awaken from sleep with long-sought answers popping into their
minds and epileptics who awaken with "terrifying prefigurations"
heralding oncoming fits? What are the similarities between these
two "hypnopompic"* events (so different in content and similar in
form) and the ideas, images, and moods that may come to any of us
on awakening?

Such questions are illuminated by attention to a group of brain
storms associated with disorganization of the brain-mind-person
system produced by rapid, rhythmic—"incantatory"—psychocere-
bral activity. When an epileptic patient has an episode of peculiar
behavior coming and going suddenly, lasting a few seconds or
minutes, and in the circumstances in which he often has a convulsion, the nonconvulsive episode may legitimately be thought of
as an epileptic fit, as genuine as any other. These equivalents are
said to be epileptic because they happen to an epileptic person in
epileptogenic conditions.

One of my patients usually got red in the face and "hot under
the collar" before his convulsions. His fits often occurred in the

---

* "Hypnopompic" events occur at awakening; "hypnogogic" ones at onset
of sleep.

heat of an argument when his thoughts were oscillating between "I'll kill him—*but*—I mustn't hurt anyone" extremes. At that time he would begin to tug at his collar and exclaim, "Phew, it's getting mighty hot in here!" According to his wife, he "did not know what he was doing," and would even try to open windows already open. His behavior was not wildly inappropriate, but it came and went suddenly, and he was amnesiac for the conversation immediately preceding these episodes, which were, I believe, epileptic-dysjunctive reactions.

Over the years I have encountered a whole class of people who have peculiar behaviors and strange experiences that fall descriptively somewhere between classic (and rather mythical) "pure" schizophrenia, epilepsy, and narcolepsy. Their symptomatic episodes have the (1) suddenness, brevity, and irrelevance to the circumstances of epilepsy; (2) bizarreness, "loose-thinking" dissociativeness, and the hallucinatory quality of schizophrenia; and (3) narcoleptic "yes-but-no" obsessive oscillations between polar attitudes: crude, almost hallucinatory symbolizations of the conflicting elements and their effect (see Chapter 24); and an unusually clear relation between symptom and an intense burst of sudden emotion, as in narcolepsy.

These strange experiences and peculiar behaviors make up a whole galaxy in the universe of fits. Their significance for us here is that similar events can be produced by drugs and physical agents (from incantatory rhythms to "shocking" experiences of one kind or another) that derange the senses, dissociate thinking into nonlogical or paralogical modes, and attenuate the "I." One of these "psychoanarchizing" agents is flickering light. Physicians in classical Greece used a whirling potter's wheel as a convulsigenic agent in medicolegal testing for epilepticity in slaves offered for sale. The effectiveness of this test depended, I believe, on its hypnoidal flickering-light effect. Certainly, through the years, epileptics have described to their physicians fit-provoking circumstances characterized by encounters with flickering light and other rhythmic influences. One patient, for example, had seizures while driving down a tree-lined road through a pattern of light and shadow made by the late afternoon sun. Today reports describe seizures of one kind or another set off by flickering TV screens, kinetic art exhibitions, rhythmic sound, etc.

In the 1940s, at the University of Chicago, Drs. Earl Walker and Ward Halstead led a research study of the "flicker-fusion" frequency at which patients and normal subjects begin to see flickering light as continuous ("critical fusion frequency").[1] They studied circumstances affecting this fusion frequency, which seemed to have a fundamental psychophysiological significance. At certain frequencies, they noted, the flickering light began to "drive" the brain's ten-per-second brain waves into synchrony with the flicker frequency, i.e., when light flickering at ten per second is shone into the eyes of a subject whose brain waves are also oscillating at ten per second, slowly increasing the rate of flicker may drive the brain waves into faster oscillations too. A surprising discovery was that some people began to produce epileptic brain waves under the driving influence of flickering light, i.e., waves would accelerate from ten to twelve to, say, eighteen per second and then break into three-per-second spike-and-dome. Here at last seemed to be a simple, harmless tool for provoking epilepticity for diagnostic and research purposes.

Long before all these clinical and experimental observations began emerging and converging, a link between flickering light and bizarre experiences had been well known in nonacademic, nonmedical circles interested in psychedelic experience (years before they were called by that term). Experimenters with intermittent light and moving images, in the era preceding modern motion pictures, concerned with mystical and artistic uses of deranged or altered consciousness in trancelike seeings, were well aware that rhythmically intermittent illumination produced trances and other strange effects on mind and body.*

In England, W. Grey Walter, a leader of research into brain waves and behavior, explored the significance of flicker-fusing, "photic driving" of brain waves, and the influence of reinforcing agents. He reports the case of a man who "found that when he went to the cinema he would suddenly feel an irresistible impulse to strangle the person next to him; he never did actually throttle anyone, but came to himself with his hands around his neighbor's throat. This impulse occurred most often when he moved his head suddenly while the screen was brightly lit. When subjected to artificial flicker he developed violent jerking of the limbs when the flash rate was high—up to fifty per second—which is about the flicker rate of cinema projectors. He could prevent the jerking by voluntary tensing of his arms."[2] Sudden movement of the head triggered this patient's fits. Sudden head movement makes some people giddy, and it activates the brain structure involved in

---

* The idea that the intelligent or superstitious laity acquires ideas and information from and after their discovery by scientists is one of our most illusory modern-day myths. Research indicates, for example, that by a kind of precognition, artists see forms only later seen by scientists using microscopes, etc.

"alerting-reactions." Closing the eyes and sudden emotion are among the reinforcing events that trigger flicker effects.

Reports by other brain-wave laboratories reveal that the effective flicker rate differs considerably from person to person, that co-ordination of flicker frequency and brain rhythms must be quite precise, that particular characteristics of the general circumstances and personal conditions and actions are important, and that effects vary from muscle twitches through strange, psychic experiences to actual convulsions.

Walter improved the effectiveness of flickering light by design-ing devices for automatically controlling the light by brain-wave changes so that flicker would be fired, fed back into the brain, and augment any shift from normal toward epilepticity. Whenever significant changes in the spontaneous brain-wave pattern oc-curred, they triggered the flickering light into action. With this self-triggering method for amplifying the effect of flickering light, in *"more than fifty per cent of young normal adult subjects, the first exposure to feedback flicker evokes transient paroxysmal discharges of the type seen so often in epileptics* [spike-and-dome waves]. This 'first time' response dies away with continuous exposure, except in the three or four per cent" whose flicker-evoked responses were "indistinguishable from those previously regarded as 'diag-nostic' of clinical epilepsy."

Walter points out that electrical discharges in the nerve-net of the jellyfish, accompanying its movements, are quite similar to those that occur in the human brain during the convulsive stage of a major seizure. He speculates that "epileptic seizures may be a necessity for this or that degree of complexity of combination between the myriad units of our Olympian nerve-net, considering that wherever two or three nerve cells are gathered together a seizure may occur." His work, and that of other electroencephalog-raphers, certainly supports his conclusion that "epileptic seizures are not the exclusive property of the clinically epileptic brain."

This conclusion is no news to physicians, who have long known that people not otherwise epileptic do have convulsions in special circumstances (children with fevers, for example). The one fact that several chemical and physical agents can produce a major convulsion in anyone shows that the mechanisms and processes for a convulsion are inherent in every brain. As Dr. Arthur N. Foxe puts it, "As odd as it may appear to common sense, the presence of epilepsy in an individual does not indicate that a mere onlooker, who never had a seizure, may not have a weaker consti-tution for the disease than the sufferer. . . ."[3]

A strong chain may break under stress whereas a weak one may remain intact if it escapes exposure to the specific amount and kind of stress that would damage its weakest link. Or experience may strengthen the originally weakest link in the constitutional make-up and weaken another; or the chain may not be stressed at its weakest link. Foxe adds, "A New Yorker, in whom the presence of malaria is unlikely, does not thereby have a greater resistance to malaria than a resident of the tropics who may be suffering from malaria."

Notes

1. Ward C. Halstead, *Brain and Intelligence*. University of Chicago Press, 1947, pp. 70ff.
2. W. Grey Walter, *The Living Brain*. W. W. Norton, New York, 1953, p. 98.
3. Arthur N. Foxe, "Antisocial Aspects of Epilepsy," in *Epilepsy*, edited by Paul H. Hoch and Robert P. Knight. Grune & Stratton, New York, 1947, p. 73.

"WHEN WE CAME TO APPOMATTOX . . ."

An incremental build-up to a fit, a sudden transition from inter-personal communication to intrapersonal absorption, and other significant fit-processes are illustrated in an episode recounted by William Golding in his book *The Hot Gates and Other Occasional Pieces.* In one piece called "Fable," the British author discusses the background of his novel *Lord of the Flies,* and tells the following story to illustrate one aspect of the complex human condition.

> But there is another kind of force which we call history; and how uncontrollable that force is even in the most detached of men was amusingly demonstrated to me only the other day. I was being driven over the last battleground of the War Between the States, a historical episode which I am able to observe with some objectivity. My driver was a Southerner and a scholar. His exposition to me of the situation was a model of historical balance. He explained to me how the South had embarked on a war they could not hope to win, in support of a pattern of society which could not hope to survive. He was perhaps a little harder on the South than a Northerner would have been; but judicially so. As the day wore on, his voice began to return to its origins. Emotion crept in—not very far, because of course he was a scholar, and scholars are detached and unemotional are they not? At a discreet forty miles an hour we followed the wavering fortunes of battle down into Virginia. Here, he told me, Lee had performed that last incredible tactical feat in the defence of Richmond; here, Grant had side-stepped—but what was this? His voice had lost all pretence of scholarship. Insensibly the speed of the car had increased. When we came to Appomattox, this educated and indeed rather cynical man grunted, "Aw, shucks!" and drove past the place where Lee surrendered to Grant at seventy-five miles an hour.[1]

The transformation from detached scholar to emotional South-erner—from quiet-spoken, careful driver to silent speeder—is as surely a fit as any other episode called by that term. Maintaining the role of detached, objective scholar by dissociating regional emotionalism required increasing tension. Prodromal signs warn of an impending crisis. His speech begins to shift from academic to Southern. Emotion creeps in. Immediate warning signs appear when his scholarly pose falters, pressure on the accelerator increases, and the car begins to move faster. At Appomattox, the grunt, "Aw, shucks!" is not unlike some of the verbal cries that immediately precede convulsions. But instead of a convulsive fit, he falls silent, presses hard on the gas, and speeds away.

"Aw, shucks!" was a warning sign that the scholar had given up the struggle, as, earlier, Lee had done at Appomattox, and the sudden acceleration to seventy-five miles an hour may be taken as a rebound reaction following that giving up. Fits are often seen as rebound reactions following intense and prolonged tension-laden activities. In a sense, the sight of Appomattox was the last straw triggering conversion of accumulating tension into an explosion. Appomattox stood for an intricate complex which could not be managed by the detached, objective scholar. How many traffic violations are set off by similar reactions equally deserving of the designation fit?

Structural and dynamic analogies between nonconvulsive and convulsive fits have been emphasized because it is difficult to overcome all at once the tendency to associate fits with some kind of paroxysmal disease. A fit, as in this example, is an effort to master dysjunctive complexity.

It is especially important in times when artists are often accused of being neurotic or worse, and many paintings and poems are said to be products of eccentric if not sick minds, to avoid characterizing all fits as symptoms, i.e., as signs of disease. Both convulsive and creative fits are outcomes of "dis-ease" in the sense of unsettling contention between disparate elements of a dysjunctive complex of contradictory ideas, images, and impulses. It is necessary to remember, however, that there are performances—often quite complex and elaborate—which are mistaken for voluntary acts of the conscious person but which really are organized and carried out by subpersonal processes for which the "person" should not be held responsible.

Notes

1. William Golding, *The Hot Gates and Other Occasional Pieces.* Harcourt, Brace & World, New York, 1965, p. 91.

THE JACK RUBY AND OTLEY CASES 19

Anyone watching a major convulsion recognizes it as a fit. And
when someone to whom we are talking suddenly breaks off the
conversation and begins to behave bizarrely, as in the "fit of
gardening," we recognize this performance, too, as some kind of a
fit. Even the "fit of speeding" can be recognized as such because of
the abrupt transition at "Aw, shucks!" from carefully driving
conversationalist to silent speeder. We recognize fits easily enough
when we see such definite transitions and clear differences between prefit and fit behavior.

But there are fits in which the transition is very subtle and
fleeting, and fit-behavior is deliberate and methodical—as if the
person were in full possession of his faculties. When, in addition,
the person is not under close scrutiny, and is unable or unwilling to
provide information about the episode, defining such purposive
automatisms as irresistible fits meets objections. This is particularly
true when crimes are committed during fleeting epileptic purposive automatisms.

During the trial of Jack Ruby, who shot and killed Lee Oswald,
the accused assassin of President Kennedy, Ruby's attorneys
introduced evidence suggesting that Ruby might have killed during
an epileptic automatism. Several prosecution neurologists, psychiatrists, and neurosurgeons (perhaps alarmed lest ancient supersti-
tions connecting epilepsy with criminal and sinister tendencies be
revived) disagreed, as did the jury. In general, it seemed that
physicians as well as laymen thought the defense's contention
preposterous, and that "fits of killing" (or killing during a fit) were
unheard of. Yet the possibility was advanced by no less an authority
than Dr. Frederick L. Gibbs, a lifelong student of epilepsy and
brain waves who had studied Ruby's brain waves.

None of the news stories I saw at the time searched the history
of epilepsy for similar happenings; it may be well to offer some

here. In 1854, Delasiauve collected many cases of court proceedings against epileptics, including one in 1808 in which a murderer was acquitted on the basis of epilepsy. Indeed, in 1824, Platner had even argued that an epileptic might not be guilty despite evidence of premeditation and intent to harm, and with no evidence of prior epilepsy.[1]

The following case from the past avoids the heat of contemporary controversy.

One day in the late 1800s, in the town of Otley in Yorkshire, England, a farm laborer who was known to be a poacher and violator of game laws saw a police officer approaching on the road leading by his house. Whether the officer was about to call upon the poacher is not known because the man went into his bedroom, took up his gun, opened the window, and shot the policeman dead. During the ensuing uproar, the man was seized. He was "in his right mind" by that time but claimed that he knew nothing about the crime. No one present believed him; he was charged with murder and tried at the Leeds Assizes. During the trial the accused's physician, a Dr. Ritchie, testified that he had treated the man for epilepsy, and that the man often had fits in which he carried out elaborate, well-organized activities for which he had amnesia. On one such occasion the man harnessed his horse to a cart, drove several miles, and came out of his fit not knowing what he had done.

Dr. Clifford Allbutt, who later reported the case, testified in the prisoner's defense as an expert witness. He had examined the accused, studied his case, and supported Dr. Ritchie's opinion that the man had recurrent epileptic automatisms and had shot the policeman during one of these. Dr. Allbutt cited similar cases of epileptic automatism from his own practice. The jury acquitted the defendant on a plea of insanity, and he was committed to a Yorkshire asylum. Some weeks later, during one of his fits, he gouged out both his eyes.[2]

We can agree with Dr. Ritchie, Dr. Allbutt, and the jury that the poacher shot the policeman during a purposive automatism, i.e., he behaved like a "thinking machine" or a guided missile. We could also cite many similar automatisms* during which individuals have taken merchandise from stores without paying for it, driven cars long distances, cooked meals, and done other things

---

* Cases of this kind were cited long ago by Gowers in his monograph on epilepsy, first published in 1885 (Dover Books, 1964). Victoria Lincoln argues persuasively that the famed Lizzie Borden killed her parents during a psychomotor automatism (*A Private Disgrace: Lizzie Borden by Daylight*, G. P. Putnam's Sons, New York, 1966).

requiring some degree of what is called "conscious control" for their performance.

Some of the mystery is removed, and the paradox of behaving "consciously" during a "fit of unconsciousness" is reduced, if we substitute for "conscious control" some such phrase as "audiovisual sensory feedback." We tend to think that the person is in charge of things if the individual behaves as if "he" (more accurately "it") saw and heard what goes on around him. But the brain can carry on hearing and seeing (and other functions requiring sensory feedback) during sleep and hypnosis, for example, when the "person" and "consciousness" are sharply limited.

In automatisms, the individual behaves as if "he" were responsive to, "aware" of the environment, and the fit persists until a particular action is completed. Sometimes these completed fit-acts terminate in sleep; sometimes they end when the person goes back to what he had been doing at the start of the fit. In other cases, interference with the fit awakens the person and he comes out of it, often surprised at where he is or at what he has been doing. Amnesia is thought to be common to all these fits.[3]

These automatisms raise important questions for psychophysiological theory, as well as for law and justice, because they blur the distinction between fits and acts. The distinction rests upon an assumption that fits are produced by the brain, that acts are done by persons. Acts can be punished; fits can be treated—although throughout history there are times when the distinction between treatment and punishment is hard to see.

In purposive automatisms, brain and person are more or less fused; the brain absorbs the person. The brain uses the inherited and acquired capacity of the individual to achieve ends which the person might well have fantasied, dreamed, wished, or intended but could not otherwise accomplish. Who or what should get treated or punished?

This argument brings to mind the concepts of possession, inspiration, autohypnosis, will power, and other processes of transcending or subverting personal, rational control of behavior. Existing theories cannot cope with such processes nor with the situations in which they arise. Distinction between fits and acts is maintained by distinctions between normal and abnormal, conscious and unconscious, responsible and irresponsible, voluntary and involuntary, and so on.

As medical ideology clings to an artificial distinction between epileptic and nonepileptic, so our general ideology clings to a distinction between fits and acts. "How could he have done it?"

(Whatever possessed him?) tends to get answered in terms of "He committed a wrongful act; he shouldn't have; he should be punished." The alternative, "He had a fit," is unacceptable to many unless the individual is lying on the floor, foaming at the mouth.

Dr. Allbutt said, in his comments on the Otley case, the "epileptic automatism is a state so marvellous, and to the inexperienced so incredible . . . I admit the awful difficulty of doing justice in some cases of this kind. . . . Heraclitus said that a city must defend its law as it defends its walls; but he was also a great prophet of dynamics and would have taught that the static mind of the lawyer must perforce come to terms with the dynamics of biology." But lawyers, of course, have no monopoly of static minds nor of difficulties in comprehending the dynamic biology of fits, especially of purposive automatisms.

The sequence of crisis and outcome is evident in fits seen at first hand, but the *point of crisis,* the beginning of the fit, is hard to find in secondhand reports. Assuming the trial verdict were correct, and that the shooting were done during a fit, when did the fit begin? Testimony from the person having the fit is not always accurate on this point. Amnesia may wipe out events transpiring just before the fit. In other cases, awareness may be retained until after a fit is well under way, so that the person believes the onset to have been later than it was.

Then, too, even epileptic automatism is not quite the same thing as an epileptic fit. If the exceptionally large, slow-and-fast brain waves recorded during convulsive fits, and in intervals between the fits of epileptic patients, are an indicator of epilepticity, these unusual brain waves may or may not be present during an automatism. If they are present, then the automatism can be thought of as epileptic fit. If they are present just before onset of the automatism, but not during it, then the performance can be thought of as a postfit automatism. Presumably, in the latter case, discharge from a focus of epilepticity in the brain inactivates higher control centers while at the same time activating lower sensorimotor centers coordinating the automatism. Abundant evidence suggests that very transitory and unnoticed fits of epileptic electrical activity within the brain may be followed by protracted performances which are absurd or destructive. They may not be technically epileptic—they are not, that is, accompanied by epileptic brain waves; they are, nevertheless, as epileptic as any other fit.

But without brain-wave recording or direct observation, we are unable to spot the onset of many purposive automatisms. Was some kind of epileptic fit, for example, triggered in the poacher by the sight of the policeman? Did it continue until he came to his senses on being apprehended? Or had he already had a small epileptic fit which left him in a postfit state of hypersuggestibility so that the sight of the policeman launched him into lethal activity?

We know that environmental cues can influence behavior in postfit automatisms and in psychomotor fits. In this sense, the person during such a fit is no more unconscious than a sleeping mother, a person in a hypnoidal state, or, for that matter, a waking person whose attention is focused narrowly on a very small activity. Thus, once again, by our difficulties in finding the transition between prefit and fit and in distinguishing between behavior during a fit and behavior after a fit, we encounter, via the problem of purposive automatism, the problem of fits and acts—the problem of how and why the brain organizes anything.

Notes

1. Cited by Oswei Temkin, *The Falling Sickness.* Johns Hopkins Press, 1945, p. 258.
2. John F. Fulton, "Clifford Allbutt's Description of Psychomotor Seizures." *Journal of the History of Medicine,* 12: 75, 1957.
3. Jackson, *Selected Writings,* Vol. I, pp. 120ff, provides many examples of the range of what he called "mental automatisms."

"IT WAS AN INSTINCTIVE REACTION"

In the Otley case and in other instances of extraordinary activities carried out during epileptic unconsciousness, the sequence of thought and feeling just before the fit and the mental processes during the fit-action are often unknown. Some light is shed on the general pattern of fit-progression by a story that recently appeared in a London newspaper.*

A barrister's wife told an inquest yesterday that she put cotton wool in her baby son's mouth to deaden the noise of his cries.

"It was an instinctive reaction," said Mrs. Anne Johnson, of Hampton Road.

The baby, four-month-old Peter, stopped crying—and died after swallowing the cotton wool.

Mrs. Johnson was distressed as she explained at the inquest how she tried to stop her son's cries last Sunday night.

She said she and her husband were visiting his parents.

Peter had been put to bed in his carry-cot and by 11 P.M. he was hungry.

He began to cry a lot, and Mrs. Johnson *became worried* that the neighbours might be disturbed. ["Worry" is one version of "thinking" in a crisis.]

She went on, "I wanted to deaden the noise and, unfortunately, I put a piece of cotton wool in the baby's mouth. *It was an instinctive reaction.*

"I continued changing him and, after a few minutes, I looked at him because there was no sound.

"The cotton wool had gone. He had swallowed it. I suppose I tried to recover it, but I could not."

An ambulance was called, and oxygen was given to the baby without success.

Dr. David Smith, a pathologist, said that death was due to asphyxia.

---

* Names and locale have been altered, as elsewhere.

In recording a verdict of misadventure, the coroner expressed his sympathy to Mr. and Mrs. Johnson. [Italics added throughout.]

Distracted by the baby's continued crying, worried about neighbors complaining, Mrs. Johnson had an inspiration to solve her problem with the cotton wool. She acted on it and then occupied herself with changing the baby. Her concentration on this task was so intense that she was relatively unconscious of anything else, including the fact that her son was suffocating. The sequence of "great idea" and its execution in a state of fascinated absorption is common to all sorts of extraordinary performances, including fits of killing, of heroism, of bravado, of foolishness, of humor, of practical jokes, of artistic performances, and other spontaneous actions. The great idea usually occurs in a setting of tension and serves to resolve it, sometimes fortunately and sometimes most unfortunately.

". . . FOR HE IS A CHOSEN VESSEL" 21

The Biblical account of the Acts of the Apostles tells the story of Saul, a Jewish "hawk," much disturbed by Christian agitators and a zealous advocate of a hard policy toward the followers of Jesus Christ. When St. Stephen was stoned to death, Saul went on to make "havock of the church, entering into every house, and haling men and women committed them to prison." But the Christians increased their agitation and Saul escalated his persecution of them. We read in Chapter 9 of the Acts:

> And Saul, yet breathing out threatenings and slaughter against the disciples of the Lord, went unto the high priest, And desired of him letters to Damascus to the synagogues, that if he found any of this way, whether they were men or women, he might bring them bound unto Jerusalem. And as he journeyed, he came near Damascus: and suddenly there shined round about him a light from heaven: And he fell to the earth, and heard a voice saying unto him, Saul, Saul, why persecutest thou me?
>
> And he said, Who art thou, Lord? And the Lord said, I am Jesus whom thou persecutest: it is hard for thee to kick against the pricks. And he trembling and astonished said, Lord, what wilt thou have me to do? And the Lord said unto him, Arise, and go into the city, and it shall be told thee what thou must do. And the men which journeyed with him stood speechless, hearing a voice, but seeing no man. And Saul arose from the earth; and when his eyes were opened, he saw no man: but they led him by the hand, and brought him to Damascus.
>
> And he was three days without sight, and neither did eat nor drink. And there was a certain disciple at Damascus, named Ananias; and to him said the Lord in a vision, . . . go into the street which is called Straight, and enquire in the house of Judas for one called Saul of Tarsus: for, behold, he prayeth, And hath seen in a vision a man named Ananias coming in, and putting his hand on him, that he might receive his sight.

Then Ananias answered, Lord, I have heard by many of this man, how much evil he hath done to thy saints at Jerusalem: And here he hath authority from the chief priests to bind all that call on thy name. But the Lord said unto him, Go thy way: for he is a chosen vessel unto me, to bear my name before the Gentiles, and kings, and the children of Israel: For I will shew him how great things he must suffer for my name's sake.

And Ananias went his way, and entered into the house; and putting his hands on him said, Brother Saul, the Lord, even Jesus, that appeared unto thee in the way as thou camest, hath sent me, that thou mightest receive thy sight, and be filled with the Holy Ghost. And immediately there fell from his eyes as it had been scales: and he received sight forthwith, and arose, and was baptized. And when he had received meat, he was strengthened. Then was Saul certain days with the disciples which were at Damascus. And straightway he preached Christ in the synagogues, that he is the Son of God.

Thus was Saul, the persecutor of the Christians, converted into Paul, their principal evangelist. This episode follows reasonably well the general fit-sequence pattern outlined earlier. There is a period of prodromal incubation in Saul's increasing fervor in persecuting the Christians. He acquires a great idea in a hallucinatory revelation that as a blinding light serves as an aura. For three days he is withdrawn and blind like a "dummy foal" (see Chapter 22) or as in human fugue states. He recovers suddenly and regains his strength. Then he resumes vigorous religious activity, only now, as in creative shifts, or epileptic deaths and rebirths, on an entirely different basis.

It is not my intention to disparage or to secularize this account; I can only comment on its nontheological aspects. From the medical point of view, and in connection with fits as structured episodes of behavior and experience, it is necessary to point out that hallucinatory experiences quite similar in form, and sometimes in content, are not uncommon in migraine and epilepsy as well as in other fits of mental illness, and that a feeling of having gone through a kind of death-and-rebirth experience, which has somehow changed one significantly, is not at all unheard of after major convulsions. Other great spiritual leaders have had similar experiences. Mohammed, indeed, had a major convulsive seizure at the time of his enlightenment and other convulsions on significant occasions thereafter.

"ONE IS A WANDERER" 22

Convulsions and related epileptic fits occur throughout the animal kingdom. Dying animals often go into convulsions; convulsions are not uncommon in serious illnesses and injuries. In other animals, as in man, fit-producing events range from the obviously critical to the seemingly insignificant, and fit-behavior ranges from the grossly convulsive to patterns of action essentially normal in form but abnormal in their inappropriateness to the situation. Fits of animal epilepsy, as well as of psychosomatic and psychoneurotic reactions, can be precipitated in animals by experimental conflicts, frustration, and excessive stimulation. Thus, in animals as in man epileptoid reactions cluster around purely epileptic convulsive fits and connect them to behaviors not ordinarily thought of in connection with epilepsy, or for that matter with any disease. The continuum of fits in race horses provides an example.

"About 1% of thoroughbred foals which are born under supervision in boxes develop convulsions very shortly after birth," according to the authoritative British *Veterinary Notes for Horse Owners,* by Captain M. Horace Hayes.[1]

> The convulsions always follow a very easy delivery after which the foal seems perfectly normal. However, sometimes as soon as ten minutes later, whilst the foal is attempting to get to its feet for the first time, or after it has got into the standing position, it commences to jerk its head up and down, then it becomes unsteady on its feet or suddenly falls into an outstretched position. It often emits a barking noise somewhat like a dog and is soon overtaken by violent fits or convulsions. Next it makes fierce galloping movements and arches its neck and back in a violent manner. Generally there is profuse sweating. The whole episode is somewhat like a violent epileptic fit and 4 or 5 men may be required to restrain the foal. . . .

After comments on immediate treatment, the account continues:

> When the convulsions have abated . . . and when very careful nursing is practised throughout the illness, a large proportion of these animals recover and do not show any subsequent untoward effects. However, during the recovery phase they pass through two very definite stages which are referred to as the dummy foal and the wanderer. The dummy usually sits silently in its box, seemingly unaware of its surroundings and free of any convulsions. The wanderer is able to stand unaided. It seems to have little appreciation of its whereabouts or even of the presence and importance of its mother. Generally it walks incessantly around the box and appears to be blind. . . . *The three phases are probably only variations in what is a single disease.* Some foals which are afflicted never show convulsions or "barking," they are born dummies or wanderers. . . . [Italics added.]

Wanderer foals may seem to be blind during their fits, but they do not blunder into things. Probably, like humans in psychomotor automatisms and sleepwalking, their visual perception operates as an automatic visual-guidance system. Adult horses who may have no history of convulsions or of wandering occasionally become stall-walkers. They have fits of incessant pacing back and forth in their stalls. Their compulsive pacing can be interrupted at times by feeding sugar lumps, and they do not appear to be blind. Nevertheless, these episodes are clearly fits; that is, even when thought of as compulsive, neurotic, rather than epileptic behavior, they are fits in the sense of "spells"—of self-limited, nonvoluntary, relatively automatic, repetitive performances.

The same situation prevails with other animals. Dogs have convulsive fits, psychomotor fits, and fits of "compulsive" behavior. Dogs such as terriers, who become both chronically bored and episodically hyperactive when confined for long periods in kennels, have compulsive fits. Terriers, in fits of running, become so absorbed that they are relatively unresponsive to any but the most vigorous stimulation. They may snap or bite anyone trying to catch them. They often run so fast that they go up the walls of a small enclosure and across its ceiling.[2]

Compulsive walking in horses, epileptic wandering of foals, or compulsive running and epileptic running fits in dogs, are closely related. These related behaviors can best be understood as outcomes of a common, fitting-together process activating different levels of organization of the nervous system. From this point of view, their interrelation makes sense, their relationship to other animal automatisms is explained, and their place in the universe of fits can be grasped.

Notes

1. Capt. M. Horace Hayes, *Veterinary Notes for Horse Owners.* 15th ed., revised by J. F. Donald Tutt. Stanley Paul, London, 1964, p. 313.
2. Drs. Herbert French and Albert Pontick, veterinarians, personal communication.

A Successfully Simulated Fit of Epileptic Convulsion Deceiving an Expert.

"LE GRAND MAL RÉUSSI" 23

The brain storm described here was selected because it has many of the aspects of all great ideas; because it was a very well-put-together performance, conjunctively creative in form if disjunctive in effect; and because it raises the question of how well conscious intention can produce the appearance of spontaneity. It involves problems of will power, of voluntary control of involuntary processes, of the taking over of persons by great ideas, and of motivation in epilepsy, hysteria, mental illness, and in ordinary episodes of behavior.

Pretended epilepsy and simulated convulsions were common throughout Europe in the 1500s; beggars and vagabonds simulated convulsive fits for mercenary and criminal purposes. Epileptic fits were also simulated to escape torture and punishment. With the rise of nationalism and national armies, epilepsy became a justification for avoidance of universal military conscription. Many who simulated epileptic convulsions could be unmasked through their ignorance of the pattern and nature of symptoms. But some simulators produced convulsive fits convincing to any but the most experienced physicians. The main procedure for exposing competent simulators was the infliction or threat of pain. In the presence of the supposedly unconscious patient, physicians made dramatic preparations for diagnostic testing and treatment (cauterization with a hot iron, castration, etc.), and the simulators promptly recovered, often begging to be spared.

When the leprosariums of Europe turned into catch-all prisons for holding all those excluded from society, and some prisons in turn were transformed into asylums and hospitals, accurate diagnosis of epilepsy became important as a means of separating epileptics from the mentally ill. The separation was thought desirable because it was believed that convulsions could be "caught" by hypersuggestible insane persons. Indeed, in the eighteenth century, many medical authorities believed that hysterical convulsions were an imitation or even a simulation of epileptic convulsions.

In French asylums, doctors took advantage of their opportunities for study of epileptics and mentally ill persons and gained confidence in their diagnostic ability. The great physicians, like Esquirol, might use the threat of burning irons to break up epidemics of convulsions among groups of children in orphanages and schools, because they prided themselves on their ability to make diagnostic distinctions between "genuine" epileptic and simulated convulsions by power of observation alone.

On one occasion, noted by Oswei Temkin in his history, *The Falling Sickness*, Esquirol, speaking to a group of doctors, claimed that it was possible to unmask any simulator of epilepsy. His authoritative disquisition was rudely interrupted when his brilliant pupil Calmeil suddenly fell to the floor with all the signs and appearances of a major epileptic convulsion. Esquirol was most concerned about this tragic occurrence, but Calmeil broke off his simulated fit and proved to the master that even he could be deceived.[1] How could Calmeil have done it?

It must be pointed out that loss of reactivity of the pupil of the eye to light, which was held even then to be a prime diagnostic sign of epileptic unconsciousness, can be seen in seizures that are hysterical in origin; that insensitivity to pain can occur in self-hypnosis as well as in other forms of altered consciousness; and that remarkable control of bodily and personal function can be achieved by those who can, to an extraordinary degree, as in yoga and Zen, "let themselves go." Calmeil, like any superb actor with a thorough knowledge of what the part requires, may have been able, by the processes of self-hypnosis, to let himself become so absorbed in the role of epileptic that "involuntary" behavior followed automatically. He nevertheless was able to keep an avenue of consciousness open so that he could wake up from his fit to confound his teacher.

Animals in the still reaction, paralyzed and unresponsive to pain, show signs that they are nevertheless alert to changes in the prevailing circumstances. Marvin T. Orne's work on hypnosis shows that the simulators of hypnosis (who have previously proved to be unhypnotizable by ordinary methods) can readily reproduce the same anesthesias and extraordinary capacities as persons hypnotized by the usual methods.[2]

Calmeil's performance certainly was well put together if it fooled so sharp an observer as Esquirol. The idea for it no doubt came to him in a flash, like any other great idea. Perhaps he was stimulated by the authoritative assertions of the master, and his great idea may well have been hatched in an incubation period of contrary-mindedness. The suddenness of his inspiration, the speed with which he acted upon it, and the apparent spontaneity of his performance are characteristics of other fits. The question of whether, and how, simulated spontaneity may be transformed at times into the real thing is of great interest. Can spontaneity be planned?

It certainly can be cut short and inhibited. Spontaneous, automatic reflex activities can be aborted by detaching attention from them and focusing it elsewhere. Many persons have discovered this in their efforts to control such things, for example, as orgasm, fits of sneezing, and even fits of epilepsy. Some people, in fact, avoid any spontaneity in their living by keeping themselves busy *not-doing* joyful or challenging things. Other people can will themselves into spontaneous performances of one kind or another by building up tension while fantasying the act and suddenly letting go. If Hughlings Jackson's hypothesis that action requires a preceding dream is correct, all that is necessary is to dream up the proper scheme, mobilize energy for doing it, distract or depersonalize the inhibiting "I," and let the dream control awareness and action.

Notes

1. Oswei Temkin, *The Falling Sickness*. Johns Hopkins Press, 1945, p. 157.
2. Marvin T. Orne, "Implications for Psychotherapy Derived from Current Research on the Nature of Hypnosis." *American Journal of Psychiatry*, 118:1097, 1962.

"MY M-M-M-MOTHER . . . I'LL K-K-K-KILL HER" 24

In and after World War II, physicians in the American military
services used hypnosis to treat psychosomatic and psychiatric
reactions to the stresses of war. Intravenous administration of
barbiturates (sodium pentothal and sodium amytal) were also
used to induce the hypnoidal condition. With this method many
patients relived traumatic experiences, discharged previously
repressed intense emotions, resolved conflicts, and were relieved
of symptoms.

After the war the hypnoidal "sodium amytal interview" was
used by several groups of researchers in the study and treatment
of reactions to the stresses of civilian life. In the psychosomatic
research group at the Cornell University–New York Hospital Medical Center with which I worked, Drs. Harold G. Wolff, Stewart
Wolf, Herbert S. Ripley, and others had observed that during sodium
amytal interviews, symptoms of asthma, hypertension, peptic
ulcer, and other syndromes were intensified during discussion of
significant problems and diminished upon reassurance. There
and elsewhere I studied the relationship between fits and epileptic patients' problems of living, using ordinary hypnosis as well as
drugs.

In the course of one such experiment, a patient went into a
major convulsion as he was struggling to communicate intense
feelings about his mother. His fit occurred at the point of transition into the hypnoidal state. The patient (who had both psychomotor and convulsive fits) sat in a semireclining chair with
electrodes fixed to his scalp for brain-wave recording. It had been
a "tough week," he said, characterized by arguments with his
mother about his wife. A control EEG showed the abnormally
large, slow brain waves said to be consistent with a diagnosis of
epilepsy. Then sodium amytal at the rate of one-and-a-half grains
per minute was given for three minutes. The relaxation usually

induced at the start of injection was, in this case, transitory. He began instead to display increasing tension. Asked, "What is the matter?" he replied, "My m-m-m-mother." He grimaced, growled, and spoke rather disconnectedly of his mother. He appeared alternately angry and in pain. Comments about his mother were interspersed with groans of "Oh . . . Oh . . . Oh . . . !" Asked, "How does your mother bother you?" he said, "I wish I could get ahold of her. I'd k-k-k-kill her. She's no good . . . She's always bothering me . . . all the time . . . all the time." He seemed to be barely restraining great rage.

"My mother killed my father," he continued. "I'll kill her sometime. She drives me crazy." He clenched his fists, raised them to his forehead, and appeared no longer able either to contain his rage or to express it. Suddenly his face went blank and he gave a short, strangled cry. Then a violent muscular spasm seized him; he went rigid; his face contorted in a great grimace; his back arched; his arms flexed strongly across his chest; his legs were straight and stiff. This rigid muscular spasm relaxed and returned in a series of alternating contractions and relaxations typical of a major convulsion. Brain waves during his two-minute seizure, and subsequent comatose state, were characteristic of a major convulsive fit. Hypnoidal reliving of reactions to his mother had been aborted by the eruption of an epileptic fit.

Dr. Stewart Wolf and I had expected to obtain a history of the patient's experiences with and feelings about his mother. We had intended to compare his brain waves during discussion of disturbing topics with those during discussion of neutral or pleasant topics. We were somewhat surprised at the rapid evolution of his reaction and its transformation into a convulsive fit, especially because sodium amytal has definite anticonvulsant properties. When we described this event in detail in a medical journal, we offered this interpretation: "The attack culminated and interrupted an increasingly violent and intense state of rage. The sequence of events suggests that the fit constituted a resolution of the conflict between uncontrollable rage and the restrictions of conscience and society."[1]

This was consistent with Freud's formulation that convulsions discharge energy that cannot be handled psychically. It was also consistent with the reports of psychiatrists postulating that convulsions discharge otherwise inexpressible aggression. A convulsive fit, in this view, reduces the level of discharge from that of a meaningful display of emotion to that of subpersonal, meaningless neuromuscular activity. Murderous John Doe "devolves" to a hostile individual, then to a snarling beast, and finally to a violently active suborganismic system.

But these psychogenic explanations of convulsions are shaped by a need for symmetry—a need to find violent causes for violent muscular activity. The violence of a convulsive fit, however, comes only from the muscles. The brain cells activating the muscles use only very small amounts of energy.

A gain in understanding this and other fits is achieved by shifting the emphasis, in the phrase "inexpressible rage," from "rage" to "inexpressible." Restrictions of conscience or society are only one aspect of inexpressibility and unthinkability. Intensity is only one dimension. Suddenness, multiplicity, contradiction, and ambiguity also shape the inexpressible.

These conjectures were borne out in this case when the patient was interviewed another time under ordinary hypnosis. This time Dr. Herbert S. Ripley and I conducted the interview. At the induction of hypnosis the patient began spontaneously to relive a series of traumatic experiences (charged with aggressive urges, feelings of guilt, and feelings of helplessness), regressing in time as he went from one episode to another. It was as if he were spreading out in time, for our inspection, a dense complex of highly charged, related experiences. The spreading out in time of a dysjunctively fused complex made up of many significant life experiences revealed that each experience was itself a complex of impulse, prohibition, and attempt at compromise. The abreactive reliving of the series seemed to convey what he usually could express only convulsively.

Were these fits triggered in the laboratory by the transition into the hypnoidal state? Were they produced by hypnosis itself? Or were they set off by the transition from waking to hypnoidal sleep? Is it possible, perhaps, that impending transitions in themselves engender a kind of hypnoidal situation?

Galen, the great second-century Roman physician, studied and wrote extensively about convulsive fits. He observed that fits could be precipitated by a wide variety of stimulus-events, especially at changes in the emotional or meteorological climate. He cautioned patients to avoid great changes of any kind. I have found in the literature since Galen, and in my own studies, that any sudden change in organism-environment relations may be followed by a fit. But change is seldom, if ever, the sole factor in a prefit situation. Usually the situation in which change seems to trigger a fit is already loaded with tension.

Notes

1. Wayne Barker and Stewart Wolf, "Experimental Production of *Grand Mal* Seizure During the Hypnoidal State Induced by Sodium Amytal." *American Journal of Medical Science*, 214: 600, 1947.

"I COULDN'T GET MAD AT MY MOTHER . . . SHE BORNED ME"

25

Illness, drugs, situational stress, hypnoidal processes, and fatigue weaken our ability to direct attention, control the content of awareness, and avoid unthinkable matters. Pressure of circumstances may require that we give some attention to such matters in order to get on with living in the situation at hand. When our control of attention is weak and a particularly complex problem demands attention, we may be overwhelmed and break down in one way or another.

Thus the young man who had a tough week of frustrating contention with his mother began explosively to abreact violent emotion toward his mother in a drug-induced hypnoidal state. Managing this sudden, intensely dysjunctive situation was beyond the capacity of the higher levels of his person-mind-brain system and he went into a major convulsion carried out by the system's lower levels.

Minor models of such events are seen in ordinary conversations with patients when one tries to explore unthinkable areas. The patient's security operations, aimed at keeping attention away from conflicts associated with feelings of shame, guilt, and helplessness, are opposed by his growth-promoting tendencies, aimed at resolving conflicts and getting rid of impediments to self-esteem. In such doubly dysjunctive situations, brief disruptions of thought and speech mark momentary breakdowns of integrative function.

With epileptic patients who have recurring major convulsions, these brief disruptions of awareness and action could be thought of as minor, or "larval" (i.e., undeveloped) epileptic fits. But they result from contention between tendencies to reveal and tendencies to conceal, between reactions in approach and reactions in avoidance, and between security-seeking and growth-promoting forces. It is probably better to think of them as minor epileptic-dysjunctive or creative-dysjunctive behavior, depending upon whether progress in understanding is hampered or helped by them.

A ten-year-old epileptic boy had been persuaded by his mother to avoid fights with other boys at all costs because she believed strongly and literally in turning the other cheek. He was asked about the disastrous consequences of applying this policy in the tough neighborhood into which he had moved just before the onset of his convulsive illness. Brain waves were recorded during this interview.

"How did you feel when you had to turn the other cheek and it meant getting beat up or having to run away?"

"I didn't want them to think I was a coward, but mother would feel very bad and make me feel bad if I got into a fight. . . ." He became tense, hesitated, then said, "I felt . . ." He stopped again, a peculiar look crossed his face, then he said, "I couldn't get mad at my mother. She's my mother. She borned me!"

In the electroencephalographic pattern accompanying this episode, there was a sequence of muscle potential associated with his tension: flat, relatively waveless patterns, like those seen in alertness reactions; and a brief burst of inverted, three-per-second spike-and-dome waves, said to be characteristic of epileptic brain-cell activity. The sequence is shown in Figure 3.

Without the EEG, the presence of an epileptic component in this seemingly ordinary blocking of speech might not have been suspected. Such minor epileptic-dysjunctive reactions provide not only a link between almost unnoticeable larval epileptic fits and fits of convulsion but also establish a connection between all epileptic and nonepileptic fits. These matters are dealt with more fully in Chapter 39.

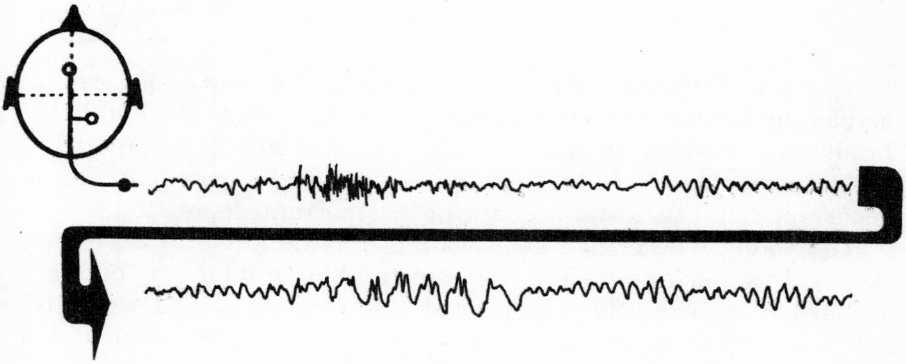

Figure 3. A sequence of tension, hesitation, speech, peculiar look, and epileptic brain waves.

"WHERE IS MY BABY?" 26

I once saw a young woman in consultation because she had a screaming fit shortly after the birth of her first child. She had been briefly and acutely confused, but had recovered promptly. Her obstetrician, however, was concerned about the possibility of a recurrence and of a more enduring postpartum depression.

The young mother had been waiting for the nurse to bring her infant daughter to her. She was musing, but "thinking of nothing in particular," she said, when all of a sudden she saw a vision of her baby being carried by the nurse and was horrified because the child was "all wrapped up for a funeral." Terror and panic accompanied the hallucination, and she began to scream, "I want my baby . . . I love my baby . . . Where is my baby?" and could not be quieted until her daughter was brought to her and she was reassured that the infant was neither dead nor defective.

She was an intelligent, pretty young woman, from fortunate family circumstances, whose early life had been remarkably free of stress. She was happily married to an attractive, successful young man. Her husband was a lusty fellow, and she half-believed that he might have sought sexual satisfaction with some other woman during the last weeks of her pregnancy and that he might be tempted to infidelity during the postpartum period. She had been ruminating on this theme just before her uncanny experience.

Exploration of her ruminations revealed that she called her husband "baby" in their intimate moments, and that she looked upon his lustful urges toward her with a sort of maternal indulgence. She saw them as occasions for babying him. She was afraid that babying her daughter might make him jealous. Her reveries about her two babies, husband and infant daughter, culminated in a kind of seesaw between love and hostility toward both of them.

She was actually trying to put such thoughts out of her mind when the hallucinatory image of her daughter prepared for burial appeared. In this image, the face of the infant, she said, was remarkably like that of her husband. The symbolic blending of the faces of her two babies is a good example of the process of condensation-compression of images and ideas that goes on in fitting together.

In her prefit musings she was in a semidrowsy state of relaxed susceptibility to things popping into the mind in dreamlike symbolization. Her hallucination was not the very vivid kind seen in typical hypnogogic and hypnopompic hallucinations that occur on going into and coming out of sleep. It was, she said, more like a thought or "something I saw in my mind rather than right in front of me." There is, of course, no hard and fast line between visions which are experienced as primarily internal and those which have been projected and are seen as being in the external environment. The difference is in the extent to which the person can accept the ideas represented in the images as arising from his own dreamlike processes.

The more these ideas are disowned, are experienced as abhorrent and alien, the more externalized and hallucinatory the image. Fortunately, the young lady was able to recall her prefit marginal thoughts, to recognize the practical, real-life significance of her symbolic death wishes toward both her babies, and to make plans to ensure that her relationship with her husband was not jeopardized by preoccupation with her infant daughter, and that the child did not suffer from her devotion to her husband.

In this example, the question "Whence came the hallucination?" is quite the same as the question "Whence came Marvin's 'whishit'?" with which we began the examination of fits. These questions have the same answer: From the brain's fitting-together capacity. Marvin was trying to spell a word and the young mother was trying to sort out her feelings about her husband and her daughter. In her case, the process suddenly came to a "plague on both your houses" hostility toward husband and daughter (the joint sources of her conflict) which was alien to her "self" as loving wife and mother. The hostility was disowned, symbolized, and recognized in this symbolic form.

Harry Stack Sullivan held that such uncanny experiences are likely whenever an individual is confronted with a part of himself that has been rejected as "not-me."[1] He believed that early childhood experience of approval generated personifications of the approved self as the "good-me," whereas disapproval produced personification of a "bad-me." When the child's action is not so much approved or disapproved, but is simply not recognized or is treated as meaningless, the concept of "not-me" is formed. It is interesting that when the hallucinatory young woman, as a child, displeased her mother, the mother had, instead of punishing her, treated her and her behavior as alien, saying, "That's not my Janet!" The patient's ideas of self were thus mostly of "good-me" or "not-me" and she often had mild but definite feelings of strangeness when she thought or did something wrong.

Notes

1. Harry Stack Sullivan, *The Interpersonal Theory of Psychiatry*, edited by Helen Swick Perry and Mabel Blake Cohen. W. W. Norton, New York, 1953, pp. 359ff.

". . . I KNOW THAT IT IS POETRY" 27

Emily Dickinson said, "If I read a book and it makes my whole body so cold no fire can ever warm me, I know that it is poetry. If I feel physically as if the top of my head were taken off, I know that it is poetry. These are the only ways I know it. Is there any other way?"[1] This description provides a link between experiences like H. L. Gold's, described in Chapter 31, in which he felt as if the top were coming off his head at a moment of prophetic "seeing," and those of artists who acknowledge uncanny feelings when they experience the mysterious beginnings of poetic creativity. Uncanny reactions, in general, are not so mysterious if we begin, as Hughlings Jackson taught, with the slightest rather than the greatest departures from the ordinary.

One such experience was described by A. E. Housman in his *The Name and Nature of Poetry.* "Experience," he said, "has taught me, when I am shaving of a morning, to keep watch over my thoughts, because if a line of poetry strays into my memory, my skin bristles so that the razor ceases to act. This particular symptom is accompanied by a shiver down the spine."[2]

Housman protected the continuity of his shaving, as others protect the continuity of their tranquillity, by excluding from awareness disturbing thoughts and memories. Some people succeed fairly well in maintaining such selective inattention. They also try to stay out of situations in which disquieting experience is likely. But now and again, pressures and needs force awareness toward the excluded. The breakthrough may visibly shake up a person, causing a change of expression or a slight shiver. In reply to "What happened?" the person may say something like "Oh, I just thought of something," or give the folk response, "Someone was walking on my grave." As Housman's little fit demonstrates, a disturbance produced by the eruption of the excluded into awareness does not necessarily mean that the excluded was unpleasant in itself. The effect of the poet's efforts to achieve uninterrupted shaving by selective inattention to poetic ideas is inevitably self-defeating. When he succeeds in excluding all thoughts of poetry, his shaving proceeds smoothly. But, as he shaves freely, less attention is required for shaving; vigilance then relaxes and his mind will wander. And in exactly these circumstances lines of poetry are most likely to pop into mind.

Many so-called obsessive-compulsive, phobic people have similar but severe difficulties in controlling the content of their awareness. Stereotyped, ritualistic defenses designed to keep disturbing ideas from awareness tend, by their hypnoidal repetitiveness, to reduce vigilance. Then, when things are going well, disturbing elements pop into mind with shocking effect. If we can view selectively inattended content, whether lines of poetry or traumatic experiences, as unresolved "disturbances," then we can see that the sudden disclosure of any of them may have a shocking effect. "Uncanny," after all, means "unknown." Any complex of ideas, images, and impulses may elaborate into unthinkable, unknowable configurations and produce an uncanny reaction. To find some way of making the unthinkable thinkable is to convert the uncanny into the creative.

Tension develops while the unrecognized is held at bay, and the shock of recognition may be significant. But whether recognition comes slowly or suddenly, the process by which thinking transforms patterns of neuronal electrical activity into patterns of personal awareness is often accompanied by notable bodily reactions. Thinking is not a "purely mental" operation.

If Housman were complaining to a physician about the fits of gooseflesh and shivering that frequently disrupted his shaving and was not aware of the association between these fits and lines of poetry popping into his mind, then his story would be that of a psychical epileptic fit. Epileptic fits are often preceded by things popping into mind. But these prefit intrusions are usually not recognized or remembered. Close investigation, however, often reveals the relevant content; further investigation may disclose that the prefit intrusion represents the patient's central difficulties in living.

Notes

1. Emily Dickinson. Quoted by Martha Gilbert Dickinson Bianchi in *Life and Letters of Emily Dickinson*. Houghton, Boston, 1924.
2. A. E. Housman, *The Name and Nature of Poetry*. Macmillan, New York, 1933, p. 48.

A Fit of Composing. A Creative Minding of a Dysjunctive
Flood of Ideas.

". . . THOUGHTS CROWD INTO MY MIND . . . WHENCE DO THEY COME?"

28

"When I feel well and in a good humor, or when I am taking a drive after a good meal, or in the night when I cannot sleep, thoughts crowd into my mind as easily as you could wish. Whence do they come? I do not know and have nothing to do with it." Thus Mozart begins an account of how his fits of composing come upon him. It is a far cry from Marvin's ludicrous spelling to Mozart's lovely music, from simplemindedness to genius, but all moments of inspiration are equivalent in form. When creative persons try to explain the source of the fragmentary ideas and faint patterns from which they fit together their creations, the terms they use have much in common with those patients use to discuss their fits of epilepsy. Housman, for example, says the source of his poetic ideas was, as far as he could make out, the pit of his stomach*— the stated source of many a prefit epileptic aura.

The sequence of events in fits of convulsion and in fits of creation is often remarkably similar. Finally, the dynamic relatedness of all fits is suggested by the fact that in both genuine fits of creativity and genuine fits of epilepsy, individual responsibility is denied.

"I . . . have nothing to do with it," Mozart continues. "Those which please me, I keep in my head and hum them; at least others have told me that I do so." Compare "the look" that attends both convulsive and creative processes. "Once I have my theme, another melody comes, linking itself to the first one, in accordance with the needs of the composition as a whole." Note that his vision in-

---

* "As I went along, thinking of nothing in particular . . . there would flow into my mind, with sudden and unaccountable emotion, sometimes a line or two of verse, sometimes a whole stanza at once, accompanied, not preceded, by a vague notion of the poem which they were destined to form part of. . . . So far as I can make out, the source of the suggestions thus proffered to the brain was an abyss I have already had occasion to mention, the pit of the stomach." (*The Name and Nature of Poetry,* p. 50.)

cludes both a general idea for and fragments of the composition as a whole. These still need to be "realized," just as thought has to be put into words. "The counterpoint, the part of each instrument, and all the melodic fragments at last produce the entire work." But the work completed is not yet the finished composition. The whole, having been "cognized," now has to be re-cognized.

> Then my soul is on fire with inspiration, if however nothing occurs to distract me. The work grows; I keep expanding it, conceiving it more and more clearly until I have the entire composition finished in my head though it may be long. Then my mind seizes it as a glance of my eye a beautiful picture or a handsome youth. It does not come to me successively, with its various parts worked out in detail, as they will be later on, but it is in its entirety that my imagination lets me hear it.[1]

This hearing or seeing it all at once, this intuitive recognition, strongly resembles the special kinds of "see-ing" described in dreams, drowsy states, and trances. All these "see-ings" are similar, and like the experience of "my life flashing before my eyes" of persons near death, they are loaded with meaning but are incommunicable except by very exceptional people, and by exceptional means.

Mozart goes on to discuss how a composition acquires his style and he compares the growth of a composition to the growth of his nose; neither has much to do with "I" or is under its control. Rimbaud made a similar comparison between the growth of thoughts and the growth of noses or warts on the face, and he insisted that no one should claim any more credit for his thoughts than he would for his nose. Nevertheless, "The work grows; I keep expanding it. . . ." Apparently the composition is dreamed up in one kind of process and written out in another. The whole sequence consists of a trancelike fitting together and a fitted-together post-trance performance.

Wilfrid Mellers, the eminent British musicologist and composer, with whom I discussed patterns of composing, suggests that in creative fits the musical vision may be expanded or unrolled in various ways. In Beethoven's Fifth Symphony, for example, he points out that the first few notes are not the true beginning, nor are the last ones the dynamic end of the composition. The first notes were added, after the body of the composition was written, to make a new, anticipatory beginning; the last notes, in which some instruments are played for the first time, are not so much the end of the music as they are a sort of rebound echo designed to illumine retrospectively the whole of the preceding music. If I have understood correctly, then, the structure of the Fifth Symphony is: onset of the music . . . gap . . . onset of the symphony proper . . . the body of the symphony . . . end of the symphony . . . gap . . . and a final, rebound reappraisal of the whole. This five-part structure, or trajectory, characterizes not only the major convulsive fit-sequence (of which the major convulsion is the main body) but all major fit-sequences.

Notes

1. W. A. Mozart. Quoted by Jacques Hadamard in *The Psychology of Invention in the Mathematical Field.* Dover Books, 1945.

TAKING A TALKING-TAKING WALK

Any psychiatric interview is both investigative and therapeutic. Identifying difficulties in living reduces feelings of alienation, because the patient knows what's bothering him even if he is not yet able to do much about it. Hence, history-taking itself may produce significant therapeutic benefit. But exploration of the patient's life history, especially of the circumstances associated with specific outbreaks of symptoms, is a two-edged tool. When symptoms have aborted awareness of painful thoughts and feelings, exploration of sensitive areas with even the most sympathetic inquisitor may activate symptomatic defenses.

No matter how tactfully one conducts inquiry—indeed, exactly because skill and tact promote meaningful communication—symptomatic reactions punctuate any effective psychiatric interview. Fortunately, these symptom-punctuations are mostly mild and brief, and can actually be dealt with as forms of communication. Occasionally, however, with epileptic patients, convulsive reactions disrupt interviews and create a conflict between the investigative and therapeutic aspects of the patient-physician collaboration. Then therapeutic benefits must be weighed against detriments. When the patient is able and willing to accept the risks, fit-producing inquiry can often be pursued, because means can be found to abort the development of full-blown convulsions.[1] The processes of fit-generating and fit-aborting maneuvers are illustrated in the following example.

My early conversations with one young man, who had major convulsions, and occasional bouts of coughing, said to be caused by an episodic, allergic bronchitis, went well enough at first. But when we got to intimate inquiry into the circumstances associated with the onset of his convulsions, our discussions began to be disrupted by convulsive fits. We discussed the problem; he wished to continue and seemed well motivated to do so. After a few trials, I found that I could interrupt his convulsive fits by painful pressure on his eyebrow, by tapping him smartly on the face, and by speaking sharply to him.

During one interview he was describing for me how contention between him and his father was subtly, but not openly, manifested. He had started to describe what went on between them when they were taking a stroll and talking together on the previous evening. "We were taking . . . [he paused as if searching for words] . . . we were talking," he said, and paused again. Then his eyes began to blink rapidly and to roll as they usually did at the onset of a convulsion. I tapped him on the cheek, pressed hard upon his eyebrow with my thumb, and said, "Snap out of it! Keep talking to me!" He opened his eyes, convulsive rigidity relaxed, he looked at me angrily, and began to cough. He recovered from this paroxysm and began to smile—a peculiar smile, as if he were harboring a secret. I said, "Come on, now. You were telling me about walking and talking with your father. Keep going with the story!" His secretive smile changed to a threatening look and he appeared to be going into a fit again. But this look was suddenly replaced by laughing. He then went on, "I was taking a talking walk . . . we were taking a walk—a talking walk. I was talking a taking walk. Either way, I was putting the old man on."

He then told me that he had suddenly seen clearly the farcelike hypocrisy of the ritual strolls he and his father took together. They usually went for a walk once a week during which the father would deliver himself of little lectures on topics he thought important to elucidate for his son. The boy would listen with feigned interest, asking leading questions at appropriate intervals because he used these tactics to obtain extra spending money and other indulgences from his father. These were, indeed, "taking-talking-taking" walks. "He talked," the patient said, "and I took—a few bucks or something else I wanted!"

Here in a single, dysjunctive sequence the boy went from the convulsive to the witty. Similar sequences in other interviews resulted as "equivalents" of disrupted convulsive reactions. The patient looked as if he were about to have a convulsion but did something else instead. The most common substitutes were simple and brief. These included coughs, sniffs, grimaces, episodes of blankness, confused loss of the train of thought, and so on.

Because a whole continuum of convulsive and nonconvulsive dysjunctive reactions was observed, it was evident that they were produced by a single fitting-together process. For some time I took this to mean that psychological factors are important in the genesis of convulsive reactions. That is, the uncovering of significant matters, whose movement into awareness and communication had previously been blocked by convulsive disruptions, seemed primarily important as evidence for the psychological, psychosomatic nature of epilepsy. But when dysjunctive sequences like that described above were considered, it was evident that junctive processes, unblocking as well as blocking forces, were also activated. Dysjunctive reactions were not merely alternatives or equivalents of convulsive symptoms; they were also crude alternative forms of creative synthesis of the previously unthinkable. That is, dysjunctive situations were resolved by exceptional conjunctions as well as by dysjunctions of behavior and experience.

Notes

1. R. C. Hamill, *"Petit Mal* in Children." *American Journal of Psychiatry, 93:* 303, 1946.

"Z, Y, X, W, V . . ." 30

One of my brain-twisting procedures for educing dysjunctive reactions during brain-wave recording was to have the patient try to recite the alphabet backward after just enough practice to enable him to begin, and to believe that he could continue to do it reasonably smoothly and rapidly. One nonepileptic patient, whose routine brain waves were invariably normal, rolled his eyes about when he came to a block in his recitation. These eye movements were not at that time of great interest for research; rapid eye movements have since proved to be reliable indicators during sleep that a subject is dreaming.* At the time of my experiments, I took these eye movements, which could be seen in channels recording from electrodes at the front of the head, simply as evidence of activation of the oculovisual apparatus in an attempt to "see" a way out of the dysjunctive impasse.

In one such experiment, the subject paused for thought after "z . . . y . . . x," and during his brief pause eye movement was visible. He went on with "w . . . v . . . u," and when he paused again eye movement recurred. After "t . . . s . . . r . . . q," there was a slightly longer pause with more vigorous eye movements before he was able to continue, incorrectly, with "p . . . o . . . m . . . n." At this point he gave up. It is not at all far-fetched to interpret these eye movements as a kind of waking-dreaming effort to see ahead with the eyes, as such, when high-level foresight fails. The brain-wave record during this experiment is shown later on, in Figure 12.

---

* Rapid eye movements as an indicator of a special dreaming state were first reported by E. Aserinsky and N. Kleitman in *Science*, Vol. CXVIII, September 4, 1953, p. 273.

"OH, YEAH? IF YOU KNOW SO MUCH, WHEN'LL THE WAR BE OVER?"

31

The word "trance" suggests mysterious, uncanny events. But trances, like fits, have only one root in the marvelous and are much more frequent in our everyday affairs than is generally recognized. "Trance" comes from Old French *transe*, a passage or crossing. In its meanings are: a state of suspended consciousness, a state between waking and sleep, a condition of abstraction or absorption, suspense, doubt, apprehension, or exaltation. Going into a trance is usually marked by transitory reactions quite like those seen at the start of convulsive fits, during precreative crises, and at the transition point into all kinds of fits. In the "fit of killing," we could not pinpoint the crisis, the passage into the fit. In some fits, however, although the fit-generating crisis in itself goes unnoticed, it can be located, because fit-behavior differs so much from prefit-behavior that the transition point is usually obvious. Many crises are signaled only by a fleeting facial expression or some other insignificant sign like those seen at the induction point in hypnosis. But there are occasions when the trance, or transition point, is outstanding.

The following example has a notable transition, and touches upon the relationship between crises, trances, and fits. For centuries, from the Dark Ages to the Enlightenment, fits of prophecy were a part of the complex of fits of convulsion, hysteria, possession, and mental illness that were seen, lumped together, as the symptom of the "falling sickness." In this contemporary example of spontaneous prophecy, significant bodily and personal reactions occur.

H. L. Gold, the editor of *Galaxy* magazine, has described what happened to him in World War II when he got caught up in the processes of prophecy.

> During the war, when the news of the Battle of the Bulge came crashing in, the C.O. of my outfit gave us a this-is-it pep talk; all

of the might of the Germans was massed against us, we were in danger of being driven into the sea, the war would go on indefinitely, etc.

As orientation man, I had war maps by the dozen and was astonished that nobody was mentioning the huge fight between the Nazis and the Russians, in, I think, Rumania, at least twice as big if no more bitter than the Bulge. Letting people know about it would have reduced anxiety.

When I gave my orientation lecture, which was shortly after the C.O. had alarmed us, I said that this was obviously a final desperate gamble and the end had to be near. "Oh, yeah?" challenged the First Sergeant. "If you know so much, when'll the war be over?"

That was in December. What happened next should interest researchers, for I felt an electric-chair shock, my muscles constricted, my eyes hurt furiously and my head built up a sudden shattering internal pressure, and I was overwhelmed by apprehension as the answer came out, "April 30th."

The First Sergeant got me to bet $2.50. The actual date was May 8th and he collected but practically over the dead bodies of the whole company. Next time was as we were crossing the Pacific. Again the First Sergeant challenged me and again the sensation paralyzed me. I said the war in the Pacific would end August 13th. . . . The actual date was the 14th and he was glad to pay off.[1]

Gold goes on to tell how on other occasions when he made predictions "out of the blue" he had the same set of bodily reactions. The challenge evidently activated cerebral discharges into the sensorimotor and sympathetic vasomotor systems producing the same "electric shock," tension, and headache before inaccurate as well as accurate predictions. A similar complex of uncanny experience, significant bodily reaction, and things popping into the mind is seen in many fits—convulsive, creative, or otherwise.

The severe psychosomatic reactions Gold experienced in his infrequent prophetic seizures call to mind similar reactions reported as characteristic of the prophetic trances of seers in general. They also accompany anxiety and other apprehensions. In the first case, the seer is trying to apprehend the future; in the second, the anxious person is fearful of what he may see if his apprehension works—he is, as it were, only apprehensive. But Gold's distressing responses to the challenge to prophesy, and the effects of apprehension, are only exaggerated versions of what everyone experiences in some degree when challenged, stumped for an answer, but required to come up with something.

When an environmental stimulus or a sudden memory makes

us pause for thought, or when we are working on a problem, various external signs show that the internal, integrative wheels are turning more or less automatically. Jacques Hadamard, the French mathematician and student of the processes of invention in mathematics, reported, for example, that his family and friends could always tell when he was absorbed in visualizing ("seeing") a problem because he had a peculiar look on his face. Most of us, in fact, get a characteristic look when we are scheming, calculating, or seeing with the mind's eye. This look, I believe, is much the same and has the same sources as the look accompanying excretory, sexual, ecstatic, and other activities in which we are momentarily absorbed and abstracted from both ourselves and the external environment. The look is an indication of a trancelike state associated with all such automatic activities. Even the peculiar look preceding convulsive fits and persisting in psychomotor fits is a manifestation of a trancelike reaction to a crisis, and reflects effort to find an answer by "seeing" when conscious effort has failed.

One of Hughlings Jackson's patients described his experience of a psychomotor fit by saying that he did not so much feel strange, he felt like himself, but as if he were "in another country."[2] So, in a sense, all those who are momentarily abstracted from the here-and-now, who are seeing into or out of another country, another not-here, not-now, share to some extent the same odd look because they share the same trancelike state.

Notes

1. H. L. Gold. Editorial, "How Now, Gray Cell?" in *Galaxy* magazine, December 1955, p. 4.
2. John Hughlings Jackson, *Selected Writings,* edited by James Taylor. Hodder & Stoughton, London, 1931; Basic Books, New York, 1950, Vol. I, p. 187.

A MOROSE SECRETARY 32

To many people, fits of creation and fits of convulsion are awesome mysteries. Some have trouble conceiving of unwilled behavior except as an accident or explosion. Others interpret fits as some form of possession—for them the person and his consciousness is shoved aside by obtrusion of the unconscious, or intrusion of the extrapersonal. Devoted as we are to ideas of self-control and will power, it is difficult to recognize fully how much of our thinking, especially in dealing with critical problems, is done for us not by "I" but by the nonpersonal, non-I part of our brain-mind system.

The German psychiatrist Hans Silberer, an early twentieth-century student of symbolization and hallucination, described a personal experience that sheds light on these processes.

> One afternoon . . . I was lying on my couch. Though extremely sleepy, I forced myself to think through a problem of philosophy, which was to compare the views of Kant and Schopenhauer concerning time. In my drowsiness I was unable to sustain their ideas side by side. After several unsuccessful attempts, I once more fixed Kant's argument in my mind as firmly as I could and turned my attention to Schopenhauer's. But when I tried to reach back to Kant, his argument was gone again, and beyond recovery. The futile effort to find the Kant record which was somehow misplaced in my mind *suddenly represented itself to me*—as I was lying there with my eyes closed, as in a dream—*as a perceptual symbol:* I am asking a morose secretary for some information; he is leaning over his desk and disregards me entirely; he straightens up for a moment to give me an unfriendly and rejecting look.[1]

Hallucinations are common at transitions from wakefulness to sleeping (hypnogogic hallucinations) and at the reverse shift from sleep to waking (hypnopompic hallucinations), and occur much more frequently than is commonly supposed. These transitions, I believe, produce a trancelike moment, between waking and sleep, in which the brain, doing the least in particular, is capable of the most in general. If one sits with a subject while his brain waves are being recorded and inquires into what was going through his mind during a brief period of drowsiness, one often gets reports of symbolic representations of problems much like Silberer's image of an irritable secretary.

These symbols of problems may, as in Silberer's example, culminate a protracted contention or they may suddenly pop into the mind without any obvious connection with what had been going on in awareness. Apparently, thinking on some subjects is sufficiently stressful to be drowsiness-inducing. Conversely, drowsiness is conducive to thinking on certain perplexing subjects. Examination of symbolizations reveals that they are compressions-syntheses, i.e., fittings-together. Sometimes they illuminate the patient's problems; sometimes they are ludicrous or absurd; sometimes they are teasingly suggestive, but their meaning eludes us like an obscure pun. It is quite likely that innumerable hallucinatory symbolizations of daily life are ignored because, like most of our dreams, they are not seen to be useful.

But what is clear is that Silberer's irritated secretary was the product of both drowsiness and a partial failure in minding of contending elements. One kind of minding was substituted for another—a kind producing a symbolization of the problem for a solution to it. The failure in minding is a question of "whose minding." Silberer-the-person's efforts were failing but suddenly the fitting-together capacity of Silberer's brain took possession of the situation. The sudden shift in minding, from the personal to the subpersonal level, took place in what can only be called a hypnoidal process. Silberer's shifting back and forth from Kant to Schopenhauer suggests the oscillation that goes on momentarily in many insoluble prefit crises. This flickering oscillation of contending content in turn suggests the swinging light used in hypnosis, and the flicker of stroboscopic light used in the brain-wave laboratory to produce fits of epileptic activity; in op and kinetic art; and in other psychedelic situations to produce fits of hypnoidal experience. There are many pathways into the hypnoidal mode of fitting together.

Notes

1. Hans Silberer, "Reports on a Method of Eliciting and Observing Certain Symbolic Hallucination Phenomena," in *Organization and Pathology of Thought*, edited by David Rapaport. Columbia University Press, 1951, p. 195.

PERSPIRATION AND INSPIRATION 33

A general developmental scheme for convulsive fits was sketched earlier and its components were described as a prodromal period of incubation or preparation; a transition period from prefit to fit activity marked by early warning signs such as the aura, cry, and alteration of awareness; the fit proper; and postdromal reactions including recovery and transition from fit to postfit behavior. This structure of convulsive fits is a particular variation of a general structure found in all kinds of trajectories of behavior and experience. A trajectory has, ideally, an anticipatory period of heightened or diminished reactivity; an on-reaction of fleeting excitatory or inhibitory reactions of brain, body, or person; a middle phase, or main course, during which the organism moves from here to there, and from now to then; a second anticipatory, preparatory reaction as the end of the trajectory approaches; an off-reaction which, as in physiology in general, has much the same character as the on-reaction; and a rebound reaction following completion of the trajectory.

In between the specific sequence of the major convulsive fit and the general trajectory pattern are a number of other sequences, the data of which have contributed to the trajectory concept. Among these are elaborate patterns of symptoms during protracted periods of life situation stress. The stressful pattern may be a mixture of several separate stresses or may consist of frequent repetitions of a single stress during a day, week, or month. The symptom sequences (alternations of asthma and depression; trains of nasal, migrainous, and gastrointestinal reaction; successions of obsessions, bodily symptoms, unsuccessful surgery, and serious psychiatric illnesses) have been described in medical journals.

Fits of creation often follow a course of development similar to that of the major convulsive fit sequence, to sequential dysjunctive reactions, and to other trajectories of behavior. For their intrinsic interest, for their contribution to the universe of fits, and as examples of the temporal organization of behavior into trajectories, we will take up two instances of fits of creative fitting together. Two men in these two episodes confront two of man's enduring problems: women and mathematics.

Harold Rosenberg, the art critic and commentator on problems in general, had committed himself to complete by a certain deadline a magazine article about women (see *Vogue*, May 1967). Pressed by other commitments, he postponed drafting the article until four days before the deadline. He wasted the first two days in general rumination about the subject. On the third day he came down with a cold, and one of his immediate family became seriously though not critically ill. Nevertheless, he managed, by working when he could throughout that day and well into the night, to piece together what seemed to be a creditable essay on women. His satisfaction with this accomplishment was short lived. Reading it over before retiring for the night, he became acutely dissatisfied with what he had written, tore it up, and went to bed weary and dispirited. When he waked next morning his eye fell upon an art magazine on his bedside table. On the cover was an odalisque. While he stared at this womanly figure, a first sentence for his essay sprang unbidden into his mind: "Loving may interfere with a woman's career, but being loved is a career." In the train of this spontaneous thought came a whole series of ideas, each a hard, unexpandable unit, linked in a rather musical progression. At that moment he had his article firmly in mind, and it remained only to write it down and get it off to the editor. His cold and associated symptoms rapidly improved.[1]

In this creative fit-sequence there is first a period of preparation, of I-directed work. Then comes a giving up of I-direction (of *reculer pour mieux sauter*, in Arthur Koestler's phrase). Finally comes essentially automatic activity in completing the fitting-together, followed by the recovery phase.

The correspondence between these sequences is that of identities, parallels, and analogies. The congruencies and incongruencies can be seen between Rosenberg's moment of illumination upon awakening and others. Often great ideas come in dreams. The chemist Kekulé, for example, saw a vision of a long-chain hydrocarbon molecule as a snake; then in his dream the snake took its head in its mouth. From this Kekulé realized that the benzene molecule was a ring made by joining the ends of the hydrocarbon molecule.

French mathematician Jacques Hadamard's own mathematical

inspirations and Wilfrid Mellers' musical great ideas characteristically appeared exactly at the moment of awakening. Hadamard's solutions also appeared when he was awakened "very abruptly by an external noise." Rosenberg was awake, though not in the fullest sense, and the picture of the womanly odalisque was relevant to his subsequent train of ideas. An aura, a dysjunctive complex of meanings, was triggered by this visual stimulus. A fit of creation followed this aura.

The second example is quoted in *The Creative Process*, edited by Brewster Ghiselin. Henri Poincaré wrote the report on the processes by which his own great mathematical inventions developed.

> For fifteen days I strove to prove that there could not be any functions like those I have since called Fuchsian functions. I was then very ignorant; every day I seated myself at my work table, stayed an hour or two, tried a great number of combinations, and reached no results. One evening, contrary to my usual custom, I drank black coffee and could not sleep. Ideas rose in crowds [compare Mozart's flood of musical ideas]; I felt them collide until pairs interlocked, so to speak, making a stable combination [compare Kekulé's "snake" of carbon atoms]. By the next morning I had established the existence of a class of Fuchsian functions, those which come from the hypergeometric series; I had only to write out the results, which took but a few hours.

This sequence of events has identities, parallels, and analogies with other fit-sequences. But Poincaré goes on to describe the unfolding of a complex sequence of creative events set off in a kind of *status creativus* (in analogy to *status epilepticus*, a condition of recurring epileptic fits) by his initial achievement.

> Then I wanted to represent these functions by the quotient of two series; this idea was perfectly conscious and deliberate, the analogy with elliptic functions guided me. I asked myself what properties these series must have if they existed, and I succeeded without difficulty in forming the series I have called theta-Fuchsian.
>
> Just at this time I left Caen, where I was then living, to go on a geologic excursion . . . The changes of travel made me forget my mathematical work. Having reached Coutances, we entered an omnibus to go some place or other. At the moment when I put my foot on the step the idea came to me, without anything in my former thoughts seeming to have paved the way for it, that the transformations I had used to define the Fuchsian functions were identical with those of non-Euclidean geometry. I did not verify the idea; I should not have had time. . . . On my return to Caen, for conscience's sake I verified the results at my leisure.

Then I turned my attention to the study of some arithmetical questions apparently without much success and without a suspicion of any connection with my preceding researches. Disgusted with my failure, I went to spend a few days at the seaside, and thought of something else [a giving up]. One morning, walking on the bluff, the idea came to me, with just the same characteristics of brevity, suddenness, and immediate certainty [quite as in many *déjà vu* and other psychic epileptic fits], that the arithmetic transformations of indeterminate ternary quadratic forms were identical with those of non-Euclidean geometry.

Returned to Caen, I meditated on this result and deduced the consequences. The example of quadratic forms showed me that there were Fuchsian groups other than those corresponding to the hypergeometric series; I saw that I could apply to them the theory of theta-Fuchsian series and that consequently there existed Fuchsian functions other than those from the hypergeometric series, the ones I then knew. Naturally I set myself to form all these functions. I made a systematic attack upon them and carried all the outworks, one after another. There was one, however, that still held out, whose fall would involve that of the whole piece. But all my efforts only served at first the better to show me the difficulty, which indeed was something. All this work was perfectly conscious.

Thereupon I left for Mont-Valérien, where I was to go through my military service; so I was very differently occupied. One day, going along the street, the solution of the difficulty which had stopped me suddenly appeared to me. I did not try to go deep into it immediately, and only after my service did I again take up the question. I had all the elements and had only to arrange them and put them together. So I wrote out my final memoir at a single stroke and without difficulty.[2]

Notes

1. Harold Rosenberg, personal communication.
2. Brewster Ghiselin, ed., *The Creative Process*. University of California Press, 1952. Quoted from Henri Poincaré, "Mathematical Creation," in *The Foundations of Science*, translated by George Bruce Halstead. The Science Press, Lancaster, Pennsylvania, 1915. See also Henri Poincaré, *Science et Méthode*. Ernest Flammarion, Paris, 1908.

"SUDDENLY I FELT A MISTY CONSCIOUSNESS AS OF SOMETHING FORGOTTEN . . . EVERYTHING HAD A NAME"

34

We began our sampling of fits with a boy's supreme effort to spell out a word despite his utter incompetence in spelling. It is fitting to conclude it with another account of spelling. In the first, a backward boy's final attempt at schooling was a bitter comment on his life, and he lapsed thereafter into social isolation and obscurity. In the present instance, a severely handicapped person suddenly grasps the significance of spelling, and of words, and begins a long journey into a useful and productive life.

Helen Keller, the famous blind and deaf author, communicated with the world through a companion-interpreter with whom she "talked" by means of finger tappings in the palms of the hand. As a child she was cut off from the world until an extraordinary young lady, Annie Sullivan, was employed as her constant companion and teacher. Miss Sullivan worked steadily to teach the child to reproduce finger-movement patterns for various words. One day, when she was seven, the girl suddenly experienced a fit of insight into what the finger movements were all about.

According to Miss Keller's autobiography, she had learned to reproduce the spelling-out patterns of words but "I did not know that I was spelling a word or even that words existed; I was simply making my fingers go in monkeylike imitation." She had not recognized that "a particular act of my fingers constituted a word" nor that things had names "and each name gave birth to a new thought." One day, however,

> We walked down the path to the well-house, attracted by the fragrance of the honeysuckle with which it was covered. Someone was drawing water and my teacher placed my hand under the spout. As the cool stream gushed over one hand she spelled into the other the word *water*, first slowly, then rapidly. I stood still, my whole attention fixed upon the motions of her fingers. Suddenly, I felt a misty consciousness as of something forgotten—a

thrill of returning thought; and somehow the mystery of language was revealed to me. I knew then that "w–a–t–e–r" meant the wonderful cool something that was flowing over my hand. That living word awakened my soul, gave it light, joy, set it free! There were barriers still . . . but . . . I left the well-house eager to learn. Everything had a name, and each name gave birth to a new thought. As we returned to the house each object I touched seemed to quiver with life. That was because I saw everything with the strange new sight that had come to me.[1]

The leap from imitative repetition to understanding was prepared by long weeks of work, but the fitting together occurred suddenly. The episode began when Miss Keller and her teacher were attracted to the wellhouse by the odor of honeysuckle with which it was covered. Since ancient times, odors have been known to activate fits of epilepsy, surges of emotion, floods of memories, and other profound reactions. One famous writer actually kept overripe apples in his desk as a stimulus to imagination. Adding to the activating effect of the odor of honeysuckle was the feel of water flowing over her hand and the rhythmic repetition of Miss Sullivan's fingers spelling out "water," at first slowly, then rapidly. Such rhythms have an incantatory, evocative effect in creating new ideas and images. T. S. Eliot said, "Rhythm may bring to birth the idea and the image." And this effect is likely to be more potent in a context which provides sensuous influences like the odor of honeysuckle and the feel of flowing water.

All these things combined to produce an arrest of ongoing activity; Miss Keller "stood still, my whole attention fixed upon the motions of her fingers." In this hypnoidal "still," the connection between Miss Sullivan's fingers spelling out "water" and "the wonderful cool something flowing over my hand" could be made— something new could happen. The new arises, as it were, when the old comes to a stop. From this beginning, a whole series of other connections between the spelling-out fingers in the palm and objects in the world around could be made. Words now could lead thought and she could see with her mind's eye.

Notes

1. Helen Keller, *The Story of My Life*. Doubleday, New York, 1954.

PART THREE

THE CONCEPTS OF DYSJUNCTIVE SITUATIONS, DYSJUNCTIVE BRAIN FUNCTION, AND DYSJUNCTIVE BEHAVIOR AND EXPERIENCE

DYSJUNCTIVE SITUATIONS AND BEHAVIOR 35

Part One essayed to "desymptomize" the concept of fits and apply it to episodic knowings, feelings, and doings not merely as a descriptive term but primarily as an indicator of the dynamic processes by which fits were fitted together by the brain-mind system to meet the needs of the person in a critically unthinkable situation. "Fit" suggests to most people an interruption of the flow of thought, feeling, and action by special kinds of behavior, or experience, generated spontaneously by the brain because of some disease, or by the mind as a result of emotional pressures and conflicts. But in its etymological development, fit also implies fitting together of multiple and incongruent ideas into structures and sequences of thought and action, and the unfolding of these into episodes of living. The term itself raises the question, "How fit is a fit?"—how does it fit into the circumstances in which it occurs?

In Part Two, a reasonably representative number and variety of fits—convulsive, conventional, caricaturing, and creative episodes of living—were described and discussed. Upon this basis we can examine in some detail just how dysjunctiveness of man's nature and nurture—the interaction of a dysjunctive organism with a dysjunctive environment—culminates in a succession of crises and resolutions. How, we can ask, are fit-patterns produced, and what role do they play in the continuing interactions between and within organism and environment? For production and purpose go hand in hand, unless one holds to the untenable position that fits are only accidental, spontaneous symptoms of some "idiopathic" disease.

Dysjunctive reaction transcends the image of sick-patient-in-medical-waiting-room projected by the symptomatic overtones of "fit." It conjures up more suitable ideas of psychophysiological fitting-together processes needed for minding the contentions of everyday life. As a complex form of "junctive," *dysjunctive* implies both *dis-*

junctive (analytical, dispersing) and *con*junctive (synthesizing, joining together) tendencies and processes. The term itself exemplifies dysjunctiveness by joining together two contradictory components.

Looking at fits, at episodes of everyday and extraordinary behavior and experience, as involving dysjunctive situations, dysjunctive brain function, and dysjunctive reactions will illuminate the mysterious processes of fitting together by which the minding capacity of the human brain manages the business of the organism-individual-person. Later, in Part Four, we can probe further into the mystery by re-viewing both fits and dysjunctive reactions as brain storms—as whirlwinds of dispersion and rearrangement of ideas, images, and impulses into patterns of action and awareness.

A LAMP AND A MIRROR 36

He is coerced and cajoled into conformity but not, we note, with complete success. He shows a capacity even from birth to resist the impact of maternal and tribal demands. While to a certain degree his group shapes his course, at the same time it seems to antagonize him, as if he realized its threat to his integrity.

If the demand for autonomy were not a major force we could not explain the prominence of negativistic behavior in childhood. The crying, rejecting, and anger of a young infant as well as the negativistic behavior of the two-year-old are primitive indications of a being bent on asserting itself. *All his life long this being will be attempting to reconcile these two modes of becoming, the tribal and the personal: the one that makes him into a mirror, the other that lights the lamp of individuality within.*

—GORDON W. ALLPORT[1]

The human condition is inherently dysjunctive, full of complexity, contradiction, and ambiguity—and so are human activities. The brain, body, personality, and environment are all characterized by elaborate spatial configurations and proceed along complicated courses of action. The human animal is a two-sided, two-faced, twin-natured, bisexual organism using a two-sided, two-part, three-layered brain in a many-sided world. Man can look both forward and backward. With his mind's eye he can see both inward and outward. He forms ideas and images from double information acquired by two eyes, two ears, and two nostrils. He moves about within and acts upon his environment by means of two arms, hands, and legs which sometimes work together, sometimes alternately, and sometimes independently.

Information and meaning leading to and from action are exchanged between an old animal brain and a new human one. The old brain, between spinal cord and cerebral cortex, coordinates sensorimotor activities of the body and integrates them with the vagaries of organism-environment interaction in the service of the individual as organism or person. The new brain is made up of two great cerebral hemispheres (two very thick-walled balloons swollen out of the old brain), each of which has arrangements for amplifying, analyzing, shuffling, recombining, and general minding of sensorimotor data into patterns of awareness and action. These patterns, their sources and consequences, are tossed back and forth between the two hemispheres and between them and the old brain in a shaking-out and a shaping-up which separates and records some for future reference, notices some for immediate information only, and organizes others into immediate action patterns. At times the old brain seems to be in charge of action, using the new brain as its computer for bending personal capacities and style to the service of the organism; at other times the new brain seems to be a higher control center, directing by feedback modulation the old brain, and the organismic functions it controls, into serving the purposes of the person. In life, ancient biological drives and newly acquired personal intentions intermingle; so, too, structure and function of old and new brain are entwined.

Information acquired through perceptive sampling of reality is necessarily as two-sided as the devices by which it is acquired and processed. But it becomes even more dysjunctive—statistically complex as well as two-sided—because perceptive devices actively take statistical samplings of relevant data rather than passively transmitting all they "see." We may not know that something is "out there" because its presence is simply not reported.

We can no longer think of our brains as super switchboards, passively making the right, or "conditioned," connections between perceptions and actions. We can no longer expect the integrative brain to fashion a timelessly true replica of external reality.[2] For the present, at least, if we must have a model of how the brain works, our image of intracerebral activity must be conceived as a moving picture filmed in a succession of probing close-ups and vast panoramics by several agile photographers and sound men, directed by a historical-minded prophet, edited by a schizophrenic given to both strict literalism and wild symbolism, and featuring a cast of thousands.

This picture of how the brain continually models the ever changing here-and-now is sufficiently dysjunctive to make for both great chaos and great creations. Dysjunctiveness in the model is also well matched by the script with which it works. Past and future not-heres and not-nows are also dysjunctive. And it is the discontinuities within and between here-and-now and these other not-heres and not-nows whose bridging over, filling in, or by-passing provides the drive and purposes of present thinking.

Experience, and the experience of experience, are necessarily dysjunctive because both sensory perception and integration-in-time are carried on by many-sided processes and structures. Experience biases perception-integration and sometimes produces a critical discrepancy between its version of contemporary reality and what others see as really there. Experience (as that which is "there" to experience in interactions with environment, with society, with culture, and with other persons) is itself quite dysjunctive.

For each of us has had two parents, each with various real and fantastic personifications. And we have had several other authoritative interpreters and predictors of what we are supposed to experience. They differ not only in sex, size, etc., but also in opinions about the world and how to live in it; in this they are often, each of them, of different minds at different times of the day.

The general culture which these people more or less represent contains its own contradictions and ambiguities. Thus we are told, "He who hesitates is lost," but also, "Look before you leap"; "A stitch in time saves nine," but, "Don't cross your bridges until you come to them." We are told that we must "Love thy neighbor as thyself," but also that our success depends on a "dog eat dog" philosophy.

With the best of intention and effort, we inevitably encounter difficulty, embarrassment, and momentary paralysis in integrating organism, individual, and person within and with those circumstances. Unfortunately, few of us live in the best of circumstances, and we necessarily go from one dysjunctive situation and reaction to another. Our progress from here to there, from now to then, would be extremely erratic indeed were it not that we have, in the very means of perception which produce momentary dysjunctions, the means also for their correction. The eye, for example, scans whatever it fixes upon some thirty times per second, thus rapidly producing thirty slightly different versions of the same thing. But this process leads to relative certainty rather than complete confusion exactly because it is a kind of averaging-out, statistical sample-taking. Our perceptive, information-acquiring activities do sample present circumstances and compare the sample with those recalled from past experience and those expected in the immediate future. When we encounter a too discrepant sample, alarms ring and emergency fitting-together operations are activated. These processes average out wild swings, center attention upon the leading elements of a complex, smooth out contradictions, and formulate pragmatic solutions for persistent ambiguities. The culture, the tribe, and the status quo also make for harmony and order even while providing contradiction and mystification. "Don't believe everything you hear and only half of what you see" can become a source of reassurance and an inducement to be content with uncertainty.

But fortunately, just when everything is tranquilized, our brains, ever busy with unsolved problems, pop some nonconforming thought into mind for "us" to deal with as best "we" can. "We" may have to change in the process, but that, too, is inherent in the human condition. And as an aid in these recurring deaths and re-births of "I," the minding capacity that produces or seeks contradiction can bring to bear its full facility for resolving it. This capacity ranges from split-second analyses of very small aspects of the concrete environment (produced, for example, by the very rapid scannings of the eye) to very large generalizations made possible by the comprehensives of the mind's eye. The ability to see, to abstract, through ever receding levels from the present to the timeless, from the specific to the general, has been used to reorganize chronic alcoholics' conceptions of themselves. This is achieved by having them watch movies of themselves watching movies of themselves discussing their problems with a therapist.[3]

Simply watching movies of themselves discussing their problems is not enough. They see nothing useful. Only when they watch themselves watching themselves (Self 1 looks at Self 2 looking at Self 3) can they begin to understand how complex their problems—and their "selves"—are. This image of "someone looking at himself looking at himself" is dysjunctive enough to make the reader giddy.* But if he can see how it might help another see himself in action for the first time, he will understand what I really mean by dysjunctive—that it is both disorganizing and reorganizing.

---

* The rich, unanalyzable dysjunctive quality of life—and its preverbal, sublogical, "unutterable" representations in the brain and mind—can be partially grasped intuitively by reflection upon the origin of "giddiness" in "god-in-ness," considering the relation between giddiness and inspiration, and contemplating the way young children enjoy making themselves giddy with brain-twisters and rolling down hills.

Notes

1. Gordon W. Allport, *Becoming* (Terry Lectures). Yale University Press, 1955.

2. W. Grey Walter, *The Living Brain*, W. W. Norton, New York, 1953, p. 22; Wilder Penfield and Theodore Rasmussen, *The Cerebral Cortex of Man*, Macmillan, New York, 1950; Michael A. Arbib, *Brains, Machines, and Mathematics*, McGraw-Hill, New York, 1964.
3. Floyd Cornelison. In a paper delivered at the December 1965 meetings of the American Medical Association, Philadelphia.

"WOULD YOU RATHER LIVE IN THE CITY OR IN THE SUMMER?" 37

When I was a boy I enjoyed exchanging jokes, riddles, puzzles, tongue-twisters, and other brain games with my peers. We were as taken with these exercises of the fitting-together capacity as we were with games of bodily strength and skill. We had a pre-Gutenberg, tribal-oral culture alive enough to have pleased Marshall McLuhan. And we were concerned enough with unanswerable questions to have gratified a Zen master.

One unanswerable question we posed to unsuspecting newcomers to the gang was, "Would you rather live in the city or in the summer?" Comparing an urban setting with a season requires matching similar differences and differing similarities—it is a dysjunctive procedure. We found no answer; arguments were endless; but we learned much about the many-sidedness of things.

Many insoluble human problems have the same dysjunctive form, and as preparation for dealing with perplexing aspects of the human condition, childhood play with puzzles and riddles comes in handy. An ageless problem for all of us, for instance, is posed in this ancient Hebraic example of dysjunctive thinking: "If I am not for myself, who will be for me? If I am only for myself, what am I?" Brain-twisters like that are timeless, produce endless argument, and have only a dysjunctive solution.

Dysjunctiveness depends upon involvement. We get stumped by things we are interested in. An appetite for play, or for whatever the playing is about, gets us involved in puzzlement and perplexities. Need, of course, can drive as strongly as desire. The role of involvement can best be seen in an illustration. Whenever a newcomer to our group made a great show of how bright he was, he was apt to be told that he was not so smart, in fact he didn't really "know his arse from a hole in the ground." Resentful, anxious to establish his intellectual credentials, he would soon find himself involved in the arse-and-the-hole-in-the-ground test. While he attended closely to the presentation of this problem, we squatted in a circle around a bare patch of earth and the examiner-for-the-day took a sharp stick and gouged out two holes in the the ground with great ceremony. The examinee was told that one of them represented his arse and the other was a plain hole in the ground. He was instructed to study them closely. Then he was led a few steps away and spun about several times as if to disorient him. He was then led back to the test site and told: "Show us where is your arse and where is the hole in the ground." Usually the neophyte would point triumphantly to the correct hole and say, "That's my arse!" and then to the other saying, "And that's the hole in the ground!" This achievement would be greeted with hoots of laughter. The test administrator would then pat him firmly on the behind and say, "*That's* your arse, not that hole in the ground, and don't ever forget it! You see you really don't know your arse from a hole in the ground." We had given the neophyte a dysjunctive experience; he had been dis-joined and reunited in his self—"he" had been "taken out of himself," shaken up, and put back together again.

When involvement is narrow, as in this example, the context is easily forgotten and we may lose our bearings, unable then to see the forest as we grimly concentrate on the bark of just one tree. Involvement is necessary in procedures calling for speed and rhythm. "She sells sea shells by the sea shore" presents no great speech problem unless one gets involved in trying to say it fast and smooth. Then the faster one goes, the more likely a breakdown —a dis-junction of speech.

Dis-junctions, as the hyphen-separated prefix implies, result from conflicts between incompatible and equally compelling elements. "She sells sea shells . . ." requires the ability to say two quite different sounds of "s"—the sibilant hiss, and the soft "sh." Anticipatory preparation for speaking this tongue-twister alerts two different neuromuscular mechanisms for producing these two sounds. If we are not involved in a speed test but are trying only to say the sentence accurately, attention will lead action by only a very slight margin. We can think about and pronounce the words one at a time; neuromuscular mechanisms are alerted and discharged in leisurely succession. But when we get involved in trying to say it fast, we are aware of the dangers of failing; foresight, looking ahead for danger spots, diverts some of our attention into scanning ahead. Scanning and oscillatory "hunting" for trouble back and forth along the sentence line not only distracts from the task at hand but also cues us misleadingly; we may be looking ahead to "shells" and thereby activating "sh" just when our motor-expressive apparatus is trying to say "sells." In our split-mindedness, the already partially activated sensorimotor devices for both sounds of "s" are put on "hair-trigger." Our next "intention to say" sets off a contention surviving embodied as "shea sore," perhaps, or by mutual cancellation of contending elements leaving us with nothing to say.

Foresightful anticipation of dangers and opportunities was essential for survival to man's ancestors. It is essential for us today. But it can prove troublesome when anticipation is ambiguously loaded with both promise and perils, and leads via static tension to reactions like the stage fright that afflicts public speakers, athletes, actors, *et al.* When foresight becomes detached from its role in leading action (because of unavoidable delay, or when oncoming events are seen to be charged with ambiguity and contradiction), anticipation itself becomes a dysjunctive experience. Anticipation turns into unpleasant apprehension and anxiety as what to expect becomes more and more unforeseeable. Anxiety, in this view, is not so much expectation of fearsome experience as it is the immediate experience of disabled expectation.

Time seems to flow forward for us, but we experience it in segments as episodes of living which have a beginning, a middle, and an end. In everyday life we seem to expect that a kind of momentum will carry us from one segment to the next. But our circumstances, and our relation to them, can be acted upon and changed only by a series of crises, decisions, and fits which move us ahead. The processes that culminate in anxiety, confusion, and breakdown begin when foresight begins to predict intensification of contradictions into unthinkable forms.

Whatever the content, our efforts to get on with the business of living are hampered in life circumstances (modeled by such performances as saying rapidly "She sells sea shells by the sea shore") because of their form. Usually we avoid, if possible, things which are unprosaically too symmetrical, asymmetrical, or uncommonly rhythmical. Foresight is not very useful in predicting their effects. The symmetry, rhythm, and sound pattern of "She sells sea shells by the sea shore" is both bad prose and bad poetry. Shorter expressions can be just as difficult. "Black bug's blood" requires expressive agility because it entails a shift from the double sound of "bl" to the simple sound of "b" and back again. This is a dysjunctive pseudoalliteration. Only practice can unify such dysjunctive sequences into a single utterance.

The playful and philosophical tasks, problems, and questions noted earlier provide practice with dysjunctive confluences of similar differences and different similarities. One can teach one-self to say "black bug's blood" quite eloquently, and gain some formal skill in minding such things. In early years we have time to play with these dysjunctive models. But living often presents us with dysjunctive situations that are novel and give us no time for practice. We may avoid or deal with them as best we can, and file them in our unconscious where they are "practiced" for future use.

Thus, in addition to problems of getting on with our immediate tasks of living, we carry a burden of problems we are dealing with outside the consciousness devoted to current living. And we find these unresolved problems popping into mind whenever current ones recall them, or even when our minding capacity is "between engagements," enjoying a rest. These spontaneous eruptions of old problems precipitate us into all kinds of dysjunctive situations.

Analysis of contexts producing or containing epileptic fits has revealed the outstanding common elements to be the formal characteristics of suddenness, intensity, conflict, and sharp phase-change. Analysis of the fit-contexts described in Part Two shows that these same characteristics pertain also to nonepileptic fits. Scrutiny of the episodes described in Part Two reveals, in addition, that the form and content of fits are shaped by condensation, symbolization, and synthesis—processes quite like those of dreaming and waking wit. The processes of wit and of fit are identical. All fits, destructive or constructive, are therefore dysjunctive reactions.

Both dysjunctive situations and dysjunctive reactions are characterized by contention between the *dis*junctive and *con*junctive components, which are fitted together. In any specific fit, one conflict may seem to be the only important one. However, close examination will usually disclose other components of a dysjunctive complex.

Dysjunctive reactions are symptomatic of the brain's ability to make labile combinations of incongruent elements. The term seems fitting for disorders of integration because it has analogies with dyspnoea, for difficulty in breathing, dyspepsia, for indigestion, dysparunia, for difficult or painful intercourse, and so on. However, though dysjunctive reactions may even be painful, interpreting all "dysturbed" processes as evidence of disease reveals a misguided tendency to conceive of health as a womblike, continuously placid existence.

Fits of convulsion and other gross disruptions of ongoing activity are, dynamically, disjunctive. Fits of creation and other syntheses of former contradictions (fits of invention or discovery) are, dynamically, conjunctive. From this dynamic point of view, the term *dysjunctive reactions* could be restricted to episodes in which the disruptive and unifying elements are evenly matched. But structural features must also be taken into account.

Fits of creative synthesis, which are to produce new modes of knowing, feeling, and doing, must disrupt the old; they are, therefore, both disjunctive and conjunctive. Furthermore, fits of convulsion are not merely disruptive. Often they produce a profound reorganization of the subjective state, and of interpersonal relations. The patient experiences this in terms of "turning over a new leaf," "as if I had gotten rid of something evil," and even as a feeling of "death and rebirth." A single fit, especially the first, or one at a critical life situation, may alter significantly an individual's relation to his circumstances and to other persons. So even fits of convulsion have their disjunctive and conjunctive creative aspects. Thus dysjunctive operations actually include the entire spectrum of continuity-dissolving-and-restoring performances. Dysjunctive activity is the means by which seemingly discrete episodes of behavior and experience are first organized and executed, and then fitted into the continuity called living.

The shuffling, reshuffling, and recombining of ideas, images, and impulses—the "turning it inside out," "standing it on its head" unification of opposites and dissolution of unities—is what is subsumed by the term *dysjunctive.* Whenever our action comes to a halt, whatever we do next is "new"; in order to do anything new, we must first discontinue the old. But to be new instead of merely novel, and to be recognized as such, the new thing must maintain some continuity with the past. The new invariably involves the old.

If we could erase all ongoing cerebral, bodily, and personal activity entirely, we could only begin living again in the condition of a newborn infant. Indeed, in a major convulsion, in the coma phase, the individual comes about as close to death as one can get. The complete inertness of some patients at that moment is just short of death; it is also just short of life, like the state of a newborn infant who has not yet begun to breathe. One feels an urge to intervene to get life going again. And the patient in recovering does, very rapidly, reenact the growth-into-person processes that had previously taken him years to accomplish. Such gross disruptions of living may seem far removed from our normal everyday life. But daily living is in fact an intermittent pattern of fits and starts. Fits of intracerebral fitting together alternate with the acting out of the fitted together as behavior. Between episodic fitted-together behaviors are many microscopic moments of psycho-physiological "death and rebirth."

These dysjunctions in thinking can occur whether we are thinking hard or whether we are woolgathering. Intense concentration (being lost in thought) and "not having a thought in my head" (having lost thought) are not so different neurologically. Finely focused attention—a small, erasable dot—is only a short step from vacant-mindedness—as procedures for inducing hypnosis demonstrate. The longer and harder we try to get the point of a joke, to solve a riddle, or to find any solution that eludes us, the closer we approach a hypnoidal state in which "we" give up and the brain's fitting-together capacity takes over. This switch enables "us" to transcend limitations on the content of awareness imposed by the ego and to reach back, out, or forward for novel or great ideas. As an ever larger number of ideas are tried and discarded during "our" efforts to solve problems, actual awareness becomes emptier; finally "we" just can't think of anything else and things start popping into "our" mind. These spontaneous ideas and images may or may not be relevant to the problem at hand.

When attention flags from fatigue, or during reverie, the things that pop into mind may seem irrelevant and unrelated. The content of awareness is then dysjunctive in the sense of being an aimless complex of ideas and images. Some larger pattern or central focus of meaning may suddenly appear or slowly emerge into and reorient awareness. These spontaneous inspirations and great ideas then lead to more coherency and meaning. Housman, Mozart, Eliot, Valéry, and other artists have described different ways of coaxing or cajoling dysjunctive patterns into creative ones. Details of their various processes for dysjunctive minding will be found in Chapter 43.

Dysjunctive awareness can also be produced directly by conditions that derange attention and disturb relevant ordering of associations. Illness and physicochemical agents (drugs, dances, drums, flickering lights, etc.) throw many people into absorbing psychedelic states. Generally, however, the means which induce these riotous, kaleidoscopic whirlings of ideas and images also deactivate the ego, or "I," and prevent its reactivation for creative use of these states. Nevertheless, someone does occasionally manage to mind the products of artificially altered awareness into creative and useful forms. Coleridge did write his poem about Kubla Khan's stately pleasure dome from an opium-and-illness-induced derangement of awareness. And Wallace, while ill in the jungles of Malaya, during a week of feverish activity managed to duplicate almost exactly the unpublished theory of *On the Origin of Species* that had taken Darwin a lifetime to work out.

If "anything from fright to flatulence" can set off dysjunctive operations, and anything from a fit of convulsion to a fit of creation can result, the fitting-together process must possess a kind of omnipotence and omniscience. A central (input) focus for convergence of endowment, experience, and expectation must also be a point of departure (output) for all kinds of divergent action and reaction. This place or process or point in time can alter the boundaries between consciousness and unconsciousness, between present, past, and future, and between brain, mind, and self. This center of centers must be activated many times throughout the day. These multiple activations may produce a wonderful variety or boring repetition of actions. The quality of the action sequence will be shaped by the past as well as by the present, causing us to mind our crises in the particular way we do. Few of us think of ourselves as being extremist in our minding operations, but a moment's reflection will show that we, too, have our fits of disruption and our moments of creative inspiration every day of our lives. We are always stopping and starting all over again; we can, if we will, recognize our opportunities and make our new beginnings more meaningful and zestful.

SIX MONTHS AND EIGHT POUNDS 38

Thinking about fits as dysjunctive reactions illuminates the interplay of their form and content, the relationship between situation and reaction. It stimulates further thinking about the brain storms of psychophysiological processes by which these episodes are generated, shaped, and guided to their conclusion. *Dysjunctive* suggests a diversity-in-unity of the apparatus, process, and time-dependent function in the brain that minds dysjunctive elements into configurations and courses.

In earlier chapters the difficulties of defining *fit* by any single criterion of location or nature were formulated in the phrase "indeterminacy of fit-ness." Defining an episode as a dysjunctive reaction accepts and incorporates this indeterminacy. And, most importantly, investigation of the episode as a dysjunctive reaction tends to proceed rather differently than if it were thought of as a fit.

For example, a pianist playing Bach could suddenly switch without a break into several bars of a Beatles song, and then back to Bach again. He might show only a slight or no change of expression during this interpolation, and seem unaware of the switch. Instances of this kind are not rare. Investigating this episode as an epileptic fit, one would proceed to diagnostic studies (X-rays of the head, brain-wave records, neurological examination, etc.). Finding no sign of brain disturbance other than occasional epileptic-type brain waves, one would call it a case of idiopathic epilepsy and prescribe appropriate medicine.

From the point of view of dysjunctive reactions, however, one would also inquire into the pianist's attitudes toward Bach, the Beatles, concertizing, the particular concert, etc. Finding conflicts within or between his attitudes, abilities, and appetites for music and money, one would then speculate about what happened at the dysjunctive moment of switching from Bach to the Beatles.

Of special interest would be the relation between dysjunctive moments and paroxysms of epileptic brain waves.

Brief consideration of the relation between disjunctive moments, dysjunctive situations, and dysjunctive behavior will bring us to the problem of dysjunctive complexes and their role in dysjunctive behavior. When we talk, every pause for thought is a *dis*junction of speech and, at the same time, a *con*junction in communication. Only when a pause is prolonged, or is followed by an abrupt shift in topic, or is in some way totally disruptive of flow, is it primarily *dis*junctive. Even so, as in the case of major convulsions, some *con*junctive action is required to reconstitute organism-environment relations. Many meaningful statements, in fact, are punctuated by stammering struggles to say precisely what we mean, and these crises are emphasized by gestures, postural shifts, and other bodily involvements in minding. Generally, if a thing has to be said, it gets uttered* in one way or another.

In psychiatric conversations and in those of everyday life, however, things which should be said, but which are difficult, are often uttered quite indirectly. Attention is called to the suppression of the almost-said only by fleeting signs—surface ripples, marking the passage of something unspoken. When one is very alert to and concerned with the individual and his talking, one recognizes that something significant has not been verbalized. From the context of this not-saying, one can have some insight into its probable content.

When these slight breaks in flow of thought and speech pass unnoticed, an opportunity has been missed. These negative signals are often the best the talker can do at the time, and the concerned listener is well advised to note the context and quality of such falterings.

A person may begin to think about previously unthinkable topics when temporary security, urgent needs for growth, and pressing life problems urge him on. Then selection works less smoothly, cracks appear in the smooth façade of pseudocommunication, and he begins to talk as best he can about significant subjects. His talking then is apt to be punctuated by many small crises as he tries to deal with the previously unthinkable. Recognizing and knowing how to help with these small dysjunctive crises in psychiatric conversations requires what Otto Fenichel called "psychoanalytic tact," which is like ordinary tact only more so.[1] Tact is necessary, for behind a small disjunctive break may lurk crucial conflicts whose sudden occupation of awareness would

---

* "Uttered" in McLuhan's sense of "outterance."

disrupt the existing design for living. Tact is appropriate, for the patient is struggling to reveal what it has seemed essential to conceal, even from himself.

Upon the tactics with which one person helps another to deal with minor crises depends the future of their relationship, psychoanalytic or personal. When small crises are dealt with tactfully, they become, like words in a sentence, units of a progressively meaningful trajectory of personal performance and interpersonal interaction.

When small crises are glossed over, the patient may give up trying to talk to the physician about more important things, and thereafter communication proceeds by each making confused and mystifying noises at the other. A second undesirable effect of ignoring small crises is a recurring pattern of approach-avoidance —of incipient expression and resuppression of the critical. Cracks in smooth communication are papered over as fast as they appear. This hectic pattern may create an aura of tension, and an impression of impending explosion. In fact, repeated suppression of minor crises may culminate in an explosion of accumulated, and by now intensified, tension. Thus are dramatic abreactions produced.

In general, it seems to me, patients, psychiatrists, and other people tend to find one of two kinds of trajectories of interaction more natural than the other, e.g., the multiple stepwise pattern of crises-punctuated progression ("two steps forward, one step back") or progression across apparently smooth plateaus to sudden, critical leaps to new heights ("take a giant step"). In terms of feeding behavior, one could think of the two patterns as "nibbling away at a problem" or as occasionally "biting off more than one can easily chew or digest."

A certain amount of testing out usually precedes any significant disclosure. But sometimes a person needs most to deal with critical problems just when his abilities for managing them are unequal to the task; such crises require effective collaboration of physician and patient. In Part Two, Chapter 16 describes an episode in which a young man under the influence of sodium amytal, overwhelmed by anger toward his mother, exploded into a major convulsion. Chapter 27 describes the prevention of a convulsive explosion by maintaining communication.

The first exploratory approaches to talking about *dys*junctive problems are often brief *dis*junctions of speech. Appearance and behavior emphasize the tentativeness of the letting down of defenses and the dysjunctive nature of the problem. Thus a patient who does not ordinarily stammer may say, for the umpteenth time, "My mother was a fine woman and took good care of us kids," but says it, "My m-m-m-mother . . ."; "My mother was a f-f-f-fine woman . . ."; "My mother was a fine woman and took good c-c-c-care of us kids"; or "My mother was a fine woman who took good care of uh-uh-uh-us kids." It is now evident that the patient has some ambivalence toward his mother; or some doubts that she was always such a fine person; or conflicts about the goodness of her care; or some feeling that one or another of "us" was neglected or favored too much. The dysjunctive locus in a dysjunctive situation may be minor, but it is useful to call the patient's attention to his moment of stammering and to suggest that perhaps relations with mother were as troublesome as his speech about them. The patient will take it from there— if he can. And he usually can, at least for a while.

When brain waves are recorded during interviews with epileptic patients, minor crises in flow of thought and feeling may be signaled by bodily and personal gap-filling activities which are preceded, accompanied, or followed by brief bursts of epileptic brain waves (see next chapter). With nonepileptic patients, outbursts of nonspecific but unusual brain waves appear at the same time (see next chapter). Chapter 16 described a dysjunctive reaction consisting of sudden tension, disjunction of speech, peculiar facial expression, and small paroxysm of abnormal brain waves that served to punctuate a boy's efforts to talk about problems in his relationship with his mother: ". . . Mother would feel very bad and make me feel bad if I got into a fight . . . [pause, tension] . . . I felt . . . [pause, peculiar facial expression, burst of epileptic brain waves] . . . I couldn't get mad at my mother. She's my mother. She borned me!"

A complex contention of emotion is clearly visible behind this disjointed speech. Elements in a similar dysjunctive complex were described in the case of the young man who had a psychomotor epileptic fit of blankness when he found himself watching others "fool around with" the fly or belt of their trousers. When he was telling me about these incidents, the break between "I don't know . . ." and ". . . I know I'm not a queer!" could have been filled in verbally with something like ". . . what I am, but . . ." and we could have gone on to discuss "what I am." But the red-faced, confused reaction which did fill the gap was an external sign of inner contention about "what I am" that was too dysjunctive to verbalize. In a series of conversations we explored the dysjunctive complex aroused by environmental cues and contained in "I don't know . . . I know I'm not a queer." The contention of thought, feeling, and memory thus condensed resulted from an unfortunate series of early experiences with his mother which had left him hostile, fearful, and aggressive toward women, and remarkably ambivalent about tender relations with them. The quality of these conditioning experiences, condensed into the dysjunctive complex, is seen in exaggerated form in one episode. Once, as a boy, he had rushed into the kitchen to tell some exciting news to his mother. She was busy at the stove, and, impatient to talk to her, he tugged at her dress. She turned quickly and, presumably inadvertently, spilled scalding water over his head.

The dysjunctiveness of his "complex" can be seen in other relevant historical detail. Equipped with an intense conflict between lustful urges and fearful, aggressive impulses toward women, he had trouble finding and keeping feminine sexual partners, and occasionally resorted to masturbation—which he thought "unmanly." He had once been seduced by the homosexual leader of the local veterans' drum-and-bugle corps and remembered this experience with disgust. Unhappy with solitary sexuality and unable to be easily lustful with other persons, he sometimes fantasied gratifying his oral and genital needs, his active and passive urges, untroubled by needs for and fear of others, by performing fellatio upon himself. Such fantasies combined with his real-life conflicts had become intermingled into a complex of hostility and yearning, fear and lust, loneliness and longing for autonomy. Such a contentious collection of urgent contradictions is a good example of dysjunctive complex.

Such things drive all sorts of dysjunctive performances, from fits of convulsion to fits of creation. Complexes, however, are not something like "psychic abscesses," needing only psychoanalytic excision and drainage; nor are they smoldering emotional volcanos awaiting an opportunity to erupt. They are also ad hoc assemblies-of-the-moment which, like nuclear weapons, become explosive only at the moment of assembly. Their dysjunctive effect arises as much, and as frequently, from their form as from their content.

Historically, complexes were first investigated by Bleuler and Jung, by means of word-association tests. In such a test, for example, a person guilty of a murderous stabbing might give the word "kill" in association response to the stimulus-word "knife" and do so after a delay longer than his reaction time to innocuous words. An innocent person might produce words like "cut," "blade," or "whittle," and so on without significant delay. Unusual delay and/or peculiarly meaningful associations are indicators of the activity of complexes of thought and feeling, and of the effort required when they are activated but suppressed—that is, the delay (and any significant bodily reaction studied later by polygraph lie detectors) reflects (as did my patient's red-faced, confused reaction) silent, inner struggle. In criminal cases, a suspect's inner struggle is carried on to prevent himself from contributing to his own entrapment. But, as Freud pointed out in 1906, we all have consciences; guilt can attach itself by unconscious associations to matters unrelated to its actual source. Thus signs of guilt may have nothing directly to do with a particular crime as such. An apprehensive individual, we now know, may produce significant bodily reactions in polygraph lie-detection procedures simply because he feels threatened. The red-faced blushing of the patient as he faltered in his effort to say "I know I'm not a queer" could have, for instance, resulted from anger at interrogation or the effects of mental effort as well as from shame about homosexual or other guilty urges. An individual who responds violently (and presumably guiltily, with great changes in breathing, blood pressure, and sweating during polygraph lie detection) to the question, "Are you the cat burglar who stole the sixty-nine dollars from the safe in Miss Jones's office?" may do so for many reasons. He may have woefully mistreated cats or loved them inordinately as a child; he might have a brother who is a burglar; he could be guilty about certain sexual practices; he might be a devout Catholic concerned about the reliability of the "safe period" method of birth control; or he might have a secret yen for Miss Jones, etc.

Dysjunctive complexes are not simply undigested clumps of distressing past experiences thrown toward awareness and action in response to appropriate stimuli. They are just as often sudden comings-together of current contradictions—that is, they are multiple and conflicting responses to ambiguity and contradiction. Complexes from the past may contribute to dysjunctiveness of current crises when they are recalled by the fitting-together capacity to broaden its search for a way out of an unthinkable situation. Past, present, and future are never as arbitrarily separated in the brain as they are in our abstractions; hence to some extent the dysjunctiveness of any situation is enhanced by elements assembled by perception, recall, and expectation.

When I said, at the end of a long series of experiments, "I'm almost finished," and my patient said, "So am I," his verbal response was appropriate to the immediate situation. But his thought and feeling, partly expressed and partly concealed, were reinforced by memories of others using him until they too were finished with him. And though the fleeting brain-wave paroxysm occurred because of his brain's epilepticity, it occurred when it did because of his conflicts about "speaking out," and these too had roots in both current and historic experience.

When I asked the young lady who had told me about a long, "sensible" discussion with her mother which had produced no new additions to her wardrobe, "And who was being so sensible, you or your mother?" her brief *petit mal* reaction was as much a response to my questioning as it was a product of conflicted emotion toward her mother. And the young lady whose frequent belches punctuated talk about her family was expressing thereby not only an active complex concerning them, she was also protesting against having to discuss her history at all.

Perhaps Father Beauchamp was conceived by Anthony Burgess as a man who tried to dispose of all his troubles by swallowing them. But there is always a first time for everything, and one can produce psychosomatic modes of problem disposal (as an alternative to solving them) when the occasion suits. When Roper says to him, "Oh, sir, we ought not to bring God into a chemistry lesson," Father Beauchamp chews and swallows before he says to Roper, "You asked the question. See if you can answer it." This disjunctive digestive maneuver is designed to dispose of Roper's current provocation. The psychosomatic aspects of the subject deserve further attention.

Dysjunctive complexes manifest themselves not only in disturbances of thought, speech, and communicative behavior, but also in alterations of bodily activity. The bodily reactions that accompany sudden shifts, in mode of operating or in the frame of reference for action, are a significant part of many dysjunctive reactions. The shivering that Housman felt when lines of poetry popped into his mind is like that some men feel at the end of urination. Shivering also marks transitions of many other kinds. Sudden phase-changes of all kinds require physiological adjustments.

Konrad Lorenz, the well-known ethologist, describes a swaying readjustment which his dog, Suzi, made when she first emerged from the water after a long swim. This had nothing to do with chilling, and Lorenz found upon inquiry among human swimmers that some of them, too, swayed when first standing erect after long swims.[2] Some such phase-change activation of brain-body mechanism may set off the convulsions of some young thoroughbred foals when they first struggle to their feet. Certainly, as Pearce and Newton point out, sudden shifts and shaking in human frames of reference produce giddiness, vertigo, nausea, etc.[3] Housman's shivering was accompanied by gooseflesh and such bristling of his beard that he could not shave. Emily Dickinson's reaction to poetry was twofold: she felt very cold and she also felt as if the top of her head were coming off. H. L. Gold felt the top of his head about to come off when he was challenged to prophesy concerning the war's end. Many people experience similar uncanny feelings when they are in church, at a concert, in the theater, and are otherwise about to have a great experience or a great idea.

These uncanny reactions are isolated and exaggerated concomitants of struggle with the unthinkable in any form. Because they are "free-floating," uncanny experiences threaten people with their alienness. They therefore make efforts to escape by disintegrating rather than integrating such situations. Physiological reactions then mix "fight or flight" bodily activities with symbolic representations of the situation. When extremely creative persons, like Mozart, who can tolerate awareness of dysjunctive collections of ideas and images, are minding them into new patterns, there may be scant visible evidence of this extraordinary inner activity. Creative people may appear abstracted or distracted and exhibit "the look" noted earlier in connection with spontaneous fittings-together. They may report only mild feelings of absorption, detachment, or inspiration. Evidently tension within and with dysjunctive complexes is dissipated constructively as the complex is unrolled, unfolded, or developed.

One example from my research studies will illuminate details of the dynamic relation between brief dysjunctive reactions and elaborate dysjunctive complexes. Persistent inquiry into the sources and significance of brief dysjunctive reactions during interviews provided many instance of this relation. For a while I used "truth drugs" and hypnosis to help patients (those who were especially inarticulate and who tried to deal with life problems by "putting them out of mind") to explore the connections between their symptoms and their problems.

A twenty-five-year-old truck driver, who was being treated for epilepsy, had a major convulsion one Sunday while "just sitting around" in his room. Ordinary inquiry revealed only that he "might have been thinking" about his two boys and of getting them back from their mother, from whom he was separated. He spoke of the older boy by name, but when he referred to the younger boy as "the kid," he spoke with an odd tone and emphasis. I asked if he had any problems concerning "the kid." His face went blank, and for about half a minute he mumbled to himself. I could make out only the phrase "six months, eight pounds." Then abruptly, he recovered from this psychomotor fit and said, "What did you ask me just then?" I repeated the question. He denied having any special problem about the boy and asserted that he had been thinking only of how to get custody of both his sons. He readily assented to my suggestion that he might be able to think and talk about his problems more freely if I gave him some medicine that had the relaxing effect of "a couple of drinks."

A small amount of sodium amytal was injected intravenously, and we discussed its effect for about a minute. Then he began to talk about his recent convulsion. I asked if he had felt lonely in his room on Sunday and he said that he had, but that mostly he had been "stewing" about his family problems. He went on, "I'm in bad shape, Doc, I think too much. You think about one thing and then another and another and then pretty soon you have yourself all worked up. I think about my two kids and how I'd like to get Pete, but there's not much I can do. That day of the fit I wasn't thinking about nothing . . . June 18th . . . that was the day the kid was born. That started me thinking . . . six months and eight pounds. Then I kept myself busy because I didn't feel good . . . kinda stomach-ache. I was singing 'To Each His Own.' . . . You want me to say I was thinking about my wife . . . to each his own means that, Doc. You start to get a headache and you stop because it makes it worse . . . my mood might have changed. She came over once . . . she hadn't been around for three months . . . you never saw anything like it . . . she was all over me. She said it was all different and it sure was . . . but then she got out of bed and left and hasn't let me near her since. The kid came six months later . . . six months and eight pounds . . . I don't want to hurt anybody, Doc, I never hurt anybody that didn't hurt me first . . . what would happen if I went ahead and then found it was my kid after all?" His paroxysm of speech after sodium amytal could be thought of as a fit of talking. Such a burst of speech was for him quite unusual.

His earlier, half-consciously mumbled "six months and eight pounds" was a condensation quite like those by which finer products of wit and dreams are made. It was, in its way, a witty statement of his problem. It was the external representation of an unthinkable, almost unutterable (utterable = outerable), complex that he could otherwise express only dysjunctively in convulsive fits.

We see again in his "six months and eight pounds," mumbled

in a half-witted or "two-witted" confusion, the two-sidedness of dysjunctive reactions that reach toward insight, wit, and acts of creation on the one hand, and toward confusion, unconsciousness, and fits of convulsion on the other.

These condensations, these dysjunctive survivals-of-the-fittest from unseen contentions (together with those syntheses of innovative and creative ideas and images), must all have a common source, which so far I have called by the noncommital term "the fitting-together capacity." Other investigators, from time unremembered, have wondered about the origins of our awareness and action, especially of the more marvelous varieties. Descartes and speculative thinkers of his time sought the "seat of the soul." In our time "psyche," usually referring to mind rather than spirit, has become as unacceptable to mechanists as "soul." Some philosophers of the laboratory pursue literary courses of thought; they speak, for example, of "where vital things happen" or of the place where Fancy is bred.[4]

To me, the fitting-together capacity has the tripartite character of (1) a place—a structure or an apparatus—in the brain; (2) both a general and specific process of cerebration; and (3) a reaction at a critical moment in time. The location and nature of the fitting-together capacity is indeterminate, like the fits, dysjunctive reactions, and brain storms it generates. Indeterminacy pervades all aspects of dysjunctive situations, fittings-together, and behavior; it is inevitable from dysjunctive structure. When Harold Rosenberg awoke to stare at the odalisque on the cover of an art magazine, the sentence that suddenly sprang to mind was, "Loving may interfere with a woman's career, but being loved is a career." This sentence is itself dysjunctive. It condensed but at the same time negated all the ideas and images he had discarded the night before. Rosenberg (whose essays are noted for their deceptive "dashed off without a moment's difficulty" quality) has long been familiar with an arduous sequence of crisis, resolution, and crisis by which he actually produces his smooth-flowing essays. Though the pattern is familiar to him, each recurrence seems, while he is caught up in it, new and different, with its own new forms, contents, and surprises. Recurrence of old patterns in new versions is characteristic of all fits. The situation culminating in and containing his creative sequence was dysjunctively crowded. His commitments (articles for other magazines, agreements to lecture, responsibilities toward family and friends) were pressing. The situation was thus freighted with competing demands for his attention. These pressures, and especially the personal discomfort of a runny nose, sore throat, and aching body, are not generally held to be conducive to composure of mind or to composition of essays bearing the hallmark of an author untroubled by circumstances or inner conflicts.

Yet paradoxically, many creative people do some of their best work under situations of stress and personal discomfort. Perhaps Rosenberg's giving up, going to bed, and awakening to a spontaneous moment of illumination can be taken as a model of similar sequences by which other creative people free their fitting-together capacities from the restrictions of circumstance. Thus they transcend the limited achievements of mere work as such and make the leap into spontaneous, all-at-once bursts of creative thought and action. This pattern is found in analysis of other fits of creation and discovery and, as noted earlier, has a similar form to the pattern of development of fits of epilepsy. There is in both a sequence of preparatory tension, sudden letting go, and automatic unfolding of the fit of knowing, feeling, and doing.

Neither Mr. Rosenberg, who was kind enough to furnish me with the details of this sequence, nor I would wish to imply that his finished article was necessarily a superlative example of his or any other author's creative abilities. Its first sentence, however, is an excellent example of a condensation midway, in form and content, between "six months and eight pounds" and some unspecified, superlative product of the contention-condensing processes of fit, wit, dreams, and creative fitting together. Its usefulness here derives from its bearing on the indeterminacy of dysjunctiveness and of the location and nature of the fitting-together capacity.

One of Charles M. Schulz's "Peanuts" cartoons demonstrates the dysjunctiveness both of an interpersonal encounter and of the artist's representation of it. Schulz's imperturbable character, Linus, is staring at the sky overhead. Lucy, the know-it-all member of Schulz's permanent cast, tells him, "Clouds are very peculiar, Linus . . . Sometimes they seem to form actual words." In the background, Charlie Brown, who is often appalled and oppressed by Lucy, once more is perplexed by her. He approaches and, in the second frame, says, "Those aren't clouds . . . that's sky-writing." He has gotten Lucy's attention but not that of Linus, who continues to look at the clouds.

The third drawing, not framed in a square as the others are, but shifted out of alignment with them, has no dialogue but shows Lucy turned for a moment to confront Charlie, staring him into silence. In the fourth drawing, now framed like the first and second

and aligned with them, Lucy returns to her instruction of Linus, and repeats her original speech as if nothing had happened. Linus, who has not moved his head in any of the four drawings, continues to watch the clouds, untouched by the goings-on around him. He is in a fit of reverie and for him there has been no change of action.

Lucy, too, in her way, is immovable. She takes note of Charlie Brown's comment in the second frame, turns and annihilates him with a look in the third drawing, and returns to the *status quo ante* in the fourth. She has excised Charlie Brown's disjunctive effect by a dysjunctive maneuver of her own. Charlie Brown, who begins in the background, comes forward and ends up in the last frame in the foreground, looking stunned. He has gotten himself into a fit of psychic paralysis from his encounter with Lucy.

I find it useful to view the unframing and displacing of the third drawing (as published in *But We Love You, Charlie Brown*) as an example of an artist's portrayal of the dysjunctive process. The others in the sequence, which are all framed in squares and aligned, have a continuity of their own. Drawing three is the kind of excessive but significant detouring, deranging activity that both creates and fills gaps in continuity, and tells a story of its own— a story that condenses that of the other three.

Notes

1. Otto Fenichel, *Problems of Psychoanalytic Technique. Psychoanalytic Quarterly* monograph, Albany, N.Y., 1959.
2. Konrad Lorenz, *Man Meets Dog.* Houghton, Boston, 1955.
3. Jane Pearce and Saul Newton, *Conditions of Human Growth.* Citadel, New York, 1963, p. 142.
4. Warren S. McCulloch, "Where Is Fancy Bred?" in *Lectures on Experimental Psychiatry,* edited by Henry W. Brosin, University of Pittsburgh Press, 1961; W. Grey Walter, "Where Vital Things Happen" (Adolf Meyer Research Lecture). *American Journal of Psychiatry, 116:* 673, 1960.

Combinations and Sequences of Miniature Epileptic, Psychosomatic, Psychoneurotic, and Creative Gestures in Experimental and Life Situations. Their Significance as Evidence for a Common Fitting-Together Capacity.

BEHIND MONA LISA'S SMILE 39

And men ought to know that from nothing else but thence [from the brain] come joys, delights, laughter and sports, and sorrows, griefs, despondency, and lamentations. And by this, in an especial manner, we acquire wisdom and knowledge, and see and hear. . . . And by the same organ we become mad and delirious, and fears and terrors assail us, some by night, and some by day, and dreams and untimely wanderings, and cares that are not suitable, and ignorance of present circumstances, desuetude, and unskilfulness. All these we endure from the brain . . .

—Hippocrates[1]

When next we examine the connotation of the word "fit" we find ourselves in no less a quandary, . . . it stands for conditions as widely separable as a convulsive movement limited to a segment, or part of a segment, of a limb, and highly elaborate co-ordinated acts of the whole person, sometimes of considerable duration. . . . The word cannot even be restricted to the phenomena of a hyperkinetic class, for it can legitimately be employed to designate certain attacks of which motionlessness is the prominent feature . . . nerve-cells store up energy in potentia . . . and in functional activity . . . liberation of energy is orderly, moderate, and controllable. We can, however, readily imagine a condition of . . . nerve-cells . . . resulting in the development of a state of high tension and instability, whereby they will discharge suddenly, with an excessive liberation of energy, either when a postulated maximum of disequilibrium has been attained, or when a sufficient stimulus reaches them. . . . I believe that the essence of a fit . . . consists in the exaggeration of a normal physiological process—that is to say, in sudden, excessive, and yet purely temporary liberation of kinetic energy in a series of . . . nerve-cells, the visible consequence of which is a sudden and excessive development of many [activities, some of which may be inhibitory] at once. On this hypothesis it is clearly possible for any constellation of nerve-cells in the nervous system to become highly unstable or overcharged, and to discharge accordingly, so that the term "epileptic fit" might be employed, and legitimately so, for any paroxysmal symptoms attributable to the process outlined above.

—S. A. KINNIER WILSON[2]

I have abbreviated both quotations and altered Wilson's statement by deleting phrases by which he restricted attention to convulsive fits. But he says, in one of the deleted parts, "The reference is solely to motor-nerve cells in this connexion, although of course the view applies to all varieties of cell." Wilson centered discussion of epileptic fits on convulsive movements partly because these show most clearly his cardinal criteria of epilepsy— "suddenness, disorderliness, 'caricaturing,' and excessiveness."

Wilson was deservedly an eminent neurologist; his two-volume text on neurology and his many scientific papers are exemplary products of the keen intelligence of a well-informed, thoughtful man who can gracefully digress and return to the central theme of his discourse. In contemporary slang, "he tells it like it is," and tells it well. But he was well aware of the difficulties that confronted Hughlings Jackson or anyone who tried to formulate the nonclinical, transsymptomatic, transmedical—the vulgar, secular, magical, and "sacred"—aspect of epilepsy.

The difficulties are many. Even if ancient wisdom about the "sacred disease" can be formulated in contemporary terms, communications about it are often greeted with selective inattention if not hostility by the "scientific" establishment. The central fact, and difficulty, is in understanding, as Wilson said further, that *healthy neural mechanisms may become epileptogenous, without being in the remotest degree diseased.* Very little in epileptic fits can be directly attributed to the activity of a discharging epileptic lesion in the brain. The rhythmic, synchronous discharge of "foci of epileptic brain waves" is incompatible with any kind of neuronal work. It is a "purely" nonintegrative activity of brain cells. Activity of body or person during fits must be integrated by nerve cells which retain their working relations with other neurones and nonnervous structures. The epilepticity of epileptic brains with or without a localized focus cannot be isolated from the inherent epilepticity of every brain. Anyone can be made to have a convulsive fit. What, then, is the source of epilepticity— the environment, the brain, the bodily constitution, or the personality?

Because epileptics with and without "discharging lesions," because people with and without epilepsy, can have the same kinds of fits, and because the brain (or some brain-within-the-brain) is the meeting ground in which environment and endowment exert their influences upon action, finding the source of epileptic fits becomes a search for the common pathway by which all kinds of events set off all sorts of episodic behavior and experience.

The time must be ripe for a fit, because the processes producing a fit on one occasion do not always do so in similar circumstances at another time. Hence, what I have called the fitting-together capacity (by which converging fit-provoking influences are integrated) has the three faces of a time-place-process. It involves not only "somewhere" and "somehow" but "somewhen" as well. And, whatever, however, or whenever it is, it must involve an interaction *between* the capacity of nerve cells to fall into "autonomous," "automatic" *dys*integrative action and the capacity of the brain to initiate and to elaborate upon these local fits of spontaneity.

The experiments described in this chapter suggest strongly that there is, in fact, some common fitting-together time-place-process for all fits. This small group of relatively undramatic observations may provide the seed from which comprehension of the entire universe of fits, dysjunctive reactions, and brain storms may grow. The following observations were made in the course of testing the effect of experimental dysjunctive situations upon the continuity of brain waves and behavior in both epileptic and nonepileptic subjects. The form and content of the experiments were derived from analysis of fit-containing life situations described by patients who had fits of epilepsy, narcolepsy, migraine, and other medical, psychosomatic, and psychiatric episodic disturbances of bodily and personal function; from study of episodes like those described in Part Two; from Pavlovian and other psychological procedures for eliciting conflict-induced disruptions of behavior; and from jokes, riddles, and other tongue- and brain-twisting maneuvers. The aim of these models of dysjunctive life situations was to "embarrass" the brain by giving it too much to do smoothly at any one time—to produce crises in continuity by engaging the person in tasks characterized by or culminating in contradiction and ambiguity.

I began my experimental studies in the brain-wave laboratory while working with Dr. Harold G. Wolff's psychosomatic medicine research group at the New York Hospital–Cornell University Medical Center. Other members of Dr. Wolff's group studied the relationship between life stress and bodily diseases by observing changes in diverse bodily reactions during periods of stress and tranquility in life and in the laboratory. Variations in blood pressure, blood flow, rates of secretions, changes in color and turgidity of mucosal tissues, etc., were observed at periodic intervals or during alternating discussions of distressing and innocuous topics during interviews.

At first I studied changes in the number and kind of abnormal brain waves during periods of trouble and tranquility in the patient's life situation. I also observed changes in the degree of normality or abnormality of brain waves, as an indicator of the effect of disturbing and reassuring discussions during interviews upon the epilepticity of brain function in epileptic, neurotic, and psychosomatic patients. Generally there was less epilepticity when the patient was calm and more when he was disturbed. But this general observation only confirmed in the laboratory what competent clinicians have known since Galen; it failed to illumine the specific role and nature of epileptigenic processes. Furthermore, some people are apprehensive when things are going well, and they are quieter, if more depressed, during difficult times. Therefore I went on to construct experimental models based upon analyses of dysjunctive-epileptigenic life situations, and to study their effects upon brain waves and behavior. Some brief additional comment on brain waves and methods for recording them may be helpful.

Routine brain-wave recording requires restraint from moving about and relaxation of tension in order that actual brain waves not be obscured by muscle potential and artifacts.* For my purposes, however, brief artifacts were useful—bursts of muscle potential signified preparatory, incipient reactions of body and person; muscle potentials and artifacts marked frowning, eye movement, and attempts to use accessory maneuvers for "seeing more clearly" the solutions to problems; swallowing, grimacing, gesturing, nail biting and other breaks of restraint can be spotted in the EEG by their associated muscle potentials and movement artifacts. These nuisances in routine examination of brain waves became, for me, valuable indicators of significant, extracerebral dysjunctive effects. Combinations of brain waves, muscle potentials, and artifacts were the means for observing complexes of neuronal, somatic, and personal reactions to dysjunctive crises in experimental situations.

These combinations of epileptic and nonepileptic, of neuronal and bodily reactions, which I think of as "minor epileptic-dysjunctive reactions," are the heart of the matter in this chapter. They

---

* Illustrations and discussions of brain waves and artifacts are provided in the following books: Frederick L. Gibbs and Erna L. Gibbs, *Atlas of Electroencephalography*, Addison-Wesley Press, Cambridge, Massachusetts, 1952; L. G. Kiloh and J. W. Osselton, *Clinical Electroencephalography*. Butterworth's, London, 1961; *Electroencephalography*, edited by Dennis Hill and Geoffrey Parr, Macmillan, New York, 1963.

are minor reactions to small crises. They dispose of and discharge small amounts of tension, have a short refractory effect, and can recur in a short time. Effective stimuli can be repeated and a clear relation, or lack of it, between cause and effect can be observed in the temporal patterns of stimulus and response. Some individual components, like swallowing, may seem so insignificantly "everyday" that to cite them as significant reactions indicating dysjunctive crises may seem absurd.

We all, it might be said, swallow "all the time." But this is not as meaningful a statement as it sounds. Many people swallow only when saliva collects in their mouths, and they do so smoothly and almost unnoticeably. Others occasionally "gulp" in unwitting astonishment at ideas or images from within or without that flicker momentarily on the edges of awareness. Still others, according to stomach specialists, swallow significant amounts of air along with their saliva and thereby acquire cramping collections of gas in their guts. Swallowing can momentarily relieve tension and can postpone the inevitable, explosive breakdown of protracted breath holding, for example.[3] We blink and move our eyes in dreams, trancelike moments, and when we are trying to "see" the obscure more clearly. We tend to swallow things that need "digestion." The flow of saliva itself varies with a whole set of avoidance-approach reactions to dangers and opportunities, real or fancied. But the important point is that swallowing, or any other minor dysjunctive bodily reaction to internal or external influences, does not occur either at fixed, periodic intervals or completely at random. "Things happen" in anticipation of, or rebound reaction to, significant episodic activities; swallowing or any other minor reaction tends to occur during action trajectories only if a dysjunctive crisis develops.

Ideas for experimental dysjunctive procedures came originally from analysis of life situations provoking epileptic fits; these fit-situations ranged from changes in the emotional climate to changes in the meteorological climate. Hence convulsigenic elements common to such a great range of fit-provoking events had to be formulated in terms of dynamics rather than descriptive content. Common epileptigenic elements are seen in widely differing fits. Thus analysis of the story of the southern scholar guiding William Golding through Civil War battlefields to Appomattox reveals a contradiction between his roles as scholar and Southerner. Trying to do, or to be, two different things at once could, it would seem, lead anyone to his own dysjunctive Appomattox, in life or laboratory. H. L. Gold's "blowing his top" fit, when he reached beyond his own predictive capacity into the realm of prophecy about the war's end, suggests that pushing experimental subjects beyond their capacities might activate similar dysjunctive processes.

Tongue-twisters split attention between, and partially activate, competing motor-expressive systems; they offer models for many fit-producing life situations characterized by conflicts. In life, fits may occur when an individual has exhausted the means at his disposal upon a resistant problem. In the laboratory this situation can be reproduced by having a subject name rapidly all the members of a given class of things until he can think of no other and comes to a halt, still trying to recall one more. Whole-part and word-and-opposite association tests (in which words that have no familiar part or opposite are given after words that do) will produce suddenly "unthinkable" situations in miniature.

On close scrutiny, these diverse conditions seem to have in common a kind of hypnoidal process. Many experimental dysjunctive maneuvers seem to induce a transient trancelike "empty-mindedness" or "crowded-mindedness." Finally, anticipatory, rebound, and "letting-go" reactions (which have as much to do with the structure as with the content of dysjunctive situations) are likely to occur in any task requiring smooth, rapid performance of dysjunctive activities.

In the laboratory, as in life, a variety of dysjunctive events produces a diversity of reactions. Sometimes a single experimental maneuver produces several different reactions (in different subjects or in the same subject at different times). These range from the epileptic (spike-and-dome brain waves with or without observable fit-behavior) to the witty (laughing, joking, and occasional bursts of insight). On the other hand, a single kind of dysjunctive reaction results from several different experimental procedures—ranging from complexly "unthinkable" problems to simple tasks involving sudden starts and stops. All dysjunctive situations produce some sudden changes in the scope, direction, and continuity of ongoing activity; and, conversely, all phase changes are in themselves one form of dysjunctive stimulus. The ultimate model—approaching a purely formal, contentless structure—for activating the fitting-together capacity is the sudden, sharp phase change after intense mental effort.

Three variations of response to such a phase change are shown in Figure 4. In this experiment an epileptic patient was given three brief, moderately difficult problems in addition, one after the other.

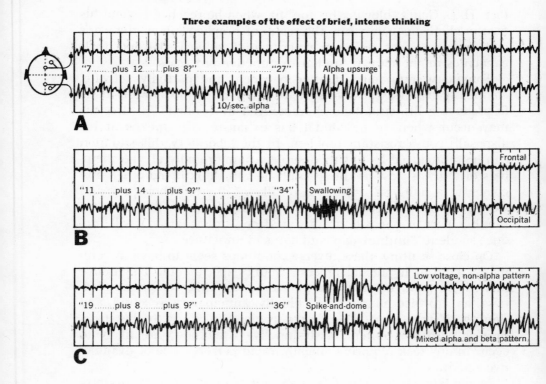

Figure 4. At a common point in dynamic time—the point of answering in rapid, brief addition—an epileptic patient progresses from a normal neuronal reaction through a peripheral "psychosomatic" one to a second level ("higher"? or "lower"?) of neuronal reaction. The shift is from center to periphery and back again. Such "equivalents" seen separately, as in this instance, in a series of repeated stimulus-events, are often seen combined in a single sequence in reaction to a single dysjunctive situation.

After the first rapid addition, an upsurge of alpha-wave voltage suggested that the generators of alpha rhythm had been over-stimulated briefly. After the second, he swallowed as if to discharge tension or to dispose of some undesirable subjective reaction (swallowing is not uncommon during experiments but does not occur randomly; subjects usually swallow at significant points in experimental procedures). After the third problem, a brief burst of spike-and-dome brain waves appeared as if the generators of alpha waves had been thrown momentarily into convulsive activity by an overresponse to overstimulation. Repeated observations of such sequences strongly suggest that the successive reactions are "equivalents," i.e., products of a single process or apparatus.

In this sequence of experiments, the patient's reactions progressed from an initial, relatively normal reaction, through a psychosomatic swallowing, to an epileptic neuronal paroxysm. There was a shift from intracerebral neuronal activity to extra-cerebral bodily-personal activity and back again to intracerebral neuronal reaction of a second kind. The movement was from center to periphery to center, and in that sense was cyclic; but since the second central neuronal activity was on a different level from the first, it is more useful to think of the shift as constituting a trajectory rather than a cycle.

Equivalent reactions seem to be products of a common agency; this view is supported by the fact that a variety of neuronal, bodily, and personal reactions was observed in other experiments at dynamically identical points. One other such point of dysjunction occurs at approximately 15 to 20 seconds after the start of the three minutes of vigorous overbreathing that is a part of routine EEG procedure. After several fast deep breaths, the content of oxygen and carbon dioxide in the lungs and blood begins to change in a direction ordinarily opposed by protective reflexes which would, on their own, slow breathing down. The subject, however, must inhibit these protective reflexes in order to keep on with vigorous over-breathing. At about 15–20 seconds, then, the unchecked effects of hyperventilation are suddenly felt, and many subjects recognize that continuing to overbreathe for three minutes is likely to be difficult. Various reactions are observed.

Figure 5, for example, shows swallowing at the 15–20-second point in the first overbreathing by a nonepileptic subject (see Strip A). On his second effort, an outburst of abnormally large and slow ("nonspecific") brain waves appeared at the same point. Patients who ordinarily produce spike-and-dome paroxysms, coughing spells, yawning, etc., at moments of stress are likely to do so at this crisis in EEG recording or at the rebound period shortly after hyperventilation is stopped. Dysjunctive reactions frequently occur at the beginning or end of any procedure which is definitely structured in time.

When, for example, the experimenter counts from one to six, with "six" as the signal for the subject to close his eyes, open his eyes, to close or open his mouth (or to stop and start any significant activity), reactions often occur between the counts of one and two. During experiments in which the subject adds five small numbers, reactions often occur between the calling out of the first

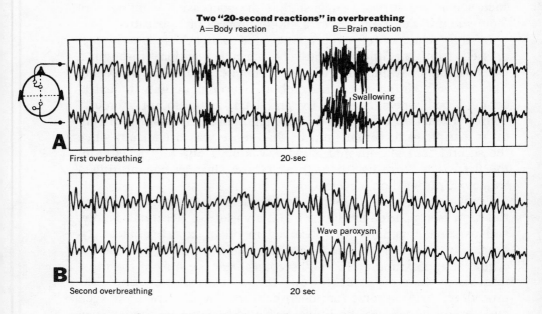

Figure 5. Swallowing and nonspecific paroxysmal brain waves as "equivalent" reactions at a definite, operational point in time. Two successive overbreathings by a nonepileptic subject.

and second numbers. Figure 6 shows three "on" reactions: a spike-and-dome, a swallowing, and an alpha voltage upsurge observed at the start of five-number additions.

The three equivalents illustrated and discussed above are by no means the only ones observed in experimental tests and trajectories. Closing the eyes, a requirement for brain-wave recording, produces a significant, and for some people a profoundly disturbing, phase change in organism-environment relations, and it also produces a significant, and for some people a profoundly disturbtrate a yawning reaction and a sniffing reaction immediately after eye closing. Figure 9 shows a sequence of alpha upsurge; a rubbing-the-nose, "nasal salute" (seen not uncommonly with allergic people and with heroin sniffers); and a swallowing reaction. In this three-part sequence, the fitting-together capacity seems to be running through a short series of equivalents. Such sequential combinations are important for theory because they link several dysjunctive reactions together as products of a common fitting-together capacity caught up in a *status dysjunctivus*.

Complexes of equivalents are seen at dysjunctive impasses dis-

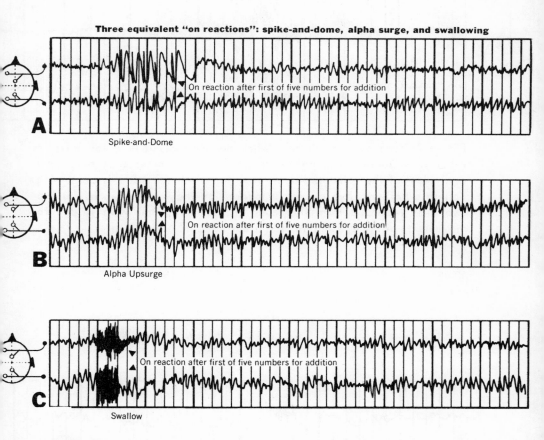

Figure 6. Three "on-reactions" as equivalents at a common, operational point in dynamic time. The EEG in strip A is from the front and from the back of the head of an epileptic subject. B and C show waves from the same locations in nonepileptic subjects.

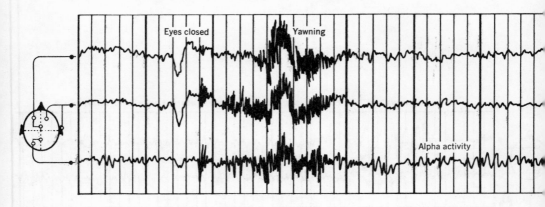

Figure 7. Yawning immediately following eye closing in a nonepileptic subject. A single yawn, not repeated for some minutes. A functional equivalent of the spike-and-dome reaction often seen at this point with epileptic patients. Eye closing is marked by the waves seen in the top two lines recorded from the front of the head; the wave is due to movements of the eye and lid, and is not a "real" brain wave.

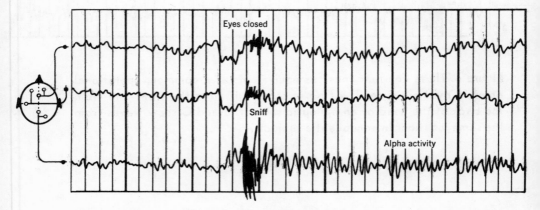

Figure 8. Sniffing following closing the eyes in a nonepileptic subject. One of many "equivalent" reactions observed at this operational point in time.

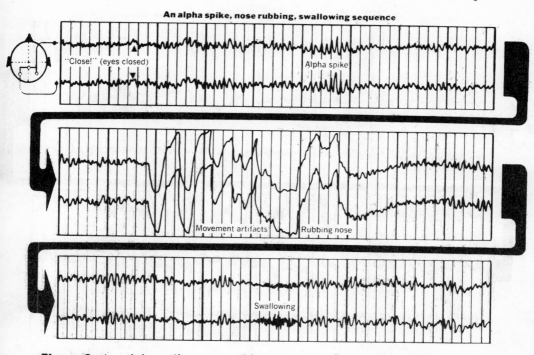

Figure 9. An alpha-spike, nose-rubbing, swallowing sequence following eye closure in a nonepileptic subject. The three strips are continuous. (Lack of space prevents showing such sequences in one horizontal, straight line. In yard-long books, one could illustrate many interesting EEG phenomena.)

rupting "impossible" experimental tasks. Experiments using opposed "tendencies to say" often result in progressive or intermittent difficulties. Reciting the alphabet backward, for example, is almost impossible to do steadily, at a reasonable speed, without considerable practice. At any particular letter, habit opposes intention. At the letter "q," for instance, instructions demand "p" as the next letter but experience calls for "r." The motor-utterance patterns for both letters are partially activated. The subject goes from one dysjunctive situation to another and sooner or later gets stuck; "r" and "p" cannot be dysjunctively condensed into a caricatured or creative solution. To maintain continuity a subject may simply repeat "q" over and over, or double back with something like "q . . . r . . . s . . . r . . . q."

Some subjects proceed steadily but give up suddenly, as if their pattern were an all-or-none one of smooth performance and sudden

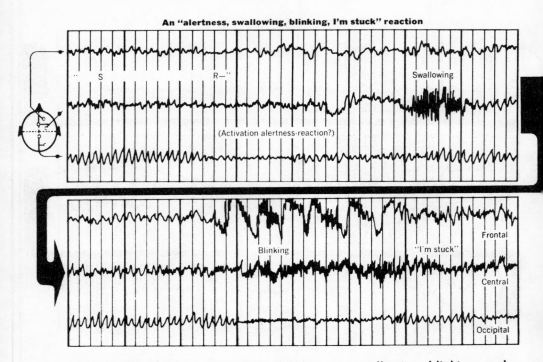

Figure 10. A sequence of alertness-response, swallowing, blinking, and speech at a dysjunctive impasse in reciting the alphabet backward. Subject is nonepileptic. A sudden breakdown in an otherwise relatively smooth performance.

breakdown. Such a development is shown in Figure 10 when an epileptic subject failed at "r." An alertness-attention response (brief suppression of alpha waves), a swallow, a spell of blinking (as if trying to clear his vision), and the statement that "I'm stuck" occurred in rapid succession. Some subjects struggle along, faltering now and then, before they give up. Such a persistent effort is shown in Figure 11. In this case, a nonepileptic subject began to frown, compress his lips, and to tense the muscles of his head and neck from time to time as if trying to "use his head" more effectively. His difficulty, reflected in muscle-tension potentials, began at "q," continued intermittently as he squeezed out pairs and triplets of letters until he gave up at "h." Other subjects proceed intermittently, with alternate bursts of activity and inactivity, from the start. They break up the task into segments, blurting out a few letters, then pausing to think up the next sequence. Such an inter-

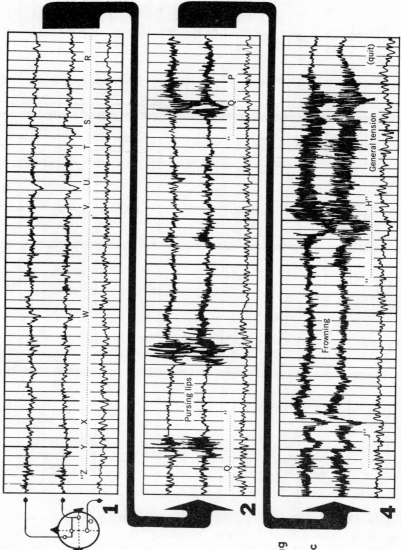

Figure 11. Stepwise breakdown of reciting the alphabet backward in a nonepileptic subject. Strips 1, 2, and 4 are essentially continuous. (Strip 3, a near-duplicate of 2, is omitted.)

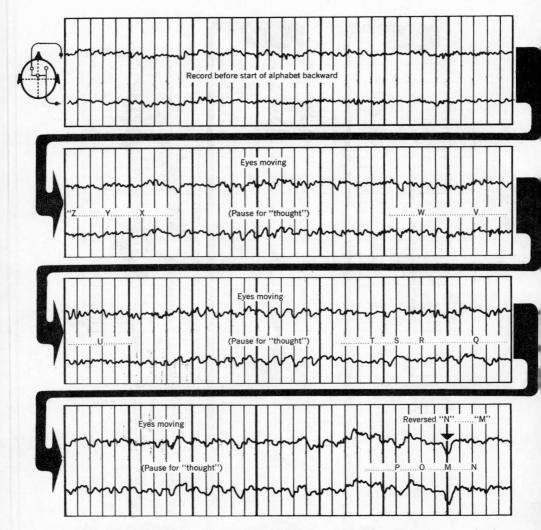

Figure 12. A segmental performance, alternating reciting and thinking. In this nonepileptic subject, "thinking" involved eye movements as if he were trying to "see" the next segment. As difficulty increases, an error appears at the end of the last strip.

mittent pattern is shown in Figure 12. In this case, rapid eye movement waves, presumably from eye movements similar to those in dreaming, filled the pauses between bursts of letters, as if the subject were using eye movement to facilitate seeing the next group of letters with his mind's eye.

These performance patterns during reverse recitation of the alphabet show that such tasks do generate acute dysjunctive situations, and illustrate some of the reactions of brain, body, and person that occur. Many of my experimental tasks set up contradictions between tendencies to say and do, much as in the alphabet-backward maneuver. Thus, alternate counting and reciting the alphabet forward ("a–1–b–2–c–3," etc.) opposes two different kinds of interwoven continuity. Serial subtraction combined with rhythmic, moderately deep breathing (answers are given at the start of expiration) also opposes two different actions, each of which requires some attention to sustain.

Any task that involves only two main elements in conflict could be called *dis*junctive. But in any experimental situation, desires to cooperate conflict with wishes to be rid of distress. Furthermore, personal idiosyncratic reaction to specific elements or some general reaction to being tested complicates a seemingly simple situation. To the extent that the subject becomes involved in a task, dangers of failing and opportunities for bolstering self-esteem by succeeding make it critical. Experiments in which the patient tries hard are complicated and dysjunctive.

Overtly complicated dysjunctive situations can be created by combining several disparate elements. Asking the subject to listen to a list of words and to signal when he hears one that is the name of an object *either* long and thin, blue in color, round like a ball, or soft to the touch gives him many things to mind at once. On the other hand, dysjunctive "empty-mindedness" occurs when the subject names rapidly all the members of a given class that he can call to mind (names of baseball players, makes of cars, composers of music, etc.) and suddenly runs out of names. A kind of "name on the tip of the tongue" paralysis ensues. A similar state is generated during word-association tests when the subject is given a word that has no ready reflex association. "Cloud," for example, has no easily named part; "putty" has no easily named opposite.

Surveying experimentally dysjunctive situations provides a necessary basis for passing on to the nature of dysjunctive reactions so produced. Some sample combinations will illustrate the versatility of the fitting-together capacity and illumine its nature. An epileptic patient was given the word "salt" after several easy word-and-opposite association-test words. He hesitated and was silent much longer than with preceding words. Then he blurted out "bitter" and began to laugh in a rather silly fashion. He stopped laughing

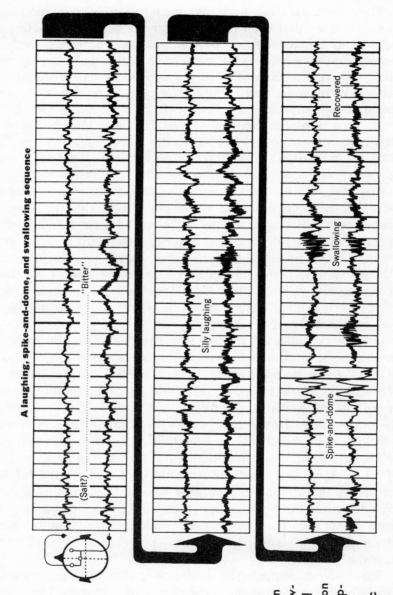

Figure 13. Laughing, epileptic brain waves and swallowing as a sequential dysjunctive reaction disrupting word-opposite association test in an epileptic patient.

and a brief burst of spike-and-dome appeared in his EEG. Then he swallowed—something he rarely did. This sequence of approximate answer, laughing, epileptic brain-wave paroxysm, and swallowing is one version of what I call "minor epileptic-dysjunctive reactions." Such sequences of neuronal, somatic, and psychological activities contain epileptic, psychosomatic, and psychiatric symptoms-in-miniature. They also include dysjunctive reactions like laughing, which, whether the humor is witty or absurd, represent at least germinal creative activity. This sequence is shown in Figure 13.

Some years ago I recorded the instructive exception shown in Figure 14. An epileptic patient, a young Negro man, blocked on one of the supposedly easy words on my word-opposite list before I got to what I had intended as the tough word, "putty." The word that stopped him, however, was "black"; he did come up with its opposite, "white," but only after a delay containing a swallowing and spike-and-dome reaction. In subsequent conversation I discovered that my "not-thinking" about the possibilities inherent in the "black-white" opposition was matched by his witting effort not to think about The Problem. This inadvertent "experiment arranged by life" shows that dysjunctive moments cannot all be planned or contained within even the best designed experimental situation—one man's innocuous word may be another's anathema.

In this example, swallowing and spike-and-dome were distinctly separated by a few seconds of time. One could argue that they were separate reactions; that one was psychosomatic and the other epileptic. If seen as a unitary reaction, was it an epileptic-dysjunctive one or a larval epileptic fit? Spike-and-dome waves plus bodily reactions do occur in more or less simultaneous combinations difficult to explain as separate products of separate processes. In Figures 15 and 16, a minimal spike-and-dome outburst is coupled with yawning in one case and with facial grimacing in the other. The proportions of epileptic, psychosomatic, and personal activity vary widely in combinations of intracerebral and extracerebral activity. Thus Strip A of Figure 17 shows a coupling of minimal spike-and-dome with minimal smiling. Strip B shows a long period of laughter and a short burst of spike-and-dome. Strip C shows a swallowing reaction as a brief bodily-personal activity in the midst of a much longer spike-and-dome outburst.

A feeling of coldness accompanied by shivering (a reaction similar to that of Emily Dickinson and A. E. Housman to poetry) seized an epileptic patient during an experiment combining rhythmic breathing and serial subtraction. This complex dysjunctive

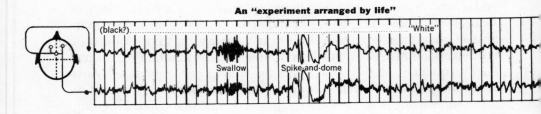

Figure 14. A dysjunctive reaction combining a sequence of swallowing and spike-and-dome. This minor epileptic-dysjunctive reaction has an extracerebral component (swallowing) and an intracerebral one (the minimal spike-and-dome brain wave). As noted elsewhere, the order and degree of such central and peripheral reactions vary from time to time—the various combinations, therefore, seem to be varieties of a single operational dysjunctive response. As with any fit, it is the operational significance of the behavior rather than any particular descriptive character that makes it a dysjunctive reaction or fit.

In experiments like that illustrated above, reactions were expected to a test word for which an opposite is difficult to find. Dysjunctive reactions, however, were also observed in response to presumably innocuous, easy test words such as "small." It is easy enough to see that individuals worried about their size might react rather unexpectedly to such a word-stimulus. Investigations of the stream of thought and feeling preceding such "spontaneous" dysjunctive reactions, i.e., those to seemingly neutral words, often reveal complexes of significant distressing personal meanings. In the laboratory, as in life, people react to what is meaningful for them, and personal meanings are often quite idiosyncratic.

The important point here is not the "cause" of these dysjunctive combinations of epileptic and nonepileptic responses, but the fact that they do occur and are evidently put together by a common fitting-together apparatus of capacity.

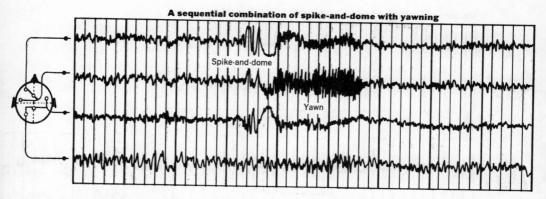

A sequential combination of spike-and-dome with yawning

Spike-and-dome

Yawn

Figure 15. Minimal spike-and-dome combined with yawning. An epileptic patient's reaction in rebound to the end of an arduous test.

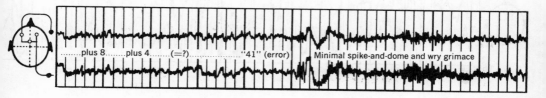

........plus 8........plus 4........(=?)........"41" (error)   Minimal spike-and-dome and wry grimace

Figure 16. Minimal spike-and-dome combined with grimacing.

Varied proportions of body, brain, and person reactions

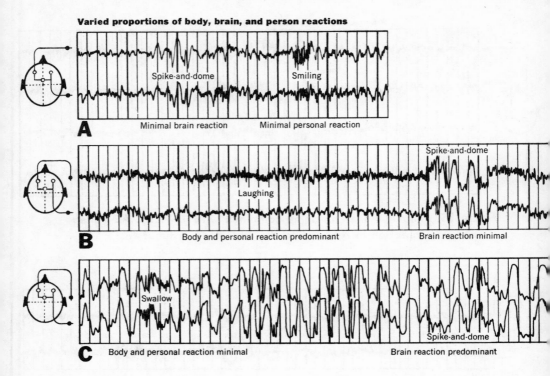

Figure 17. Strip A shows a combination of spike-and-dome with smiling: an epileptic patient's reaction during an association test to a private joke that popped into his mind. Strip B shows the EEG during open laughter. The laughing ends with a brief burst of spike-and-dome. Without the EEG, one would not have suspected that his laughing had any epileptic component, though in the context—the patient was laughing at one of his mistakes—the laughter was not one hundred per cent pure joy. Strip C shows a combined intracerebral and extracerebral reaction dominated by the spike-and-dome paroxysm.

reaction began with swallowing; included spike-and-dome brain waves, shivering, and an "icy breeze" sensation; and ended with yawning. At the same time, her "mind went blank." This sequence is shown in Figure 18. Shivering and shudderings, with or without accompanying sensations of coldness and outbursts of unusual brain waves, accompanied other subjects' sudden recognition of failures and errors in experimental tasks. They also occurred with sudden disturbing memories. The shock of recognition produced by poetic and other artistic effects seems also to occur with more mundane instances of sudden recognition.

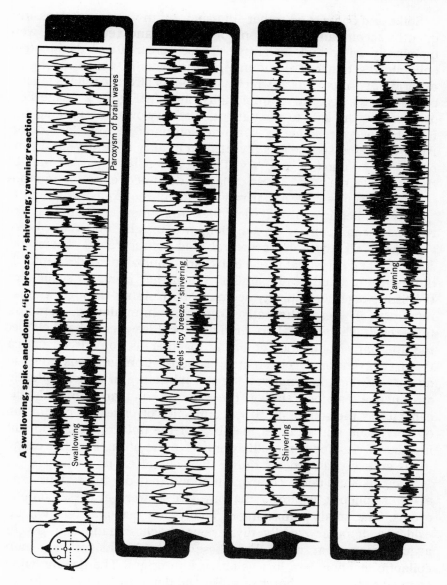

Figure 18. A fit of swallowing, epileptic brain waves, "icy" sensation, shivering, and yawning—a variation that has close connections with the Mona Lisa smile sequence and the icy-shivering reactions of poets to poetry. No doubt also related to the common someone-is-walking-on-my-grave shivering reaction to erupting, but fleeting, thoughts and memories.

Spike-and-dome and other unusual brain-wave reactions frequently accompanied eruptions of thought and feeling that were incipiently witty and insightful. These "precreative" dysjunctive-epileptic reactions were common at moments of strain during an experiment—moments at which some joking effort to relieve tension could be expected. An example illustrated in Figure 2 (page 56), occurred when I said to one patient, "Let's try overbreathing again." His only overt reaction was a brief outburst of spike-and-dome. His unspoken response was revealed on inquiry to be, "What do you mean, 'try'? I don't have to 'try,' I'm an expert by now. *You* may be trying to give me a fit." These epileptic, dysjunctive, protohumorous reactions seem to be a halfway stage in the transformation of "purely" epileptic-neuronal activities into more personal-human responses characterized by emotion, wit, insight, and relatedness.

Clearly, all these intracerebral and extracerebral (neuronal, somatic, and personal) reactions are equivalents—descriptively different but dynamically similar. When they occur in sequences, the fitting-together capacity seems to be running through a small repertory of these alternative symptoms-in-miniature; combinations result when several are fired at once. Elsewhere I have classed the alternative outcomes of fitting together as convulsive, caricatured, conventional, or creative actions. Combinations and sequences of these alternatives, seen in miniature in minor epileptic-dysjunctive reactions, support the idea of a common fitting-together capacity as the source of all the outcomes of crises. They link fits of convulsion and all other members of the universe of fits including acts of creation; they call attention to the fitting-together capacity as an everyday process rather than one of exotic pathology.

The spike-and-dome component shows that the mysterious processes of epilepsy, whatever they are, are at work in these complex events. The small paroxysms of bodily and personal reaction are evidence of other equally mysterious psychosomatic and psychiatric processes at work. For these relatively insignificant non-epileptic reactions are just as obscure in origin. The fleeting smile coupled with a brief burst of spike-and-dome in Strip A of Figure 17, for example, signals a personal reaction as evocative and elusive in its way as the mystery of epilepsy—indeed, in my view, the two problems are identical. An illustration and some comment on this ultimate mystery will show, perhaps, where the answers are to be found.

Not infrequently, particularly in experiments with adolescent girl addicts, I would see at dysjunctive moments a brief, secretive smile which sometimes affected me quite uncannily. I had little success in elucidating its subjective accompaniments. Just why getting useful information about the thought and feeling associated with these fleeting smiles should be so difficult is itself a mystery to me. Even articulate and communicative patients were unable to describe clearly their subjective concomitants of what I came to think of as the "Mona Lisa smile."

I had encountered this fleeting smile at the transition into hypnosis and also during conversations with schizophrenic patients. My patients sometimes used it to express something like condescending amusement at my inability to grasp the simplicities of complex issues—or the complexity of simple ones—as easily as they. The subjective component may be quite autistic and uncommunicable; in this it resembles certain experiences produced by mescaline, nitrous oxide, LSD, and other trance-inducing agents. It also, no doubt, has much in common with "the look" seen in ecstatic absorption or intense preoccupation, and described by Jacques Hadamard as associated with the fitting together of mathematical discoveries. A similar look precedes many major convulsions and signals the occurrence of many great ideas.

The ineffable Mona Lisa smile was sometimes accompanied by other reactions. Some, like swallowing, shifting about, and frowning, were signs of restlessness and tension; others, like yawning, drowsiness, and sudden giving up of effort, indicated boredom and fatigue. At times, signs of tension and relaxation alternated. One young lady would suddenly smile, yawn, and go to sleep. A combination of swallowing, paroxysm of large, slow, nonspecific brain waves, and of smiling and yawning is shown in Figure 19.

If these sequences of minor cerebral, somatic, and psychological reactions are in fact produced by a common omniversatile fitting-together capacity, and all the examples of the universe of fits are produced by the same device, then that capacity has at its disposal all the actual or potential abilities of the individual as biological organism or socialized person. Leonardo da Vinci was himself a living example of how great that capacity can be. It is not outrageous to suggest that he might have recognized and portrayed the uncanny suprapersonal abilities of the fitting-together capacity in the mysterious smile of his Mona Lisa—at least this supposition is no more farfetched than many others put forward in all seriousness. In any case, it is clear that in some moments of crisis, a relatively omniscient and omnipotent transpersonal capacity can summon up any behavior in the universe of fits—of episodicity —from epilepticity to creativity.

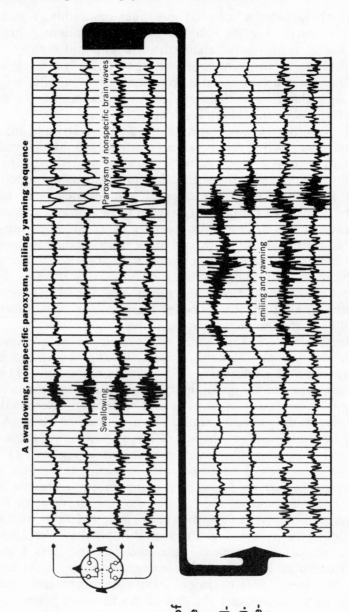

Figure 19. A fit of swallowing, large "nonspecific" brain waves, smiling, and yawning. The Mona Lisa reaction.

Notes

1. Hippocrates. Quoted in *M.D.*, Vol. VII, July 1963.
2. S. A. Kinnier Wilson, *Modern Problems in Neurology.* Edward Arnold & Co., London, 1928, pp. 4–5.
3. Albert B. Craig, Jr., "Regulation of Respiration in Exercise and Breath Holding," in *Regulation of Respiration. Annals of the New York Academy of Science, 109:* 901, 1963.

PART FOUR

THE FITTING-TOGETHER CAPACITY— ITS BIOLOGICAL, PSYCHOLOGICAL, AND SOCIAL ORIGINS AND FUNCTIONS

BRAIN STORMS **40**

Brain storm is a familiar term for a common experience of being suddenly possessed by a great idea, of being suddenly moved into spontaneous action. The dictionary defines the term as a sudden idea or inspiration. To the person overtaken by one, a brain storm seems at the time to be *the* answer to a problem, or *the* thing to do under the circumstances. Brain storms include impractical ideas, practical jokes, and truly inspired solutions to problems.

If a fit is a two-part sequence, combining a subfit of whirlwind fitting together of patterned action and awareness with a second subfit of automatically acting-out or experiencing the fitted-together pattern, then the whole sequence may be thought of as a single brain storm. The term shifts responsibility for the fit from the person, and his thinking and feeling, to presumably autonomous, spontaneous explosions of cerebral activity.

In a brain storm, it is implied, the wheels of fitting together spin faster than one could deliberately drive them, and produce, in a flash, a great idea that the person could not have thought up all by himself. But despite the air of spontaneous inspiration, only some brain storms are really great; many are quite uninspired and inappropriate; others are rather half-wittedly intriguing and amusing.*

The familiar brain storms of everyday life are closely related to all others, both ordinary and extraordinary. Within the group as a whole are: hypnoidal ideas and experiences at transitions between waking and sleep; ideas, fantasied actions, and bodily disturbances that comprise nocturnal dreaming; brain storms that give rise to fits of convulsion and fits of creation; and all sudden, spontaneous behaviors and experiences. The conception brain

---

* One of William James's great ideas, conceived in a dreamy state, was, "What kind of a take is a mis-take?"

storm provides us with a third view of the continuum of episodes sampled and discussed in Parts Two and Three as fits and dysjunctive behavior.

In studying episodes as fits, attention was centered upon the descriptive content and dynamic structure; viewed as dysjunctive behavior, fits were considered as a means for minding critically dysjunctive situations. In their aspect of brain storms, fits and dysjunctive behavior can now be scrutinized in terms of the psychophysiological processes which produce them at moments of crisis. However, it will not be necessary or desirable to describe and discuss a third set of episodic behaviors and experiences. Reflection upon the brain-storm aspects of the fits and dysjunctive behaviors already presented will be sufficient to illumine that side of their three-sided nature. Additional data will be concerned with the time, place, and process of fitting together.

The gathering and breaking of brain storms was clearly visible in the fits of convulsion, creation, and prophecy—when "My m-m-m-mother . . . I'll k-k-k-kill her . . ." gave way to a convulsive fit; when Harold Rosenberg's sudden idea for his article on women popped into his mind after a tiring day of writing and a restless night; when H. L. Gold burst out with a prophecy upon being challenged to prove his predictive competence, and so on. Sudden lightning flashes and distant rumbles of stormy feelings are evident in "All of a sudden it comes in my mind I'm a queer." Episodes like "It was an instinctive reaction" are lit dimly by a kind of "heat lightning" over the horizon, heralding, perhaps, a remote storm which yet may break. Discharges of stormy tension into convulsive seizures, confused speech and action, visceral commotion, and elaborately organized behavior, both convulsive and creative, have been described in various examples. In some minor *petit mal* reactions, the intracerebral energy of an "intention to do" was apparently dissipated in paroxysmal neuronal discharges producing abnormal brain waves. In some instances, as in the Otley case, the occurrence of a most serious brain storm, as the cause of a coordinated purposive automatism presumably set off by it, can only be inferred.

When ordinary people are moved to discuss a brain storm they have had, they stress how great the idea seemed at the time and how it "just came to me." They often report a sense of utter conviction, of revelation and illumination, and they seem to have had a minor uncanny experience of possession and inspiration. Even when ordinary people talk about other things, they unwittingly reveal that they also have very frequent, if very slight, brain storms. A person will say, for example, "An idea just struck me,"

"Something just occurred to me," "I don't know where I got this notion, but . . . ," and so on. The person saying such things does not mean to say that he has not been thinking all along; he means that suddenly he "had a thought," perhaps one seeming entirely irrelevant to his existing train of thought and one that he had not consciously been seeking. He may be a bit suspicious of such spontaneous intrusions of something relatively alien, and he may avoid discussing these experiences.

When It-just-came-to-me and I've-just-had-an-idea experiences are discussed, these impressions emerge: The individual as "I" did not participate in producing the idea; in fact, his "I," being absorbed elsewhere, could not prevent its occurrence. Something-told-me experiences differ from I-told-myself ones. Having something "come out of nowhere" produces mixed feelings; inspirations are intriguing, but trying to fathom out-of-nowhere activates attitudes about the uncanny. There is interest in the process but uncertainty about its significance; having great ideas seems to question whether one is creative or crazy, blessed or damned. Thinking somehow involves progressive transformation of nerve-cell interactions through stages of ever increasing abstraction conceivable as neuronation, cerebration, mentation, ideation, and personation. Through these processes nerve impulses are changed, via information and meaning, into ideas. At the end of the process, "idea" comes before "I," the thought before the thinker.

In a brain storm, things move rapidly. Both the thought and the personified thinker suddenly burst into awareness more or less at the same time, like twins. Whether this double birth of "idea" and "I" is experienced as inexplicably uncanny (or which of the pair is felt as cause and which as result) probably depends on the circumstances associated with the crisis as well as upon individual inclination. "I" may seem the source of "ideas," "ideas" may intrude into "I," or the whole thing may seem entirely mysterious.

Thinking, as the fitting together of both thought and thinker, is a two-sided process—one side or the other of which we tend to put first, causally and in time. But the true cause of both is a crisis in the continuity of integration. Systematic thinkers have special aversion to simultaneous two-sidedness; therefore we have controversies about thinking in which each side sees its kind as a unitary process. Rationalists like Descartes say, "I think, therefore I am." Inspirationalists like Rimbaud say, "You should not say, I think. You should say, I am thought." Both are right and wrong. "I" thinks itself into crises which something "not-I" then resolves, and, in doing so, thinks "I" into existence again to explain "its" action.

In fitting together (of brain storms, dysjunctive behavior, and fits—whatever way an episode is viewed), the evidence indicates that "I" is not around to do any thinking: it has been transported into something more or less approaching ecstatic trance or hypnoidal fascination with horror. Indeed, a new "I" has to be thought up as part of the fitting together in order to be there to *have had* the fit. "I" does not convulse or create; it is dis-integrated and reconstituted. Only then, if at all, can the individual know about it and say, "I convulsed," or, "I created." Just so with small fits of disruption and creation—subclinical *petit mal* or reasonably bright ideas. We do not notice the disappearance and reappearance of "I" because the changes are slight and the gaps are brief.

Small fits, especially of constructive ideation, are experienced as natural events—as punctuative discontinuities which heighten the impression of continuity. And from the "I's" of two successive such episodes, there is abstracted a more enduring, embracing, and generalized "I" whose job it is to mind operations, to have experience in longer periods of time. Thus is created an entire hierarchy of "I's," the topmost of which, being at the end of a long chain of increasingly smaller abstractions, seems to be a relatively unchanging "I" which can contemplate if it cannot master the fate it experiences. It is this "I" that can aim or will "to be good," "to stop smoking," and so on. But its Jacksonian dreams of effective action, and of affecting action, have to be couched in general terms and to pass down a long chain of command. Like a colonel giving the military command, "Pass in review!" to a regiment, "I's" commands may, at the end of the chain, activate an awkward squad of privates with two left feet.

This scheme is especially applicable to the mythically average person for whom the generation of awareness, action, and "I" is relatively smooth because it progresses by means of extremely small, rapid fits of fitting together. Such fortunate people have an impression that living, at least for them, is simple, pleasant, and orderly. Their "I" is never very far removed by abstraction from the immediate scene of action and awareness—they do not have to, nor can they, lift their mind's eye very far to see where the action is. The chain of command between dreams and action concocted by their highest centers, is relatively short and reasonably effective; hence they have a great faith in will power as an everyday exercise. But usually they fail to notice that the scope and significance of their "dreamed-up," but seemingly willful, action is necessarily quite limited. The imaginative reach of "I" is not for them much greater than its actual grasp, than the series of episodes from which it has been abstracted.

Other, less fortunate people seem either to live for the moment, from one episode to the next, or under the direction of a star-gazing "I." Among these are the "epileptic," the "obsessive schizoid," and the "creative artist" (the quotation marks signify diagnostic imprecision). The obsessive schizoid is continually busy avoiding being or doing "wrong" by not doing whatever is "wrong"; absorbed in dipping his "I" in and out of small, repetitive "not-doings," he avoids any sudden, significant uncanny experience, pleasant or horrifying, and, thereby, exists in a permanent quasi crisis of "not-quite-I." For the epileptic and the artist, on the other hand, living shows a succession of significant, relatively infrequent crises about being and doing—a series of discernible deaths and rebirths of "I." It should, of course, be kept in mind that we are all alike more than we are different. Being or doing epileptic, average, or creative is not a matter of rigid diagnostic categories but of an averaging out of what most of our episodes of living add up to.

To me, the continuing, recurring, double creation of I and idea— of both thought and thinker, of knowing and knower, of doing and doer—resolves the "unresolvable" contradictions and dualities of the so-called mind-body problem. For some readers this idea may lack elegance and satisfyingly quantitative precision, but as a rude working hypothesis it will do until a better one comes along. The fitting together of successive ideas, actions, and "I's" occurs repeatedly every day of our lives. It is much the same, formally, in the unremarked thought-discoveries of ordinary people about their immediate situation, or in the fitting together of intricate patterns of sounds into a great musical composition by Wolfgang Amadeus Mozart, who then struggles to explain the process as an extended "I don't know how I did it." In each case, thoughts come crowding into mind when "I" is weakened or relaxed or the fitting-together capacity is stimulated into relatively spontaneous, autonomous activity.

Fitting together gives rise to all sorts of ideas and actions whose form and content fall in between our small everyday brain storms and those of truly creative artists and confirmed epileptics. All kinds of things—clumsy and clever, lovely and ludicrous, mundane and marvelous—occur as brain storms, as manifestations of the constructive and destructive processes of witting and fitting which make up the fitting-together capacity. They are sometimes interchangeable, as when disturbances of bodily and personal function—sudden weakness in the knees, sudden blankness of mind, etc.—appear in circumstances in which bursts of laughter, anger, and other emotions might well be expected.

Thus brain storms are both good and bad, fruitful and foolish; the term has a certain ineradicable ambiguity. It shares with "fits" some implications of disruptiveness, but it also shares with *dysjunctive reactions* implications of conjunctive synthesis. With both it shares the idea of suddenly doing something about a problem. It takes up, where dysjunctive behavior leaves off, an emphasis on the intracerebral devices and processes of fitting together. Its very elasticity and ambiguity make "brain storms" a useful viewpoint for considering the elusive activities by which the human brain escapes from servile responses to environmental changes, and by which it evades the rigid restrictions upon action and awareness exercised by the personified "I." As climatological storms "clear the air" so neurological storms "clear the way" for improved or continued action by removing crisis-induced roadblocks.

The emphasis in Part Four, then, is on the neurophysiopsychology of fitting together. Fitting together is not a "thing" easily described, nor is it a process whose dynamics are easily charted. It, too, has a triune, three-sided nature, and requires approach from three slightly different points of view. With this transition from "brain storms" to "brain storming"—from "fits" to "fitting together" —the term "brain storms" will hereafter be of little use. Instead of further examination of fits, dysjunctive behavior, and brain storms as three different descriptive aspects of episodic behavior and experience, attention will be devoted to the reactions, times, and processes by and in which the three-sided episodes are fitted together.

Fitting together will be discussed as (1) a biologically ancient and important process-apparatus for survival in emergencies, the *still reaction;* (2) a peculiarly significant though often fleeting moment in time, the *pregnant interval* between stimulus-events and responsive activity a kind temporal fringe state of, and between, awareness and action, during which integrative capacity can be organized for meeting an emergency; and (3) an *integrating trance,* an ego-diffusing, minding-expanding, process-state assumed by the brain-mind-person system when the existing "I" falters in a crisis and transpersonal fitting-together capacity is required to restore continuity of organism-environment relations and to reconstruct an "I" to experience them.

Theoretically, a still-interval-trance is a true pause, very near to an absolute stop in ongoing organism-environment integration. Dynamically and descriptively, it is a compromise fusion of excitation and inhibition concomitant with an arrested but activated and content-less "intention to do." If it could have a subjective reflection in conscious experience, it would be something like an intense urge to do something-in-general transformed by an equally intense everything-is-wrong inhibition of any specific action into an "I can't stand this" kind of feeling. Beginning as an arrest of the elaboration of action and awareness (without, however, any suspension of energy-accumulating metabolic processes or cessation of energy-arousing if unnoticed environmental stimulation), it can become a highly labile condition of intense, "pure," unorganized tension increasingly demanding some outlet as time passes and the energy level mounts.

In this qualitative state of utmost tension, all organizing and discharging systems are partially activated, but held in check because no one of them can resolve the contradictions and ambiguities of the momentarily unthinkable situation. The fitting-together capacity may run through, in backward- and forward-looking "as if" scanning, seemingly relevant parts of its repertory—or even the whole of its store of interpretations and actions, like the proverbial drowning man's experience of his whole life flashing through his mind.   •

Absorbed in a standstill of thinking and doing, the organism enters into a kind of hypnoidal trance derived by evolutionary development from the ancient *still reaction* for surviving in emergencies by extraordinary feats of seeing and doing. In this process-state, cogitative integration consists of a subpersonal, transrational "seeing" and "dreaming-up" which, free of the ordinary restrictions of "reality" and "I," can organize otherwise inconceivable solutions for the unthinkable.

In a sense, in discussion of the still reaction, the "Why?" will be of primary importance, although "How?" and "When?" also play significant roles. In the chapter on the pregnant interval, "When?" is the leading question; in that on the integrating trance, "How?" Although the still reaction is well known to biologists, *pregnant interval* is a term used only casually by Herrick in discussing the delay between arousal and action. *Integrating trance* is an idea of my own, though derived in part from the "moment of contemplation" and "waking trance" mentioned by Yeats and others interested in the creative moment. Both formulating and comprehending these three concepts, and their unification in the still-interval-trance of fitting together, are novel experiences, likely to be attended by novel errors—but, perhaps, likely also to be attended by novel rewards.

The Evolutionary and Biological Basis for Crisis-Induced
Discontinuities in Ongoing Action and Awareness and
for all Forms of Fitting Together.

THE STILL REACTION 41

. . . the still or "still"* reaction in many instances appears to be a
necessary, preparatory step in the transition whereby an animal reacting in avoidances or "avoidance" to a nocuous element in a given
situation may be brought to react in approach or "approach" to some
non-nocuous or pleasurable element in the same situation.

But even after the still reaction has been induced the situation may
not be altogether safe and the animal may resume flight instead of
reacting in approach to the bait. It seems, therefore, that the still
(precurrent, anticipatory) reaction represents a vantage point from
which the situation may be evaluated instinctively, with the animal set,
in full readiness, for the execution of the consummatory (final) reaction by way of approach or flight.

—J. G. BYRNE[1]

In the seventeenth century Descartes postulated an activity which
suppressed activity. It waited for factual confirmation until the nineteenth century. Then at first it was not believed. Several who witnessed
the fact did not report it, hesitating to accept it as true. Descartes had
made this postulate when thinking out his supposed Robot-man and
how it should work. The nerves of the muscles which turn the eye-ball
sidewise he had particularly in mind. Those muscles are arranged as
antagonists. Instead of one pulling against the other, he supposed one
paid out as the other drew in. It was paid out by inhibiting its activity.
He was right. The inhibition is however actually exerted not directly
on the muscle, as he thought, but on the nervous centre driving the
muscle. It acts within the nervous system itself.

A nerve-centre is a place of junction of nerve-lines, and of departure
for fresh ones. It is at such junctions that inhibition occurs. It can
there suppress action, or, no less important, can grade it by moderat-
ing it. In the network of conductors it can switch off one line as
another is switched on. The real importance of Descartes' step was
that it handed the work of the nervous system over to the nervous
system itself. It had been worked by Galen's spirits and the soul.

—SIR CHARLES SHERRINGTON[2]

---

* By quotation marks Byrne denoted static and symbolic equivalents of
overt reactions.

Watch any freely moving animal—a cow grazing in a field, a child playing in a yard, a woman working in her kitchen, a carpenter building a house—and you can see that living action is intermittent. It is episodic, an alternation of action and inaction. Continued and closer observation will suggest that the periods of inaction are not merely a passive waiting for sufficient stimulus to come, from within or without, to set off the next action. The gaps between episodes are filled with formulating what to do next, and this formulating activity includes contemplative rumination and tightly focused concentration.

In its everyday living a freely moving animal repeatedly reorganizes the direction, scope, quality, and intensity of its action according to the solicitations and instigations of bodily needs and environmental events. In these reorganizations, its ability to "see" what comes next is aided by hindsight and foresight. Its difficulties in seeing clearly, because of fuzzy ambiguities and contradictory double images inherent often in both bodily and environmental events, are compounded by congenital and acquired tendencies to see and to interpret certain things in highly personal ways.

If what comes next depends upon whether cues for it are seen clearly, any fuzziness or blurring of relevant stimulus-events may shift perception from trying to see exactly what is there (as a guide to differentiated, cue-specific behavior) to trying to ascertain whether it is promising or threatening (as a clue for nonspecific activities in avoidance or approach). Dr. Stewart Wolf, a long-time and careful student of those protective behaviors called psychosomatic symptoms, has said that their immediate cause is "the perception of an event as threatening."[3] One might add that approach and attack behaviors can ensue when an event is perceived as promising.

Professor Adelbert Ames, whose lifelong studies of how we see have provoked much thought and considerable revision of our ideas on seeing, believes that in all his behavior, symptomatic or otherwise, man is concerned primarily with the threatening or reassuring aspects of his situation. He once said, "While in no way denying the existence of the 'external world' our disclosures apparently show that the only aspects of it man can know anything about are those aspects which are either helpful or thwarting in carrying out his purposes."[4]

Thus, an important element determining what comes next— whether it is a particularized action or a generalized movement toward fight or flight—is the appraisal of the balance of peril and promise, of danger and opportunity. When promises and threats (present in some proportion in all situations) are equally evident and energized, the animal can only go into a state of readiness for nothing-in-particular and everything-in-general called a still reaction. This totally ambiguous, multipotentialed (and, relative to the animal's own capacity, omniscient and omnipotent) metastable state is a zero point from which all "negative" and "positive" behaviors diverge. It can give way to actual or symbolic behavior in total or partial patterns of fight or flight, offense or defense, approach or avoidance; be prolonged into exhaustion; turn into sleep; or differentiate rapidly into any activity of which the organism-individual-person is capable. Clearly, it is a central, fundamental fact of behavior. As a biological wellspring—concomitant with the temporal pause for thought, or pregnant interval—it is the operational source of all episodic behavior and experience, and as such, requires incorporation into behavioral theory.

The still reaction has long been known to naturalists as an emergency-activated protective device by which animals avoid attack and injury. By unusual actions or inactions, the animal assumes an appearance—suggesting that it is invincible, invulnerable, or insignificant—such that a would-be predator avoids it. In 1846, for example, Kirby and Spence[5] reported that the common dung chafer (*geotrupes stercorarius*), when touched or frightened, freezes rigidly with limbs extended as in actual death. Thus chafers deceive chafer-loving rooks. Confusion arose from the fact that the still reaction was first noted in "death-feigning" and "playing 'possum." These terms, unfortunately, have prevented full understanding of the ubiquity and significance of the still reaction as a fundamental fact of everyday psychophysiology.

For the death-feigning version of still reaction can be evoked by simple, not particularly threatening means and by reassuring maneuvers such as petting and stroking. Mere contact is sufficient to throw the aquatic insects *Nepa* and *Ranatra,* for example, into the still reaction. Lifting *Belostoma* out of the water or digging the sand flea *Talorchestia* out of its burrow evokes a protective freeze.

Sometimes, however, animals will, instead of freezing, go into vigorous action. *Belostoma* may not freeze but kick and struggle; *Talorchestia* may lie curled up and tolerate rough handling only to spring suddenly to life and hop away.[6] Some shore birds when come upon suddenly, or otherwise surprised and threatened, will fall into a most dramatic fit of tumbling and flopping around.[7] Vigorous, even convulsive movements might be considered an "I am dying" form of protective reaction, but images of "dying-feigning" and "frenzied still reactions" as forms of death-feigning and still reaction stretch these conceptions into paradoxical contradiction and ambiguity.

Nevertheless, the still-freeze, in either limpness or rigidity, and the protective agitation, convulsive or purposively patterned, are closely related dynamically; furthermore, both are intimately involved with the processes culminating in sleep. Cats actively displaying the violent "rage reaction," for example, may be quieted into docility and on into immobility by careful, gentle approach and subsequent petting. And in a quiet, dark room, with continued stroking they easily pass into sleep.

Juxtaposition of corresponding opposites is generally characteristic of fits and fitting together. Indeed, the contradictions in death-feigning are clues to understanding it. Darwin pointed out in 1884 that the freeze attitudes of *Julus, Spider,* and *Oniscus* were quite different from their postmortem appearances.[8] Severin and Severin observed that *Belostoma flumineum* displayed two versions of sham death, neither of which was the posture of actual death.[9] Because of the misleadingly restrictive connotations of death-feigning, Piéron, the French authority on protective immobility in animals, suggested the generic term "still reaction."[10]

But this term is also too restrictive; crisis-induced behavior often simulates injury, for example, and other active behaviors. Indeed, various rigid and flaccid still-reaction postures and passive and active performances seem to say, "I am uninteresting," "I am inedible," or "I am dangerous," etc., and might be called avoidance-inducing or distance-creating behavior.

Yet there are also such behaviors that are approach-inducing in their effect—as when a nesting mother bird plays wounded and tries to lure the threatening animal into following her away from the nest. Here again we find that contradictions cannot altogether be eliminated, even though some are disposed of by shifting consideration to a higher, more comprehensive level. For example, "still reaction" seems appropriate enough as a descriptive term for those immobilities displayed by some animals before, during, and after mating, and for those induced by petting, stroking, and other modes of evoking animal "hypnosis." Dynamically, then, *still reaction* bears a double burden of denoting immobility during an emergency—as in the case of rabbits who freeze when a dog is near—and immobility during a tranquillity.

J. G. Byrne, the British student of mammalian still phenomena, achieved some dynamic unity of contradictions by focusing attention on the anticipatory, preparatory in general but not in particular, potential character of the still reaction as such. In itself, the still reaction is descriptively between, and dynamically before, any actual behavior of the fight-flight, offense-defense, approach-avoidance categories. Byrne saw that a standstill might be necessary to an animal reacting in avoidance to a threatening situation to enable it to change the direction and nature of its action into an approach to an attractive aspect or element of the situation. A standstill, that is, allows a "change of mind." As Byrne said, "It seems, therefore, that the still reaction represents a vantage point from which the situation may be evaluated . . . with the animal set in full readiness for the execution of the consummatory (final) reaction by way of approach or flight."[11] Thus the standstill not only allows for changing the mind; it provides a temporal-dynamic gap in ongoing minding and acting in which, and by which, the organism-individual-person can in a real sense "make up its mind" about novel, contradictory, and ambiguous matters.

But neither Byrne nor anyone else, to my knowledge, seems to have been able to stay with the contemplation of the standstill and its mind-body significance. Instead of a still reaction *about* the still reaction, we experience an excruciatingly urgent avoidance reaction, as if to stay with it produced irritating-tension-about-nothing instead of germinal ideas for thinking-about-thinking-in-a-crisis. Thinking-about-thinking is not so difficult. But thinking-about-thinking-in-a-crisis—about not-thinking—is something else again. Perhaps that is why there is so much said and written about anxiety—"about" in the sense of "in the vicinity of"—but not too much of it is precisely centered upon the experience of anxiety as a felt encounter with the unthinkable. In any case, even Frieda Goldman-Eisler, who set out to study pauses in speech and thought, was herself surprised to find that so much of our utterance time is taken up by standstills and silence.[12]

We talk so much, do so much, and are so busy just living that we forget that it took us a long time to learn to do all these things with any smoothness. Our illusions of orderliness, smoothness, and continuity in thinking and acting are maintained, in part, by un-witting comparisons with our earlier but forgotten incoherence. These illusions are also maintained by smoothly unrolling habitual performances. Any new idea or action we are forced to formulate to get out of a crisis is used time and again before we find it necessary to make another new one. And just as we sedulously avoid, if we can, getting into a crisis and organizing new ways of knowing and doing, so we desperately avoid thinking and learning about crises themselves—even when we seem to be ardently trying to do so. Thinking inevitably culminates in a crisis. And thinking-about-crises culminates in a crisis in thinking-about-thinking-in-crises. This is too much for us. Even saying or reading it over makes us a bit giddy. But "giddiness" has something to do with "god-in-ness," and if we can tolerate momentary discomfort, maybe inspiration (to be possessed by the spirit) or enthusiasm (to be en-theos-ed) will come to us in a moment of illumination.

But while we are willing to accept the fatigue that goes with logical intellectual labor (because it offers the reward of feeling ourselves to be successful rational persons), we seem to be unwilling to let ourselves go sufficiently to recognize the fact and significance of the discontinuities in our thinking and doing and living. For standstills threaten the illusions of orderliness, smoothness, and continuity seemingly so necessary for our hard-won, shaky identity as rational animals—which we translate as "thinking persons." In a still reaction we are confronted with paralysis of "I"-directed conscious, voluntary action, and with our tendency to react as nonrational animal or irrational person.

In any notable standstill, evidently, we feel threatened with loss of "our" personality and mind—with our personal identity. And we react to the anticipation of this eventuality like an animal threatened with loss of existence—we display all sorts of actual, static, and symbolic postures and performances of fight-flight, offense-defense, and approach-avoidance. "Our" security and satisfaction, and even those ideas by which we achieve and defend these, depend upon a feeling of continuity in the spatial and temporal configuration of awareness and action, of our "I," and our "mind." We rewrite Descartes' "I think, therefore I am" to read, "I think continuously or I am not."

Our ideas of "I" and of "thinking" are acquired in a masculine-oriented, Western civilization that distrusts Eastern or "womanly" intuition and is overcommitted to ideas of stepwise logical deduction as the only real thinking. Our distrust of the nonrational merges with our fear of the irrational. And to our sex- and geography-based bias, we add our "scientific" hostility to the spontaneous nonrational, which we misconceive as irrational or supernatural. For we are still, many generations after the Enlightenment, vigorously defending an impossibly constricted concept of the personal against any, even momentary, takeover by forces in the vast realm of the nonpersonal, subpersonal, or suprapersonal —as if we might otherwise become possessed by the demons and demonology that plagued our ancestors.

And that is only one side of our fearful avoidance reaction to contemplating discontinuities in our thinking and doing. If a break in continuity threatens dissolution of our identity as rational persons, we also fear losing voluntary control of our behavior. We seem to anticipate that if we are brought to a standstill, we might then give way to "brutish" passions and begin to behave in "beastly" ways. We seem as frightened of animal ways as we are of nonrational and nonpersonal human behavior and experience. Perhaps in our concepts of ourselves, rational and animal elements oppose each other. Maybe the Darwinian idea of struggle for survival still overrides post-Darwinian evidence concerning cooperation and peacefulness among animals. Perhaps the idea of "possession" by nonpersonal influences is still too loaded with visions of malevolent demons rather than of divine benevolence. Perhaps it is simply that our "I" cannot easily conceive of its own discontinuity—or can only see it as deadly.

In any case, elaboration of a theory of thinking and doing based upon recognition of the still reaction as a continuity-generating discontinuity was not pursued even by Byrne. Instead, he pursued the offense-defense function of still reactions and their derivatives. Their purpose, for him, was that of sleep—"the maintenance or refitting of the organism for the adequate performance of dynamic functions. . . ." Byrne traced this restorative function from death-feigning as a response to an acute danger, through pseudo death-feigning as an avoidance reaction, to sleep as a protective way of dealing with the chronic threat of fatigue. Other offensive and defensive maneuvers could then be linked together as still-derivatives activated by acute and chronic threats. According to Byrne:

> In man the death-feigning instinct has been conditioned to social purpose, and it is utilized to the advantage of the individual upon a large scale in the normal reactions of daily life, whilst in those afflicted with mental disorders of every description and degree it is the main factor in the mechanism which permits release . . . in what seems to the patient to be a perfectly proper socio-ethical disguise . . . of the repressed energy which furnishes the dynamic of their persistent troublesome symptoms.[13]

Indeed, theorists in psychosomatic medicine (Harold G. Wolff, Stewart Wolf, *et al.*) postulated later that a large group of symptomatic disturbances of bodily and personal function were in fact partial and total biological patterns of offense and defense precipitated when no better solution to seemingly insoluble life problems could be seen.[14]

But the protective usefulness of these various purposive automatisms is only one half of the story—the survival-promoting side. For purposivity involves not survival alone; it also implies growth, and growth requires improvement in ability to deal with crises and problems. In itself, the concept of protective still reactions is one of passivity, reflectiveness, and backward-looking atavism. It explains much of the "Why?" and "How?" of crisis-induced disruptions of on-going living. But it has little to say about what goes on during a still-induced discontinuity, and about the relationship of "what goes on" to the development of the various outcomes that terminate still reactions.

This is a crucial question which leads back to the other implications of purposive automatisms. When I pursued my researches into the meaningful aspects of spontaneous epileptic fits my center of interest was the question: What was responsible for the variety of convulsive and quasi-convulsive fit-behaviors? Was it something in the nature of the stimulus-events that provoked the fit? The kind of brain or "lesion" therein that organized the fit? Or were the problems and purposes of the person who had the fit somehow expressed thereby?

Put another way, was the form and content of the unfolding fit predetermined by an in-built or acquired automatism? Or was the fit-pattern, once triggered, subject to modification, even profound alteration, by the circumstances in which it occurred? Hughlings Jackson and other British neurologists, not too convinced by French insistence on a rigid separation between epilepsy and hysteria, long ago established that circumstances can shape the development of a fit, however it is triggered, but this truth has constantly to be reestablished to those unfamiliar with the facts and history of epilepsy. It has profound significance for *any* theory of behavior.

Passive observation of the variation in fit-behaviors displayed by a patient or group of patients over a long period of time, and active intervention to change the course of a convulsive fit, made it clear that whatever the neurological process-apparatus producing a fit, it was by no means entirely automatic. Why then the variation in fit-behavior from time to time and person to person?

This question was a variant of a still larger one evoked by our research group's context of a diversity of "psychosomatic" patients and symptoms: Why the variation or inflexibility of psychosomatic symptoms from patient to patient and time to time? And both these questions are subsumed by an even larger one: Why the flexibility or stereotyped automaticity of episodic behaviors and experiences displayed by a group of people at any one time or by one person over a period of time? Why the spectrum of fits, from fits of convulsion to fits of creation? What is the relation between episodicity, epilepticity, and creativity? And finally, in this relation, what are the roles and the nature of "purposivity" and "automaticity"?

Some ideas about the implications and answers to these questions arise when we begin to contemplate the interrelations of all the active and static, actual and "as if," fight-flight, offense-defense, and approach-avoidance behaviors. For the continuum of death-feigning-derived *immobilities* and approach-avoidance-derived *actions* shades into a galaxy of "as if" ritual encounters between animals and ritualized activities of man. This galaxy, in turn, is absorbed into a universe of as-if "imagination experiences," imaginative actions, and all creative combinations whereby hindsight and foresight are transformed into new seeings and doings.

The key to a new idea about epilepticity, episodicity, and creativity is recognizing that *all* episodes have some qualities of purposive automatisms. For whether an individual is trying to do something he has done before, and fails or succeeds, or is trying to do something he has not done before, and succeeds or fails, the sequence of events is an *intention* followed by an *acting out* of that intention. And whether the acting out is conventionally habitual or creatively novel, it unfolds "automatically" according to a goal-directed plan dreamed up at the moment, or dredged up from the past in the pregnant interval provided by a still reaction.

These and other bio-physio-psychological processes that go on in a still-interval are the subject of the next chapters. Suffice it to say here that the still reaction, by bringing ongoing organism-environment interaction to a halt in a static tableau—by disconnecting the present here-and-now from immersion in a continuous flow of organism-environment time—thereby disconnects the psychophysiological activities of the still interval from "what-has-been-going-on" and allows "what-now-goes-on" to create, more or less spontaneously, stimulus-context Gestalts relatively free from influence by those which precipitated the crisis by their unthinkability. This spontaneous or quasi-spontaneous fitting together can then be involved in resolving the crisis in continuity and getting on with the job of living, without the burden of an unchangeable flow. *In the still-interval, the unthinkable past can be rewritten, or written off. The fitting-together capacity can devote itself to attaining a new future.* The purposivity of fitted-together patterns of action and awareness produced by the fitting-together capacity in a crisis is an averaging out of the aims and drives of the organism-individual-person complex interacting with the push-pulls provided by the environment in its past-present-future totality. This purposivity transcends that of the body or person because the "I"-dissolving, trancelike nature of still-intervals frees the fitting-together capacity from servitude to either side of the critical organism-environment configuration. The purposivity of the purposive automatisms generated by still-interval-trances, therefore, allows the entranced organism-individual-person to get out of the crisis that a limited part of the fitting-together capacity, personified as "I," got it into. The automaticity of these processes ensures the completion of actions and ideas so that "I" can come back into existence as their knower and doer. The episodicity of behavior and experience is a necessary consequence of the periodicity of crises and resolutions, which themselves are necessary for survival-by-growth.

A still-reaction is an initial phase, or temporal aspect of, and the biological basis for, human crisis-resolving operations. The concept of still-interval-trance (or "integrating trance," perhaps) emerges in following the process to completion. A second phase or aspect can be abstracted from the process-complex. This is the *pregnant interval,* in and by which psychological modes of minding elaborate when "as if" biological methods are unsuitable or un-availing. "Psychological" implies the use of the processes of reasoning and intuiting one has available from endowment and experience. It seems to have a physiological basis in the manipulation of neuronal analogical models of relations between the here-and-now and other not-heres and not-nows. In everyday life most crises in the continuity of living are probably resolved on either the biological *still* or psychological *interval* phase levels.

In the evolution of man, near failures and anticipated failures in biological crisis-resolution probably lead through as-if minding, in repeated still-intervals, to increasing use of psychological modes of problem-solving. In everyday life we can, and often do, shift back to biological substitutes for problem-solving in our efforts to get out of crises. But occasionally we shift to a third phase-aspect, the integrating trance.

The integrating trance is a transpsychological mode of crisis-resolving in which patterns of relation between here-and-now and not-here, not-now are abstracted by as-if operations upon other as-ifs instead of upon reality. A kind of transcending of problem-solving into "transcendental problem-solving" is the only alternative to an epileptoid retreat when ordinary and biological problem-solving fail. Whereas everyday crises are mostly resolved by ordinary continuity-restoring problem-solving, fits of convulsing and fits of creating do not so much restore the disrupted continuity as they tend to shift it to a different level.

How this happens will be examined next.

Notes

1. J. Grandson Byrne, *Studies on the Physiology of the Eye: Still Reaction, Sleep, Dreams, Hibernation, Repression, Hypnosis, Narcosis, Coma, and Allied Conditions.* H. K. Lewis & Co., London, 1942.
2. Sir Charles Sherrington, *Man on His Nature.* Doubleday Anchor Books, New York, 1953.
3. Stewart Wolf, in discussion of "Life Stress and Bodily Disease—A Formulation," edited by Harold G. Wolff. *Publications of the Association for Research in Nervous and Mental Disease*, Vol. XXIX, New York, 1950.
4. Adelbert Ames, "Architectural Form and Visual Sensations," in *Building for Modern Man*, edited by T. H. Creighton. Princeton University Press, 1949, p. 82.
5. W. Kirby and W. Spence, *An Introduction to Entomology.* London, 6th ed., 1846, p. 447.
6. H. H. P. Severin and H. C. Severin, *Behaviour Monographs.* Cambridge, Massachusetts, 1911.
7. Peter Matthiessen, personal communication.
8. J. G. Byrne, *op. cit.*, p. 285.
9. H. H. P. Severin and H. C. Severin, *op. cit.*
10. H. Piéron, *"L'Immobilité Protectrice Chez les Animaux."* *Revue Scientifique*, Série 1, 1904, p. 523.
11. J. G. Byrne, *op. cit.*, p. 440.
12. Frieda Goldman-Eisler, "Hesitation, Information, and Levels of Speech Production," in *Disorders of Language*, edited by A. V. S. de Reuck and Maeve O'Connor. J. A. Churchill, London, 1964, pp. 101ff.
13. J. G. Byrne, *op. cit.*, p. 440.
14. Harold G. Wolff, "Protective Reaction Patterns and Disease." *Annals of Internal Medicine*, 27: 944, 1947.

The Psychophysiological Aspect of Fitting Together in a
Still-Interval-Trance. The Time-less Moment Between Onset
and Resolution of a Crisis in Continuity of Living.

THE PREGNANT INTERVAL 42

. . . As Sherrington pointed out long ago, in a free swimming animal
there is a time lag between reception of the stimulus from a distant
object and the consummation of the response. The pregnant interval
between the anticipatory and consummatory phases of the reaction
gives a clue to understanding of the entire history of forebrain evolution.

During this interval there is a central resolution of forces, which
eventuates in appropriate behavior; and with increasing complication
of patterns of behavior, this central apparatus of adjustment* assumes
more and more structural complexity and physiological dominance over
the entire bodily economy.

—C. JUDSON HERRICK[1]

. . . The human animal is an attentive animal, and his attention
may be given to stimuli that are relatively faint. One can pick out
sounds at a distance. Our whole intelligent process seems to lie in the
attention which is selective of certain types of stimuli. Other stimuli
which are bombarding the system are in some fashion shunted off. . . .
Not only do we open the door to certain stimuli and close it to others,
but our attention is an organizing process as well as a selective process.
. . . Our attention enables us to organize the field in which we are
going to act. Here we have the organism as acting and determining its
environment. It is not simply a set of passive senses played upon by
the stimuli that come from without. The organism goes out and determines what it is going to respond to and organizes that world. . . .
Such is an approach to what goes on in the central nervous system
which comes to the physiologist from the psychologist.

—GEORGE HERBERT MEAD[2]

The phrase "pregnant interval" was used casually by Herrick; at
other times he used "moment of inhibition" and similar terms
to denote the pause necessary for the "central resolution of forces

---

* Much of the confusion and controversy about the mind-body problem,
focused on the nature and location of the highest centers of control of
awareness and action, can be organized around the question: Is the "central
apparatus of adjustment" a part of the brain (cortex or subcortex), a functional division of the mind (ego or unconscious), or a moment in time (the
pregnant interval and its multiverse fitting-together abilities)?

that eventuate in" any behavior. But when he did use it, as above, he clearly meant to signify that the interval between anticipatory and consummatory phases of behavior was gestational—that it was pregnant with more possibilities than a passive time lag between perception and motion. It was, in his conception and in mine, an active inhibition of organism-environment interaction which allowed active, contentious resolutions-of-forces to occur.

Other theoreticians of behavior and brain function use various terms to denote the arrest of the ongoing (in which activation of continuity-restoring cerebromental processes takes place in reaction to ambiguous stimuli and complex overloaded situations). Among these are: "arrest reaction," "attention response," "alertness reaction," "regarding reaction," Pavlovian "delay," a "stage of inhibition and facilitation of reflex response," "activation of a subconscious complex," "period of association formation," "moment of contemplation," "waking trance," and, of course, "still reaction."

This collection of terms is itself pregnant with meanings. Mainly these refer, as in the case of *fits,* to what leads up to the event, what goes on during it, or what comes after. Any one term is insufficient to convey the three-sidedness of the whole process-moment-state. They all denote fits of fitting together.

"Pregnant interval" has not, to my knowledge, been used as a central organizing concept by anyone as it is here. It serves here to center consideration upon the temporal features of a complex biological, operational, and psychophysiological process-state produced by the time-suspending effect of the still reaction. This moment is indeed pregnant with all the potential capacities of the organism-individual-person. And in this moment of relative freedom from fleshly urgings and socioenvironmental push-pulls, patterns and processes within the minding system can be shuffled to produce convulsive, conventional, and creative behavior. The tendency to form particular patterns can also be weakened, reinforced, or transcended in this omnipotentialed moment.

The fitting-together ability of the minding system thus grows, and becomes more rigid or flexible, by means of successive fits. Fits of advance or retreat occur in response to repeated challenges by encounters with contradiction and ambiguity in the converse between organism and environment. In the pregnant interval provided by a still reaction, Jackson's "highest centres" can engage in a "struggle for survival of the fittest under the circumstances." And this contentious construction of a pattern for resolving a dysjunctive situation is what Herrick meant by his "central resolution of forces." The result is not only an immediate solution for a crisis but an increase in the complexity and power of the "central apparatus of adjustment" to respond habitually or to organize novel and ever new patterns.

This concept of the role of the pregnant interval in the working and growing of the brain's minding ability is consistent with— indeed, is an elaboration of—George Herbert Mead's thesis that "*the psychical is* a temporary characteristic of the empirical inter- action of organism and environment *concomitant with the inter- ruption of that interaction* [emphasis added]."[3] But it is an extension of Mead's thought on the roots of the self and "I" in crisis-induced "psychical" activity that has origins also in synthesis of ideas provided by many other investigators and philosophers.

Formulating a really novel or new idea is often exceedingly difficult because it requires simultaneous contemplation of both the similarities and differences (and Sullivan would add "the different similarities and similar differences") between it and the older ones from which it is derived. For there is no easy stepwise progression from the old to the new; there is always an inter- posing gap, a pregnant interval filled with trancelike "depersonal- ized" playing with words and ideas in a nonconformist or even a "sacrilegious" way. And this playing with words and ideas (really a playing together of the nervous arrangements underlying words and ideas) takes place in the region behind words. All of us, to some extent, are reluctant to enter this region, to experience shaking our frames of reference by passing through the "sanity barrier." We are all reluctant to experience even momentarily the uncanny effect of immersion in the unthinkable. For just as we can get "goose-flesh and shivers" from the poetic effects of the tensions between images, so too we can get "all shook up" from the noetic effect of the tensions engendered by similar differences and different similarities between contradictory and ambiguous noetic, intellectual ideas and images.

Considerable repetition and reworking is sometimes essential in communicating the scope and specificity of reference for the new concept. Definition is best accomplished by placing and differentiating the new idea within its historical and theoretical context of derivation and significance.

Recognition and explanation of fit-producing discontinuities in the continuity of behavior and experience go back at least to Galen's catalogue of "similar things that stir up and trouble the body violently, remind it of the disease and produce a paroxysm." But the idea that critical emotional and environmental events produced moments of spiritual vulnerability to demoniacally and divinely inspired fits must be attributed primarily to Christian theologians like Origenes and St. Hildegard. Origenes assumed the task of explaining away naturalistic explanations of fits because it was theologically necessary that the Biblical account of Jesus' miraculous healing of an epileptic (by casting out the causative demon) remain unchallenged by medical science. He argued persuasively that demons were clever enough to take possession of people only at times of crises and changes so that their demoniac influence would be concealed behind naturalistic screens. St. Hildegard advanced the doctrine of possession by explaining that moments of passion weakened the soul and made it susceptible to either demoniac or divine influence.

When, centuries later, the doctrine of possession was more or less outgrown, supernatural inspiration was replaced, causally, by instinctual drives and environmental stimulation. But scientific, mechanistic theoreticians were fearful that any recognition of nonrational processes would open the way to a return of the "irrational" as supernatural. Instead they postulated a lifeless machine in whose continuous operation there was no place for passion and no time for passion-induced standstills in which "vital" or "supernatural" forces could take possession of the machinery.

But in cleansing the precincts of mechanistic science from all theological contamination, these theoreticians produced a situation too sterile for everyday use. By eliminating the soul and its susceptibility to supernatural influence, they also got rid of the person and his moments of passion and crisis. Troubling noises, however, soon were heard above the quiet continuous hum of the mechanists' Newtonian machinery. With the decline of ecclesiastical authority, secular activity in the universities flourished, and inquiring minds turned to psychology as well as to nature studies. Soon ideas such as "learning," "consciousness and unconsciousness," and "motivation" abounded. Thus the Freudian and Jacksonian doctrine of "psychophysical parallelism"—an irreconcilable duality of machine and mind—became the only way neurology could come to terms with psychology. This structural duality could lead to a unity of common purpose shared by "scientifically" oriented psychologists and neurologists, namely, preserving the explanatory primacy of stimulus-response dynamics.

But discontinuities between and within consciousness and unconsciousness, noticing and ignoring, awareness and action, and other processes of living are facts of life. So too are the discontinuities at synaptic junctions within the brain that keep the brain from responding as a single big nerve cell to any stimulus.

And at these discontinuities of time and place, "vitalistic" things like purpose and desire tend, like St. Hildegard's divine and demoniac spirits, to insinuate themselves into the works. For it is evident from everyday observation of the intermittency of animal and human thought and action—in some pauses we can almost see the "wheels turning"—that discontinuity plays a significant role in the organization of behavior. Hence even during the nineteenth-century expansion, refinement, and entrenchment of mechanistic biology, attention was occasionally paid to things like "consciousness" which could be sandwiched in between stimulus and response.

Thus in the mid-1800s Herbert Spencer, an early modern philosopher of behavior whose ideas influenced Jackson, and whose concept of "psychical" antedated Mead's, said, "Between the reception of certain impressions and the performance of certain appropriate motions there is some inner connection. If the inner connection is organized, the action is of the reflex order, either simple or compound. If the inner connection is not organized, then the psychical changes which come between the impressions and motions are conscious ones. . . ."[4] In his view, consciousness and psychical changes arise from the inadequacy of existing inner connections for "unthinking" reflex response. Psychical changes, then, establish the needed new connections.

It is a short conceptual leap from Spencer's psychical changes, establishing new connections, to Herrick's pregnant interval in which an active "central apparatus of adjustment" functions, and in so doing develops "physiological dominance over the entire bodily economy." But in the century covered by this leap, knowledge about the inner connections between and within input and output grew enormously. Today the central apparatus of adjustment is seen to be an indeterminate, shiftingly structured complex mysteriously endowed with more freedom of action than any existing or anticipated man-made "electronic brain." Stressed from within by contradictions, shaken by the impact of cybernetics, stimulus-response psychophysiologies lie in ruins. The first fatal cracks in the edifice were made by observations like Herrick's.

> The flow of nervous impulses from receptor to effector is not one-way traffic. The excitation of a peripheral sense-organ may be followed by an efferent [outgoing] discharge back to the receptor. An instructive illustration of this is seen in the auditory apparatus of mammals. Excitation of the cochlea [the analyzer of auditory sense information in the inner ear] is followed by efferent

return to the tensor tympani [the muscle whose tension "tunes" the eardrum] . . . and also to the cochlea itself.[5]

What we see now is no longer a simple inflow of sensory nerve impulses from passive sense receptors, but an active analysis and selective transmission of relevant information by analyzers whose active exploration of the environment is guided, as it proceeds, by a to-and-from converse with the directing brain. Because all contracting muscles report back to the brain centers controlling motion (not muscles, per se), ideas of simple, one-way motor outflow have been replaced by conceptions of "commands" whose execution is guided by sensory feedback to completion. Instead of a "reflex arc," we must begin to think in terms of a "circulation of thought" between and within both organism and environment. Instead of Sherrington's "enchanted loom" passively weaving only what is fed into it, we must begin to think of "an entranced weaver." Instead of a complex switching device dependent on environmental input, we must imagine a fitting-together capacity reaching into inner and outer time-space via logic, intuition, and other modes of "seeing." It recurringly confronts itself with contradiction and ambiguity in the resolutions of which it facilitates living and creates the future.

Herrick's transformation of Sherrington's "time lag" into a "pregnant interval" recognized and foreshadowed the significance of new but ill-understood directions in the course of development of work and thought concerning the structure and function of the brain and its fitting-together devices. For what happened in Herrick's pregnant interval was not merely a confluent flowing of contending perceptions and impulses into appropriate motor channels but an active time-traveling appraisal of the here-and-now as such, and in its relation to not-here and not-now, so that the consummatory action was not only an appropriate "grammatical" solution for the present crisis but also an effective "syntactical" link between past and future.

A very significant but generally unnoticed implication in Herrick's transformation of passive time lag into active pregnant interval—and one not sufficiently pursued even by Herrick—is that a pregnant interval is, operationally, an effective discontinuity in the flow of organism-environment integrational time. The "present" has a real existence only during the suspension of ongoing integration represented by a pregnant interval. The "present," thus, is an occasional, crisis-induced occurrence and not merely a hypothetical ever moving "now-point" in the uninterrupted flow of time. In this sharp though often subtle break with the past, the "central apparatus of adjustment" can promote a resolution of forces by the "quasi-spontaneous" activities of "higher centres" exactly because fitting-together activities are freed from functional subservience to the stimulus-events which, in being so contradictory or ambiguous, activated the crisis-induced pregnant interval instead of a reflex response. *The break in bondage* to the immediate past and the contemporary environment *is a necessary temporal condition for any truly novel or new behavior and experience.*

Active fitting together of the new requires special conditions and the pregnant interval provides the temporal answer. In it all possible conditions of person and minding can arise; in it the conditions for creative fitting together are themselves created. For the discontinuity in the ongoing linkage of awareness to action allows momentary dissolution of the boundary between conscious and unconscious; then, too, attenuation of the zone between voluntary and involuntary follows upon detachment of attention and intention from supervision of on-going action. The suspension of on-flowing time abolishes the separation of here-and-now from not-here, not-now. Only at this moment does the brain become anything like an "enchanted loom," a self-guiding one.

Clearly, these special conditions must also have effects upon the body and "I" as well as the brain-mind system. Biologically, prolongation and intensification of a time lag into a still reaction and pregnant interval has the possible effects discussed in the previous chapter. In particular, the everything-activated, nothing-discharged state of tension must provide a peculiarly fertile basis for "ideomotor" reverberating amplification of quasi-spontaneous activity in higher sensorimotor centers, now liberated from environmental influence. The psychophysiological effects of emancipation from the time-place restrictions of here-and-now must alter consciousness. But it does not seem likely that consciousness arises only now to establish the necessary new connections as supposed by Spencer. Rather, it seems more likely that the ordinary relation of consciousness to unconsciousness is at this moment altered by expansion of the usually narrow boundary zone, so that awareness is something like that of a half-conscious, neither conscious nor unconscious intermediate state.

In this hypnoidal state of entrancement, the fitting-together capacity can combine the aims and style of "I" with the drive and manner of the organism-individual to shape ideas, images, and impulses provided by memory and anticipation. And the forward-outward-inward-backward-looking generalizing-and-particularizing abilities of the brain-mind system can "see" many ways out of the situation. This is how the still-interval as an arrest in the flow of organism-environment integration and interaction, and a discontinuity in operational time, can be so pregnant with possibilities for all sorts of knowings, feelings, and doings.

Notes

1. C. Judson Herrick, *The Brain of the Tiger Salamander*. University of Chicago Press, 1948, p. 41.
2. George Herbert Mead, *Mind, Self, and Society*, edited by Charles W. Morris. University of Chicago Press, 1934. Reprinted in *George Herbert Mead, On Social Psychology*, edited by Anselm Strauss. University of Chicago Press, 1964, p. 138.
3. Quoted from the article on the philosophy of George Herbert Mead by T. V. Smith in the *Encyclopedia of Social Sciences*, Vol. X, p. 241.
4. Herbert Spencer, *Principles of Psychology*, Vol. I, p. 496. Quoted by John Hughlings Jackson, *Selected Writings*, Hodder & Stoughton, London, 1931, p. 189.
5. C. Judson Herrick, *op. cit.*, pp. 75–76.

The Continuing, Recurrent Disintegration and Reintegration of Action, Awareness, and "I." The Fitting Together of Fits.

THE INTEGRATING TRANCE

The purpose of rhythm, it has always seemed to me, is to prolong the moment of contemplation, the moment when we are both asleep and awake, which is the one moment of creation, by hushing us with an alluring monotony, while it holds us waking by variety, to keep us in that state of perhaps real trance in which the mind liberated from the pressure of the will is unfolded in symbols.

—WILLIAM BUTLER YEATS[1]

Thanks to the protection of the highest sensory centres by the lowest sensory centres (which are "resisting positions" as well as "reservoirs of energy"), the highest sensory centres can energise uninterfered with by the environment. . . . There can be activities limited to the highest links of the great sensori-motor chain. . . .

Thanks to the "protections" spoken of, there occurs internal evolution in our highest centres; we can have combinations never actually experienced . . . as, indeed, we obviously must have when dreaming, and certainly have, too, during much of our waking lives. . . .

We acquire numerous different ideas: that is to say, there is, on the physical side, an organisation of many different nervous arrangements of our highest centres during actual converse with the environment.

When, as in sleep, and in "reflection," this actual converse ceases, the quasi-spontaneous slight activity of the highest sensory centres is uninterfered with by the environment . . . the nervous arrangements of the highest centres, or some elements of them, are "left to fight it out among themselves"; new combinations arise. . . ."

—JOHN HUGHLINGS JACKSON[2]

Great figures in history bring about very fundamental changes. These profound changes . . . are only the extreme expression of the sort of changes that take place steadily through reactions which are not simply those of a "me" but of an "I" . . . the ego or "I" that is responsible for changes of that sort appears in experience only after its reaction has taken place. It is only after we have said the word we are saying that we recognize ourselves as the person who has said it . . . this something that we are continually bringing in and adding to is what we identify with the self that comes into the level of our experience only in the completion of the act. . . .

We can state what is going to happen and take responsibility for the thing we are going to do, and yet the real self that appears in that act awaits the completion of the act itself. . . . It is that "I" which we may be said to be continually trying to realize, and to realize through the actual conduct itself.

—GEORGE HERBERT MEAD[3]

The cumulative and instantaneously total effect of these three citations—the incantatory effect of an unfolding series of ideas; the noetic-poetic tensions within the quotations, between the ideas, and behind the words; and the mind-stretching in contemplation of the whole all-at-once—may bemuse the reader, induce a real "open-mindedness," and encourage a relaxedly excited playfulness toward words and ideas—all of which is a sample of what is meant by "integrating trance."

In a small way, this experience models the processes (of focusing attention and dilating awareness) by which understanding the concept of fit was sought in scrutiny and contemplation of the universe of fits in Part Two. In a larger way, contemplating these citations is an expanded "pause for thought," i.e., a still reaction and pregnant interval. The hypnoidal qualities of this biological reaction, critical moment, and psychophysiological state—the trancelike aspects of the still-interval-trance as a moment of fitting together, of seeking and "seeing" real and fanciful solutions for crisis-induced discontinuities in living—concern us now.

As an extraordinary mode and moment of seeing and doing, the still-interval-trance must inevitably acquire hypnoidal qualities *exactly because the dysjunctive pause-impasse constitutes a failure in ordinary logical and intuitive thinking.* Such a crisis in the ordinary thinking that supervises the continuity of everyday activity necessarily calls for a crisis-resolving leap to a more effective kind of thinking—a transpersonal, hyperlogical, direct "seeing" that comprises a creative step forward into clairvoyance, and an atavistic falling back upon empathic perception and other biological capacities for surviving in emergencies. The triune still-interval-trance adds another mode, one of spontaneous unthinking-thinking, to thinking by logic and intuition.

The concept is not entirely new; many of its elements have been derived from discussions by others of such matters as the two-way traffic between the unconscious and conscious, the relation between incremental learning and sudden flashes of insight, and, in general, the various alleged dichotomies between slow, stepwise progressions and sudden, step-skipping leaps in various modes of knowing, feeling, and doing.

"Integrating trance" as a concept, however, is not simply offered as a solution for the problems of learning vs. insight, of conscious volition vs. involuntary instinct, or any other versions of the mind-body problem. Instead it grew out of a search for the "real" problem—a problem that is unseen, at least unclearly seen, by those concerned with the mind-body dichotomy. For all the various solutions of this problem are necessarily substitutive pseudo solutions because the problem itself is substitutive—it has no "real" existence outside the minds of those preoccupied with it. It can have no solution when it is posed in terms of "mind" and "body"—it must be approached in terms of "minding" and "bodying."

The real problem has always been the relation between continuity and discontinuity—and this is not between the "mind" and "body" but between "mind-body" as a unity and "mind-and-body" as diversity. This relation presents a psychological version of Zeno's paradox about the static and flowing qualities of motion. In human terms, this is sometimes seen as the relation between knowing and doing, between thought and action.

Here, too, the problem is more effectively conceived as one of the relation between "thinking-doing" and "thought-and-action" in their unity and diversity. Our contemporary awareness of the supposed separateness between thought and action ("Them as can do, them as can't teach," etc.) obscures an older recognition of the essential unity of awareness and action. The "participant consciousness" (now obscured by the contemporary "observer consciousness" of the post-Gutenberg era) made no great distinction between knowing as represented by the Scotch *ken* and doing as embodied in the Teutonic root *kan*. We are now, to some extent, healing this breach by such terms as "know-how" and "can-do." In life, if not in our ideology, the breach is closed in the still-interval-trance.

For many years, knowing and doing were conceived as functions of separate sensory and motor nerve trunks and brain centers. In keeping with early twentieth-century emphasis on localization of functions within the brain (a kind of scientific phrenology), great emphasis in physiological work and thought was given to mapping areas in which various sensory and motor functions were thought to be sharply separated and highly localized. But refinements of surgical and electronic technique soon allowed delicate explorations of nervous structures and functions and soon sensorimotor processes were no longer seen as sharply separated and localized. For example, it was long an item of neurophysiological doctrine that the functions of speech were confined to a highly limited "speech area." But neurological, psychological, and linguistic evidence now suggests that the act of selecting one word can involve the entire anterior cerebral cortex. Recent recognition of the intermingling of "sensory" and "motor" structure and function counsels a return to older ideas of the unity of thinking and doing expressed in the pre-Gutenberg language of an era of "participant observation" and "participating consciousness." Such a reunification would be consistent with the neurophysiological fact that, whatever "we" are knowing, feeling, and doing, the unified basis for all these behavings and experiencings is the electrophysiological nerve impulse. This traveling "wave particle" of electrical activity is at the bottom of all brain-mind operations. The nerve impulses that subsume sensation and motion, cerebration and mentation, are all the same; there are only different patterns of them in cerebral time-space.

Thus the real problem of the relations-between-relations (i.e., of thinking-doing to thought-and-action) is what goes on in the "region behind words" where contradictions and ambiguities are woven into unities and diversities, and into unities-in-diversity, etc. And this noetic problem turns out to be the same poetic problem posed by philosophers of creative action and awareness. As posed by Viereck,[4] it is how we pass beyond "reading between the lines" to "reading between the betweens." It is the problem of the differences and similarities in the relation between these two quotations: "What happens to all the experiences we have had and the things that we have done that we remember so clearly some of them and not so clearly others?" and "Where are the snows of yesteryear?"

Diverse theoretical problems of continuity-discontinuity have their base in the problem of continuity and discontinuity in the brain itself. As a student of Dr. George W. Bartelmez in the Department of Anatomy at the University of Chicago, and of Dr. Ralph W. Gerard in the Department of Physiology, I spent many hours peering through microscopes at the synaptic junctions between brain cells. These junctions are structural discontinuities and functional continuities which both delay and pass on nerve impulses from one brain cell to another. I spent many days wondering about how these synaptic discontinuity-continuities at one time allowed the brain to function as a single large harmonic whole, synchronizing its billions of units into the massive chords of muscle action seen in a major convulsive fit, and speculating how they could at other times integrate, by the most delicate timing of millions of nerve-cell discharges, the intricate sequential sensorimotor complexities of a Bach fugue. For whether the brain, or significant parts of it, functioned all-at-once or in elaborate temporal sequences depended upon the fact, and the pattern, of delay by and at synaptic junction-disjunctions between nerve cells transmitting patterned bits of nerve impulses. And it is from the patterns in time-space of nerve impulses that patterns of information and meaning, of awareness and action, are made.

Patterns of living are configurations in space and courses in time. We move through organism-environment time-space by moving in time to change our place and postural configuration in the environment, and vice versa. Our flip-flops between behavioral configurations and courses are, no doubt, based upon flip-flops in the brain between spatial patterns of nerve-cell electrical charges and temporal patterns of nerve-cell discharges. A temporal train of nerve impulses can be switched to arrive at a series of single receptor nerve cells so that the "train" is transformed into a spatial arrangement with one car at each receiving station. And in the reverse way, a spatial arrangement can be discharged sequentially to become a pattern in time. These transformations are made possible by the fact of synaptic continuity and discontinuity, by synaptic delay or expediting.

From such transformations it is but a step conceptually (though it involves many steps of neuronation, cerebration, and mentation) to transformations between "mind-body" and "mind-and-body," "psychophysiological" and "psychology-and-physiology," "consciously intended" to-and-from "unconsciously-reflexively-instinctively," and so on. For the still-interval-trance of everyday living, as a process-moment-state analogous to and derived from the electrophysiological phenomenon of synaptic continuity-discontinuity within the brain, is the moment of such transformations. Making the leap from one concept to the other has been my personal way of dealing with the perplexities of the mind-body problems and its congeners; it is a way that uses a combination of both avoidance and approach. This way was opened up by my studies with Dr. Douglas N. Buchanan, in the University of Chicago clinics, of the fittingness of fits in the circumstances in which they occurred. For Dr. Buchanan believed with Hughlings Jackson that no matter how odd fit-behavior may seem as behavior, it is nevertheless behavior, and must involve the same processes as any other. Suggestions in the work and thought of many investigators (especially Drs. Jules Masserman, Ives C. Hendricks, Frank Fremont-Smith, and Harry Stack Sullivan) that the key to the mystery of fits lay in analysis of the aura, of the uncanny moment at the transition from prefit to fit behavior, lighted the rest of the way.

"Integrating trance" is both dynamically and descriptively more inclusive than Yeats's "moment of contemplation" or "waking trance." It also is more time-located than Harold Rugg's "off-conscious thinking" or "transliminal mind." Arthur Koestler's *reculer pour mieux sauter,* a Darwin-Byrne-Wolff biological protective "still reaction pattern of offense and defense," and Herrick's "pregnant interval" have time-situation references, but they have other limitations. Integrating trance locates the genesis of all fits, of convulsing or creating, in the strivings of the organism-individual-person and in failures of ordinary minding to achieve goals; it identifies the mythical cave of oracular clairvoyance, removes it from the zealous and jealous monopoly of self-appointed custodians of the sacred, and makes it common property of everyone to use in moments of secularized "all-seeingness." It goes on to unify body and mind by conjoining bodily instinctive "drives" of tension-reducing behavior with suprapersonal teleological pulls educing goal-directed action toward ideal-ends-not-as-yet-accomplished. It does this by conceiving a larger moment of fusion, the still-interval-trance, in which biological appetitive-consummatory "purposive automatisms" and "consciously intended" behavior are merged and transformed by a "letting-go" of biological-environment push-pull and personal volition. All these marvelous things happen in an indeterminate psychophysiological "instant" of organism-environment integrational time. This time-process-state is a dysjunctive discontinuity-continuity in living—a fundamental, necessary operational unit of behavior and experience.

These multitudinous, mundane, and magical moments seem to be the reaction-process-condition in which all dreams of action are dreamed, all lovely and ludicrous schemes are schemed, and all fancies bred. Their almost miraculous fittings-together arise from the truly uncanny characteristics of confrontations with the unthinkable. The failure of ongoing integrative function to avoid, or deal successfully with, a crisis leaves an integrative vacuum— an urgent but empty "intention to say or do." To fill the vacuum with form and content, attention goes free-ranging in search of a useful organizing clue; awareness opens wide, ready to provide a frame of reference for interpreting any possible grain of truth spotted by attention. With attention tightly focused for fine scanning, and with awareness freed from any single point of reference, the line between conscious and unconscious, the boundary between self and circumstance, and the border between here-and-now and not-here, not-now are all tenuous and blurred. These qualities of a critical pause for thought are exactly those of the hypnoidal state, a state supposedly reached only by suggestible people, on special occasions, by special methods. The data already presented in Parts Two and Three reveal, however, that in the everyday still-interval-trance one sees to a greater or lesser extent the same weakening of the constraints of rigid verbal concepts and mental "sets," the same utilization of "somnambulistic" modes of seeing and doing, and the same transcending of conventional limitations on action and awareness as in any of the usually described instances of bemusement, entrancement, and hypnosis associated with magical, religious, or naturalistic processes and situations for hypnoidally accumulating, organizing, and discharging tension.

Because a large part of our everyday living consists of "pauses for thought" and "intentions to say or do," i.e., of brief still-interval-trances, we must conclude that the integrating trance is an everyday marvel. It is a magical moment in prosaic affairs, but its origins are the prosaic ones of striving to continue crisis-disrupted action, to get on with the business of living. It is not, however much it might seem to be, an intrusion of the supernatural into the ordinary. Rather, it is the other way around—the dramatic hypnoidal trances of theatrical entertainments, in bizarre mental illness, and of both popular and scientific interest are only exaggerated forms of this most fundamental everyday event.

Notes

1. William Butler Yeats, "The Symbolism of Poetry," in *Essays and Introductions*. Macmillan, New York, 1961, p. 159.
2. John Hughlings Jackson, *Selected Writings*, edited by James Taylor. Hodder & Stoughton, London, 1931; Basic Books, New York, 1958, Vol. I, p. 375.
3. George Herbert Mead, *Mind, Self, and Society*, edited by Charles W. Morris. University of Chicago Press, 1934.
4. Peter Viereck, "Russia's Conspiracy of Feelings." *Mount Holyoke Alumnae Quarterly*, XLIX, 144 (fall 1965).

THE STILL-INTERVAL-TRANCE 44

. . . To deny that artistic creation involves problems and purposes would be to admit that an artist creates without premeditation, without design, under a spell. Therefore if an artist boasted to me of having written a story without a previously settled design, but by inspiration, I should call him a lunatic.

—ANTON CHEKHOV[1]

I can aver that all the poetry that I have written which I continue to regard as authentic poetry was written immediately, instantaneously, in a condition of trance.

—HERBERT READ[2]

Action is the product of the qualities inherent in nature. It is only the ignorant man who, misled by personal egotism, says, "I am the doer."

—THE BHAGAVAD-GITA[3]

Byrne concluded that in man the still reaction is manifested primarily on the psychic level of organism-environment integration. He believed there were three levels of still reaction and still outcomes. The lowest level, evoked when any action was blocked, centered upon death-feigning and symbolic-static fight or flight. An intermediate level, evoked by chronic and acute threats, eventuated in sleep and various patterns of "pseudo-death-feigning" and "avoidance" and "approach" maneuvers. On the highest psychic level came all the multitudinous fits and starts that comprise human reactions to surprise and perplexity.

In man the still reaction is manifested in stage fright and other anticipatory experiences of entertainers, athletes, and ordinary persons. In some of these, tension dominates the picture; in others there is excessive relaxation, yawning, and even sleep. Any prolonged or intensive arrest of the ongoing is, *ipso facto*, trancelike, and man's entranced behavior reflects both personal and situational influences. His entrancement also effects the resolution of the crisis that brought it about.

The still-interval-trance has been discussed in terms of the form, dynamics, and significance of the pregnant interval; now it can be considered in terms of its inner content and processes. It is the moment of "psychical" change, postulated by Spencer and Mead; it is also the interval in which the fitting-together capacity consolidates and extends its abilities. A survey of the processes that go on in the pregnant still-trance will give substance to our concepts for unifying the "psychical" and the "neuronal."

The ordinary pause for thought is a good place to begin exploration of the psychophysiological processes of the still-interval-trance. Fitting thought, words, and gestures into communication requires matching sound and sense, syntax and grammar, and selecting words which have the "fittest" center and circumference of reference. In addition to these complex operations, the fitting together of the intended utterance must also surround whatever is actually said with signs of the sayer's attitude and intention-in-general. "Saying something" is far from a simple operation, and repeated pregnant pauses are necessary to get it done.

Stating even a simple proposition is a two-sided operation, as Hughlings Jackson noted:

> It is not enough to say that speech consists of words. It consists of words referring to one another in a particular manner; and without a proper inter-relation of its parts a verbal utterance would be a mere succession of names embodying no propositions. . . . Now, a proposition is not—that is to say in its effect upon us is not—a *mere* sequence. When we apprehend a proposition, a relation between two things is given to us. . . . We receive in a *two-fold* manner, not the words only, but the order of the words also.
>
> *Within the speaker's mind, the complete process must correspond to this double gift* [emphasis added]. There is (internally) something like a reduction of (apparent) relations of sequence to relations of co-existence (i.e., alternate sequence) of the *two* terms of a proposition.[4]

Here Jackson, in describing the dynamics of noetic propositions, foreshadows, in neurophysiological terms, discussions of poetic communication couched in terms of inducing in the reader the poet's own tensional experience of the relation between words and images, and evoking in the reader a model of the creative effort by which these relations were experienced by the author in the first place. Jackson's formulation is also most pertinent to understanding direct, empathic communication from one brain-mind-person to another; it provides a neurological basis for "imprinting," "imitative," and other mysterious effects believed by some researchers, including this author, to be involved in those phenomena discussed as "telepathy," "contagious spread of fits by imitation," and the more extraordinary varieties of "intuition" and "sensitivity."

Formulation and communication of propositions, mundanely noetic or marvelously poetic, proceeds by means of doubled processes in the minds of speaker and listener. Jackson used as example, "Gold is yellow." In this noetic proposition each of the two names interacts with and modifies the other in much the same way that poetic images and ideas interact. The two processes, noetic or poetic, are flickeringly and alternately associated and dissociated. But for this to happen some dissociation of the two simultaneous processes is necessary. And dissociated carrying on of two such independent processes uses the same operations as the dissociations observed in mental illness and in the trancelike states induced by hypnosis, drugs, and other psychedelic influences.

Clark Hull, a stimulus-response mechanist of the Pavlovian persuasion, once posed the problem thus: "Is the dissociation . . . of such a nature that two distinct intellectual processes may go on quite or nearly independent of each other?"[5] His own experiments, and his evaluation of those of others, made him dubious of the possibilities of genuine dissociation. To the problem of whether the left hand can operate without knowing what the right hand is doing, so to speak, hypnotists of the organic school answer yes. From studying the same material as Hull, Lawrence Cole, for example, drew the conclusion that "We are of two minds, not one. Or perhaps we should try to conceive of a hierarchy of systems, of levels beneath levels, with a top level where full awareness and capacity to verbalize give us an illusion of unity, integrity, and rationality that the study of hypnotic phenomena belies."[6]

The inherent dysjunctiveness of organism-environment integration was thoroughly explored in Part Three, and from the evidence presented there, and from Jackson's formulation of the dysjunctive unity-and-separateness of the two sides of a proposition, it would seem clear that neither the "conjunctive" nor the "disjunctive" school of thought is either entirely right or wrong. We do, indeed, have, and are of, "two minds" as Cole argues. But we are also at other times clearly "single-minded." And it is in still-interval-trances that dissociated processes can come together and complex associations can be dissociated for analysis and resynthesis. These discontinuities are necessary for "making up our minds" by unmaking and remaking. *And in the interplay of dissociation and association, still-intervals acquire their quasi-conscious and quasi-unconscious trancelike characteristics.*

Among the many things we repeatedly have to make up our minds about (for which we have to have repeated pregnant intervals) are the "right" words, propositions, and actions in particular situations. What is right, alas, is not always "right." For actual situations do not always jibe with our assumptions about the nature of the circumstances. The difference between what is right and what is "right" is rather like Byrne's distinction between avoidance and avoidance reactions—the truly right may be imprudent or dangerous. Hence many of our realistically "right" performances are substitutive, "as if" derivatives of the still reaction on Byrne's "psychic" level. John Holt, for example, in his studies of the defensive-offensive behavior of school children observed that in recovering from their "stunned" reaction to difficult questions posed by teachers, school children very often seek a socially approved "right" answer even if they know it is actually wrong.[7]

Confusion about the relationships between "right" and right answers is one thing Holt finds most distressing about schools. When people are free to play with words, unconcerned with being examined, and with exam-passing "rightness," a word-hunting pregnant interval can be pleasant instead of frightening. The Zulu writer Lewis Nkosi describes this scene from his growing-up days in Africa: "I walked about the streets of the bustling noisy city . . . with new English words clicking like coins in the pockets of my mind; I tried them out on each passing scene, relishing their power to describe and apprehend experience. I used words to delineate faces I saw in the streets and through them I evoked the luminous figures from the closed world of the imagination."[8]

But in using words to evoke images from "the closed world of the imagination," Nkosi was entering the region behind words where play the flamelike, flickering transformations of association-dissociation, and the nervous arrangements which subsume these generators of thoughts, words, and images. In this nonverbal, subverbal, subnoetic and subpoetic world of Viereck's "between the betweens,"[9] Nkosi was no longer playing with words; he was entrancedly watching his fitting-together capacity play with neurophysiological "atoms" from which words and ideas are made into images. From there come Nkosi's "luminous figures," Marvin's "whishit." Villon's "Where are the snows of yesteryear?" and "E = MC². " For this is the process common to all fitting together of fits; it is the fundamental function of the pregnant interval, and the source of its dreaming and other hypnoidal features.

Just as one is not likely to notice at first, in Nkosi's account, the transition from playing with words to reverie and entrancement with "luminous figures," so one is unlikely to notice the frequent moments of reverie that make up much of everyday "thinking." Sullivan called attention to this often overlooked fact of life, and to its nonverbal processes: ". . . a great deal of covert living—living that is not objectively observable but only inferrable—can go on without the use of words. The brute fact is, as I see it, that most of living goes on that way. . . ."[10] It seems evident that searching for words and actions suitable for the moment must go on in the region behind words, and that the trancelike pause in which these processes go on will vary with the success of the hunting.

When we cannot find a word for a thing or an event, our experience of it is incomplete; we cannot think about it as a "real" phenomenon without a defining center of relevance or circumference of reference. We may notice it but we cannot conceptualize it without giving it a name. On the other hand, words may become almost empty of meaning through overuse—as when in an acute form we experience this by saying a word over and over. William Burroughs believes that all too many words become images of words and no longer represent the "thingness" of reality. He uses "permutation points"—suggested to him, he says, by Brion Gysin—or what he calls "intersections" to refresh the impact of words and propositions by use of their coincidental and other nonlogical fittings together. Burroughs, like Baudelaire, is using the processes of the integrating trance.

When the right or "right" word fails to come to us (or we fail to find it because we can't conceive it, or it has lost meaning for us), we can be stuck in an "intention to say" (or in similar circumstances with an "intention to do"). Then we find ourselves truly at a loss for words (or action). Then the psychophysiological processes of fitting together, in the ensuing still-interval-trance, may transform into metaphor the directly inexpressible relation between subverbal nervous arrangments. For as Susanne Langer says, "In a genuine metaphor, an image of the literal meaning is our symbol for the figurative meaning, the thing that has no name of its own."[11] Or as Walter Lippmann said years ago, ". . . lacking words, we use images and build up pictures in our heads."[12]

When we are at a loss for words, or for images of postures and performances with which to lead our thought and action, sub-verbal and submotor fitting of the nervous "atoms" of image-ing may shift to other fields of imagination by what Peter McKellar calls synesthetic shift.[13] Instead of "seeing," we may experience an odor or hear a voice, which may or may not then lead to a resumption of seeing. Any momentarily unthinkable situation may also be described as "pointless," and there are various modes by which the fitting-together capacity may try to "see" or otherwise "get the point." Burroughs' "intersections" and "permutation points" may be thought of as efforts to find or to make sense of otherwise "pointless" configurations in a "pointless" world situation or mo-ment in history. And we, too, use similar devices; both "ours" and "his" may seem alien to "us," but that is because these "uncanny" processes go on in "I"-dissolving, trancelike conditions.

In his studies of thinking during drug-induced states of dis-sociation, Peter McKellar observed a progressive shift from per-sonal through egocentric to autistic modes of symbolization and metaphor.[14] Increasing concretization and simplification produced "silly" ideas and obscurely pointed jokes very much like those noted in schizophrenic and autistic thinking by Arieti.[15] For in-stance, dissociation may educe new relations by substituting predicates for unrelated subjects. Thus, "John Doe was born in the United States" and "The President is a person who was born in the United States" are seen to mean "John Doe is President" because identity of the predicates (born in the United States) seems to validate identity of the subjects. But this is not merely dissocia-tion—it is dissociation interacting with association. And in a pregnant interval, the processes of matching "it is so" against "it is as though," and of "seeing" with "believing," may thereby go astray. "Is as if" may be taken as "is"; we may see what we believe or believe what we see. And when contradiction and ambiguity prevent a leading element from guiding elaboration of awareness and action, the content of consciousness may become a polyphony of multitudinously swarming ideas, impulses, and images.

Of this Wilhelm Stekel, a pioneer explorer of compulsion and doubt, said, "I picture thinking as a stream of which only the sur-face is visible; orchestral music of which only the melody is audi-ble." "What we are after," said Stekel, "lies in the middle voices or even in the counterpoint."[16] But without an organizing, leading center of awareness or action, what we often have is a disorganized swirling of "atomic" particles of ideas, images, and impulses, and to make even autistic sense and action by any one process like metaphor-making or predicate-pairing is impossible. To deal with a situation overloaded with information but empty of organized meaning, a real shake-up is required.

In his study of imagination, Harold Rugg discusses the processes of "shaking up," and of selecting likely new combinations so produced.[17] He cites Jacques Hadamard's coupling of Max Müller's nineteenth-century observation (that the Latin verb "cogito," *I think*, derives etymologically from *to shake together*) with St. Augustine's fourth-century observation (that "intelligo" comes from *to select among*). Rugg and Lawrence Kubie hold that these two operations of shaking up and then selecting take place in two separate zones of consciousness; cogitation goes on in a preconscious, selecting newly created patterns of action and awareness takes place in a conscious phase. Arthur Koestler believes that the two-sidedness of this creative process is responsible for the controversy about whether creativeness involves mostly perspiration and some inspiration or is almost entirely spontaneous. But whereas Rugg, Kubie, and McKellar see all creative fitting together as requiring two phases of consciousness, Koestler sees a spectrum at one end of which are discoveries "due to more or less conscious, logical reasoning, and at the other end sudden insights which seem to emerge spontaneously from the depth of the unconscious."[18] Controversy between the "perspiration" and "inspiration" schools of creativity seems to me to be at heart a controversy about responsibility for behavior and where to place it—in person, circumstance, body, mind, etc. This "problem" (like those of consciousness vs. unconsciousness, voluntary vs. involuntary, hysteria and epilepsy, and so on ad infinitum) is a matter of both and neither. Either active or passive minding can culminate in a still-interval-trance. And in this magical moment all these different things and processes are repeatedly unified and separated. The duration, concomitants, and other characteristics of the still-interval-trance may or may not call attention to its critical nature as a unique time-place-process where responsibility and irresponsibility, consciousness and unconsciousness, and perspiration and inspiration are repeatedly conjoined and disjoined. *But whether it is noticed or not, studied or not, this is the temporal meeting place where all the processes of fit and wit diverge and reconverge.*

Whatever the intensity of intention, and the level of consciousness, in "dreaming up" great creative activities, the dreaming up is produced by quasi spontaneity in the highest neurophysiological centers and the psychological processes directing attention. But the unusual quality of these physiopsychological processes lies not alone in the unusual qualities of creative persons but derives from the peculiar nature of the moment of creation. For the moment of fitting together, and whatever is fitted together during it, is, in its form, no different from the moment of crisis in everyone's everyday living. The still-interval-trance is the source from which flows all convulsive, conventional, and creative behavior. How this flow is organized requires some further consideration.

Koestler uses "thinking aside" to denote a shift of attention to a previously ignored element in a situation, or to one now hovering on the fringes of awareness. Rugg uses "off-conscious thinking" to describe the same process. Whence come the suddenly attended things whose recognition leads the way to fitting together of a fit—of a more or less fitting solution? What makes attention suddenly turn to them? Is there some intrinsic attraction that "draws" creating attention to them? Or is there some kind of "hunger for creating" that "directs" attention to them? These questions are important ones, for, as Koestler says, all great innovations require sudden shifts of attention and emphasis onto some previously neglected aspect of experience. And, we should add, any innovation, even the slightest change in our habitual ways of doing and seeing that mark the small leaps forward we make in our living, involves exactly the same processes.

Evidences of spontaneity in creative and ordinary living suggest that noticing, naming, and thinking about the previously unthinkable, by shifting attention to some transforming item or quality, have to do with the time at which they happen. "The time was ripe for it," as it were. But noticing the time element has failed to lead enough people to thinking accurately about it. Attention to time shifts all too easily back again to accustomed concerns with "circumstance" (time as conditions prevailing externally) or to the "intentions" of the person (time as conditions prevailing internally).

But the ripeness of the moment of fitting together also has much to do with its unique qualities as a moment in time. These derive from the peculiar quality noticed by James in his "intention to say" and by Jackson in his "intention to do." The fullness-in-potential, but emptiness-in-actuality, of the still-interval produces not only its hypnoidal openness but also its trancelike ripeness for anything. The outcome of the moment of fitting together, therefore, may be shaped by the ripeness of personal intention and contextual conditions, but that there can be any outcome at all depends upon the ripeness of the trancelike vision of the relation between the here-and-now and the not-here, not-now. That is, the ripeness of the "central apparatus of adjustment" is also involved. In this moment, it is the interaction of intention, circumstance, and readiness of the fitting-together capacity that determines whether the outcome is cliché, creative, or convulsive. And the pertinent frame of reference for this interaction is what can only be called the "commitment" of the individual to more general circumstances and to longer-term intentions.

For the enduring central commitment of the individual to these larger configurations, courses, and circumstances has much to do with what goes on in the interactions of limited immediate ones. A really critical crisis, therefore, occurs when an everyday one models and evokes decisions about the individual's larger commitment. The more a seemingly momentary crisis approaches a point of decision about commitment itself, the more fitting together of a solution for here-and-now tends to reorganize all the individual's not-heres and not-nows.

Thus it comes about that the commitment of the person, which allows us to describe him as "epileptic," "artistic," "neurotic," and so on, can itself be refitted when it can no longer stand above and contain the mode of interaction of present intentions and circumstances. But while it functions, by being a superior abstraction, an enduring intention to participate in certain circumstances for certain ends, it directs the interplay of conditions and intentions toward facilitating the style and purposes to which we are committed.

The higher the level of abstracting and the longer the term of our commitment, the greater the scope and freedom of the fitting-together activities. But since freedom is not too useful without a frame of reference and a focus of attention to shape activity, our most productive pregnant intervals will be those which are most critical—that is, the value of their outcome will depend upon mobilization of the formally free fitting-together capacity in the face of formally crucial problems. The most critical crisis, in short, presents us with the most formally exquisite balance of danger and opportunity. The maximum of peril and promise lies in those moments that pose a decision about the form of our commitment as a decision in the time-less now of an everyday still-interval-trance. And, to some extent, every still-interval is pregnant in just this way.

The work and thought of Professor A. R. Luria[19] in the Soviet

Union, and of psycholinguisticians throughout the world, on the temporal sequences of communicative and other behavior seem to support the psychobehavioristic speculations offered here. These speculations are given point by the opinions of Hughlings Jackson and the researches of Frieda Goldman-Eisler about the pauses that precede and give rise to bursts of speech and action. They are given substance by the observations[20] of Birdwhistell and other students of paralanguage on the fitting together of communicative utterances by both contradictory and complementary combinations of words and gestures. They can be documented further with relevant supporting data about the processes that go on in the pregnant interval.

Before considering these data, a final comment about commitment can serve as introduction. At one point in his discussion of the "creative flash," Rugg phrases what others concerned with the subject have said. "The history of science is packed with discoveries resulting from the precisely needed juxtaposition of events and the presence of a curious observer, whose mind is organized with tightly related concepts. Köhler's learning experiments on chimpanzees supplied examples of the facilitation of the flash [in chimpanzees] when favorable conditions of perception were juxtaposed."[21] Creative, crisis-resolving flashes can occur, that is, in monkey and man. And what I mean by commitment is so arranging one's life, or having it arranged for one by a fortunate fate, that one is more likely than not to be in the right time, at the right place, under the right circumstances, and equipped with the right information, ideas, and impulses.

Rugg goes on to cite Lawrence Cole's conclusions about Gestalt-closing interactions of elements and contexts. "Very slight transformations in the spatial arrangements transform a difficult problem to a soluble one . . . the perceived relationship is the essential factor."[22] Just as in a dissociated state perceived identity between two predicates can lead to a mistaken identity between two subjects, so in a learning situation crisis a perceived new relationship between two elements can lead to suddenly seeing the situation itself in a new light, and to a solution for a problem which had previously been, and in a logical sense still is, unthinkable. Unthinkable situations lead to unthinking-suddenly-seeing of unthinking-spontaneous-solutions. But, how is the "seeing," the perception of "perceived relationship" done? Is the "relationship" out there in the "real" environment only waiting for a ripe time to be seen? Or is it up here in the "model" of reality in nervous arrangements within the brain? This problem is most puzzling when we are thinking about relationships "right now" within the environment or the brain's models of it. Our thinking can become clearer if we recognize that what the brain sees is not "seen" through actual eye-ear perceptive apparatus but by inspection of its model of the environment with its "mind's eye." And that inspecting appraises the differences and similarities between at least two neuronal models, not of the environment, but of the total organism-environment interaction. The discrepancies between similar differences and different similarities are then checked by use of the perceptive apparatus to predict whether or not the gaps will be narrowed or widened by the ongoing course of events. But when "perceived relationships" are those between elements in the here-and-now and in past or future not-heres and not-nows, we have less trouble in seeing that the things related are located somewhere in the brain and its neuronal models of a historical temporal sequence of configurations of many here-and-nows.

From a career of studying the temporal organization of behavior, Karl Lashley concluded that anticipatory "running through" of alternatives would partially activate all the elements in an animal's behavioral repertory that were foreseen as of possible use. He also postulated that some of the neuronal devices so activated could scan others in what could be called an "as if," running-through evaluation of alternative solutions.[23] There are sound reasons to believe that the brain does have devices for appraising alternatives, and for abstracting from similar differences and different similarities novel and new patterns of seeing and doing. "Imagination," "thinking aside," and "off-conscious thinking" do occur, and these observed functions must have an anatomical and physiological basis, just as the pregnant interval in which they occur has a physiological basis in synaptic delay of neuronal transmission, and perhaps in the workings of the "activating reticular system." In current neurophysiological literature, many cybernetic circuits are described which can "see" and compare many relations.

John Livingston Lowes, who systematically studied Coleridge's creative activity as an example of creative process, has pertinent things to say about the problem of perceived relations and their transformations. He gives as an example what happened when he recalled a passage from Oliver Wendell Holmes's *Autocrat of the Breakfast-Table* thirty years after he had originally read it. The passage of Holmes's reads, "Put an idea into your intelligence and leave it there an hour, a day, a year, without ever having occasion to refer to it. When, at last, you return to it, you do not find it as it was when acquired. It has domiciliated itself, so to speak—become at home—entered into relations with your other thoughts, and integrated itself with the whole fabric of the mind."

When Lowes recalled this passage three decades later, it was remembered "as if" Holmes had described a plantlike growth spreading white tentacles like a plant growing under a stone or in the dark depths of a pool. When he checked this memory against the original passage, Lowes was astonished to find no such image had been described by Holmes. However, on reading further, Lowes did find that Holmes had elsewhere used, in an entirely different context, a growing-thing metaphor of uncanny life breeding beneath a stone. Lowes points out that his memory-image was a fusion of Holmes's verbal passage and figurative metaphor with something added by Lowes's own fitting together. The result was neither Holmes's nor Lowes's, but something new out of both.[24]

Were Holmes and Lowes contemporary neurochemists, they might have ideas about images breeding and spreading in the memory like viruses, to infect in time many different cells throughout the brain. Or they would be familiar with W. Grey Walter's conclusion that a perception is transmitted throughout the brain as a memorandum to whom it may concern, whenever it may concern them. There come to be many memoranda and many changes in relations between and within them. Sometimes, as in Lowes's example, the relationship is almost proportionate. Holmes's passage on the storage, generalization, and transformation of a memory is related to his metaphor about plants growing under a rock; this relation in turn is related to Lowes's image of Holmes's passage as being a spreading fungoid growth and that image's relation to something else born, Lowes says, in the "subliminal deep" of his mind or brain. This proportion could be written as $H_1 : H_2 :: L_1 : L_2$, with L_2 being the "x" with which students of creativity are concerned. How one solves for "x" depends usually on whether one is a neurologist or psychiatrist, a "mentalist" or "mechanist." These disparate calculations result in two different identities for "x," and in irreconcilable controversy. However, it would seem better to view the differences between them as the differences between "imagination" and "quasi-spontaneous activity of the higher centres"—and to see this difference as only that between two slightly different names for the same thing. "Imagination" and "cerebration" are two seemingly contradictory forms of the ambiguous unity "neuronation."

The same situation holds in the relationship between the "spontaneous" and the "looked for" perceptions of meaningful relations between hitherto unrelated things in the creative activity of artists, scientists, and everyday people. In discussing this problem, Arthur Koestler quotes and paraphrases one of N. R. F. Maier's experiments in stimulating "unconscious," inspired guidance of perception. "In one of Maier's ingenious experiments the problem set to the subject was to catch hold at the same time of two thin strings hung from the ceiling so wide apart that he could only get hold of one at a time. The only available tool was a pair of pliers. The solution is to tie the pliers to one string and set it in pendular motion." The crucial point of the experiment, however, is described as follows: "If the subject had not spontaneously solved the problem within *ten minutes,* Maier supplied him with a hint; he would accidentally brush against one of the strings, causing it to swing gently. Of those who solved the problem after this hint, the average interval between the hint and solution was only *forty-two seconds. . . .* Most of those subjects who solved the problem immediately after the hint *did so without any realization that they had been given one.* The idea of making a pendulum with pliers seemed to arise spontaneously. Here we have a beautifully ambiguous example of what looks like 'unconscious' guidance."[25]

It is also, because those who "saw" the answer immediately may truly not have perceived as such the implications of the hint provided by Maier, a beautifully ambiguous example of what looks like subliminal cuing, but might be coincidence. As Jan Ehrenwald concluded from his extensive studies of the relation between coincidence and clairvoyance, situations which most suggest spontaneous clairvoyant seeing are at the same time most suggestive of coincidence.[26] Situations that are ripe for one thing are often equally ripe for its supposed opposite. Ripeness is multipotentiality, and multipotentiality is ambiguous. A nonspecific stimulus may trigger a ripe situation into fruition.

Whether one gets a sudden insight from clairvoyance, intuition, or fortunate accident has much to do with whether one is committed to a given line of exploration and has been working at it enough to be entitled to a bit of luck, or is weary enough to deserve a bit of inspiration, i.e., with whether one is committed. But how one feels about it, what the moment of illumination is thought to be, probably depends upon one's "taste" in such matters.

Sudden flashes of "seeing" answers do resolve protracted struggles with problems; they do terminate paralyzing crises in seeing and doing that are centered upon contradictions and ambiguities resolved by the flashes of creative comprehension. It may be that contradiction and ambiguity can be resolved only by a process that is itself essentially ambiguous and contradictory. Poincaré, Coleridge, Lowes, and others who have thought about the matter try to make room for both the nonrational and rational by postulating a sequence of nonrational and logical operations. An ambiguous two-sided "one part perspiration, one part inspiration" configuration of creative being is transformed into a two-stage temporal course of creative doing. Rugg makes this temporal solving of a configurational problem explicit by postulating two phases in the act of creation—a mysterious phase of transliminal "seeing" followed by a logical stepwise filling in of the details of the envisioned temporal or spatial pattern.

But all such operations only transform the shape, not the quality, of the mystery. The fit of fitting together may be briefer by far than the fit of acting out the elaboration of the fitted together. What is acted out, or logically figured out, however, is contained, compressed in the almost instantaneous flash. And the mystery of the "flash" is itself intensified.

But however we approach the mystery, we sooner or later must come somewhere to "our wit's end." And the end, and beginning, of wit is in flickeringly kaleidoscopic rapid neuronal precogitational juggling of forms whose essential ambiguity occasionally resolves itself, at one time in sudden dramatic patterns that "shock" the fitting-together capacity into seeing them, and at another time in subtle suggestions from which the fitting-together capacity can build its own meaningful picture. Because our wit, rational or intuitive, cannot, any more than we can, envision its own conception very clearly, we can probably never know just how it is done. For just as the "I-that-was-trying-to-say-a-word" comes into our experience only as the "I-that-said-it," so the "thinking-that-was-thinking-up-a-thought" comes into existence only after "the-thought-is-thought," only after the thinking stops. At least this is the case when a crisis converts unified, integrated simultaneous seeing-thinking into a sequence of seeing-followed-by-thinking.

Rimbaud's "You should not say: I think. You should say: I am thought" is one answer to Descartes' "I think, therefore I am." It is a contrary answer and not the best one, but it leads to the proper answer by synthesis of the contradiction: "You should say: I *thought*, therefore I am." "I had a thought" is true only if one means also by that statement, "The thinking produced both I and the thought." "I was thinking" tends to refer to a crisis in which the both-and-neither neuronal-and-psychological cogitation and neuronal-psychological cogitation goes on. It can have only a certain dysjunctive validity, for in the ordinary sense, in a crisis, neither "I" nor "thinking" exists.

But if we cannot directly know what goes on and how, we can know something about "When," and from the time-conditions infer, as we have been doing, something about "How" and "What." Either too little or too much success in thinking verbally, by word-formation and word-organization, can put us at a loss for words and lead us into a crisis during which "impersonation" and "mentation" fall back on "cerebration" and "neuronation." When Walter Lippmann was at a loss for words, pictures came into his mind. When Lewis Nkosi was full of words, he began to see "luminous figures." One picture may or may not be worth a thousand words, but many pictures in the mind seem to precede and to be alternative preverbal substitutes for the word or words that cerebromentating cannot at the moment produce.

And how are these pictures produced? Probably from atomic wave-particles of subidea and subimage size and significance, i.e., of elements from which ideas, images, and impulses get put together. And how do these pieces of the picture puzzle come to the attention of the fitting-together capacity? Probably just as Housman's germinal fragments of poetic ideas came into his awareness accompanied by vague conceptions of the whole poem, as a frame of reference within which to assemble the parts. Between this "higher level" kind of assembly and that depicted by Grey Walter, in terms of sensorimotor data being projected throughout the brain as both "memoranda" and "propaganda," there is no doubt some middle ground and process, whatever its nature may turn out to be.

Poincaré put it this way: "How can we explain the fact that, of the thousand products of our unconscious activity [of the quasi-spontaneous activity of our highest centers], some are invited to cross the threshold, while others remain outside? Is it mere chance?"[27] To Poincaré, a swirl of Epicurean atoms of form filled space in all directions and "their mutual collisions may then produce new combinations." I gather that some of these combinations then go "nova," as it were, and radiate sufficient attraction to become "points of departure for calculations" in the "second period of conscious work which follows the inspiration." Poincaré's own long sequences of fits of seeing inspiring new combinations and fits of fitting them together have been described in Part Two. In form, his process was quite like that by which Housman made his poems. This sequence suggests that a germ of an idea or image comes into existence together with an incipient frame of reference for giving it more meaning.

I believe that in ordinary thinking there is a double-creation of thought and thinker to correspond with Jackson's double-natured propositions and the two-sidedness of proposing. The communicating of propositions, i.e., the duality ("gold is yellow") of the propositions, links a double-effect in the mind of the speaker with a similar responsive effect in the mind of the audience. In the same way, in thinking-in-a-crisis there is a double-creation of proto-idea and proto-frame-of-reference which makes for the same kind of oscillation between information and meaning as goes on at higher levels between memoranda and propaganda—between thought and thinker, speaker and hearer.

This oscillation, or vibration, goes on between all forms of contradiction and ambiguity and generates an "aura," or "field," of higher significance wherever it occurs. Thus, on the neuronal level it generates waves of meaning and particles of information. And from the interaction between one pair of oscillators and another pair, still other oscillators pick up vibrations and make even higher level information and meaning from similarities and differences. On the everyday level, oscillations between the contradictions and ambiguities of unified integrated thinking-doing and separated but interacting thinking-and-doing produce a spectrum of felt experience of living ranging from "Look, Ma! No hands!" to the panicky "I'm stuck" experience.

"Look, Ma! No hands!" is the experience of smooth-flowing continuity in living. But just as a boy on a bike cannot forever keep on in that mode, so continuity characterized by temporary unity of configuration and course, thinking and acting, self and circumstance, and all erstwhile syntheses and unities comes to an end by developing or encountering ambiguity out of unity, and contradiction out of ambiguity. Nkosi's flow of verbal thought gets bored with itself, the glow of word after word fades into repetitive noise, and has to be refreshed by dipping down into the "well" of Lowes and Coleridge—the region behind words. Lippmann's flow of words stops when the right or the "right" word fails to come, and his fitting together, too, dips down into the source spring of images.

So continuity, by the contradictory ways of "fullness" and "emptiness," breeds discontinuity. And in moments of discontinuity oscillations between various content-clothed forms of information and meaning give rise to new ambiguities and contradictions from which sense and sensible action must be made. We can see the "energy" of these generative oscillations as a spark whose light illumines its own surroundings or as a flicker between two seemingly separate lights. We can see the spark or the flicker as lighted or exhibited to us and our conscious by the unconscious or the subliminal ego. We can see them as being generated spontaneously from ignitible material collected in some storehouse of the brain-mind-person. Or we can think of the creative power and imagination as personified forces that go out looking for, and examining selectively and critically, a whole set of flickering sparks, shining in the region behind words, in the hope that one of these will-o'-the-wisps will prove to be a godsend.

But it seems most fruitful, and consistent with all of what we know, to conceive of the interaction between imagination and its objects as the interaction between the information-processing and the meaning-comprehending abilities of the brain's fitting-together capacity. It is also useful to see that our way of handling the tensional relationships of poetic all-at-once statements of dynamic-descriptive, simultaneous interrelations is to transform these static-dynamic configurational relations into temporal sequences by means of analysis, by spreading them out in time. This transforming of poetic into noetic in turn gives way to a succeeding poetic reunification, a synthesis which heals by transforming disjunction into dysjunction. So we are all, by turns, to some extent or another in content, and to a large degree in the form of our minding, both poetic and noetic. Some of us are more one than the other, at one time or another, but all of us are both-and-neither in a crisis in continuity of thinking, acting, and living. It is how we get out of the crisis that makes the difference.

John Livingston Lowes, who in hundreds of pages explored the processes of creation, was one of the few to see relatively clearly the true relation between creation of pieces of art and pieces of everyday living. He saw it in terms of how the noetic-poetic simultaneity of consciousness and unconsciousness, of imagination and object, of self and circumstance, was spread out in time. He spoke of "the thronged yet sleeping sub-liminal chambers; the summons which unlocks their secret doors; the pouring up of images linked in new conjunctions provocative of unexpected *aperçus;* the conscious seizing and directing to an end, of suggestions which the unconscious operations have supplied."[28] He went on to say that this process was "the stuff of which life weaves patterns on its loom" and "the ways of the creative faculty are the universal ways of that streaming yet consciously directed something which we know (or think we know) as life."

This chapter represents, in form and content, my own trance-like vision of what goes on in a still-interval-trance. It is trancelike because that is the qualitative effect of rhythmic oscillations between the ambiguities in the empty-fullness of the pregnant interval on which attention was centered, and the contradictory fullness in the ideas of others used as a frame of reference and meaning. With attention focused on the flickering events in the still-interval, and awareness wide open to shining hints in the referential context, we can have a poetic comprehension of what it all means. This set of poetically perceived relations has then to be unfolded in time with as much noetic, straightforward-moving, logical, Gutenbergish linear coherence as possible.

But since the thinking required in unrolling the "seen" content proceeded by leaping from ambiguity to contradiction, an aura of intuitional all-at-once meaning began, perhaps, to be generated as one went along. Tuning in with this aura of contextual total meaning requires using a kind of McLuhanish, tribal, Davy-Sullivan participant-consciousness resembling wide-open awareness. Thus the reader with attention fixed upon the linear incantatory hypnoidal sequence of words and ideas, beginning to develop his own tensional experience of his own double-minded apprehension of the dualities of the various propositions, is further entranced (pleasantly or unpleasantly, or something of both) by the expansion of his awareness to oceanic wide-openness to his own meanings. I know of no valid other way to confront the reader with the truth of the proposition that thinking in a crisis, experiencing a still-interval-trance, trembles on the brink between fits of convulsion and fits of creation.

The unity of epilepticity and creativity in formal sharing of episodicity, and the relationship of both to everyday living, it should now be apparent, lie in the relation between fits of condensation in fitting together and fits of expansion of the fitted together.

Notes

1. Anton Chekhov. Quoted by Brewster Ghiselin, ed., *The Creative Process*. University of California Press, 1952.
2. Herbert Read, *Collected Essays in Literary Criticism*. Faber, London. 1938.
3. The Bhagavad-Gita, written down in the Mahabharata by Vyasa, circa 500 B.C.
4. John Hughlings Jackson, *Selected Writings*, edited by James Taylor. Hodder & Stoughton, London, 1931; Basic Books, New York, 1958, Vol. II, p. 227.
5. Clark Hull, *Hypnosis and Suggestibility: An Experimental Approach*. Appleton-Century-Crofts, New York, 1933, p. 176.

6. Lawrence E. Cole, *Human Behavior: Psychology as a Bio-Social Science*. World Book Co., Yonkers, N.Y., 1953, p. 675.
7. John Holt, *How Children Fail*. Pitman, New York, 1964, pp. 32ff.
8. Lewis Nkosi, *Home and Exile*. Longmans, London, 1964.
9. Peter Viereck, "Russia's Conspiracy of Feelings." *Mount Holyoke Alumnae Quarterly*, XLIX (fall 1965).
10. Harry Stack Sullivan, *The Interpersonal Theory of Psychiatry*, edited by Helen Swick Perry and Mabel Blake Cohen. W. W. Norton, New York, 1953, p. 185.
11. Susanne Langer, quoted by Harold Rugg, *Imagination*. Harper & Row, New York, 1963, p. 285.
12. Walter Lippmann, quoted by Rugg, *ibid.*, p. 287.
13. Peter McKellar, *Imagination and Thinking*. Basic Books, New York, 1957.
14. *Ibid.*
15. Silvano Arieti, "Special Logic of Schizophrenia and Other Types of Autistic Thought." *Psychiatry*, XI, 325, 1948.
16. Wilhelm Stekel, "The Polyphony of Thought," in David Rapaport, *Organization and Pathology of Thought*. Columbia University Press, 1951, p. 313.
17. Harold Rugg, *op. cit.*
18. Arthur Koestler, *The Act of Creation*. Hutchinson, London, 1964, p. 120; Macmillan, New York, 1964.
19. A. R. Luria, *The Nature of Human Conflicts*, Liveright, New York, 1932; "Factors and Forms of Aphasia," in *Disorders of Language*, edited by A. V. S. Rueck and Maeve O'Connor, J. A. Churchill, London, 1964, p. 143.
20. Ray L. Birdwhistell, "Paralanguage: 25 Years After Sapir," in *Lectures on Experimental Psychiatry*, edited by Henry W. Brosin. University of Pittsburgh Press, 1961.
21. Harold Rugg, *op. cit.*, p. 13.
22. Lawrence E. Cole and William F. Bruce, *Educational Psychology*. World Book Co., Yonkers, N.Y., 1950, p. 469.
23. Karl Lashley, "The Problem of Serial Order in Behavior," in *Cerebral Mechanisms in Behavior*, edited by Lloyd A. Jeffress. John Wiley and Sons, New York, 1951, p. 136.
24. John Livingston Lowes, *The Road to Xanadu*. Houghton, Boston, 1927.
25. Arthur Koestler, *op. cit.*, quoting N. R. F. Maier from C. E. Osgood, *Method and Theory in Experimental Psychology*, Oxford University Press, 1960.
26. Jan Ehrenwald, *Telepathy and Medical Psychology*. W. W. Norton, New York, 1948; and personal communication.
27. Henri Poincaré, in Jacques Hadamard, *The Psychology of Invention in the Mathematical Field*. Dover Books, New York, 1945.
28. John Livingston Lowes, *op. cit.*, p. 431.

The Fitting Together of Living by Transformations of Contradictions in Mind-Body Patterns into Temporal Courses
of Minding and Doing.

TRANCES AND TRAJECTORIES 45

The basic problems of both science and philosophy from the earliest
times of which we have record stem from a very practical question.
What are the relationships between our bodily organization as mechanism in action and those mental capacities which seem to control the
actions of the body and to give man increasing control over his surroundings? . . . no one has succeeded in explaining how this control
is effected or the nature of the relationship between the world as we
know it in objective experience and the conscious life of the knower.
—C. JUDSON HERRICK[1]

In the quotation cited at the head of the previous chapter, Hughlings Jackson laid the conceptual basis for approaching an understanding of the highest or most central centers within the brain-
mind system and of how they might work, both autonomously and
in the service of immediate needs for adjustment of organism-
environment relations. Our understanding of the structure and
function of the "brains within the brain" has been deepened and
broadened by the arduous work and imaginative thought of many
men and women since Jackson.

In many ways, witting and unwitting, pursuit of central sources
within the brain—which can initiate, guide, and complete episodes
of mundane, conventional, and marvelous behavior and experience—takes on the character of a struggle of neurological science against metaphysics and superstition. For too many scientists
seem bent on finding a materialist equivalent with which to abolish
any yearning for an idealist soul as the source of inspired possession manifested in fits of both convulsion and creation. But such
scientific people overlook the ease with which even an amateur
theologian could remark, upon witnessing the demonstration of the
soul's material equivalent, "But how marvelous the ways of God to
so endow man with such a structural embodiment of the spirit, to
give him the very means for formulating 'the word.'" Hence, re-

cently, under the specific influence of cybernetics and the general nature of the times, sophisticated investigators have abandoned stimulus-response concepts. Instead of viewing the brain's centers as a passive switchboard integrating sensorimotor input and output, they now stress the cybernetic possibilities for autonomy, spontaneity, and creativity in the highest centers.

Though we now see some of our behavior and experience as being goal-directed, in the service of the organism-individual-person complex, too much attention, perhaps, is still paid to drives originating in the physicochemical nature of the organism. Great consideration is given to the push-pull upon the person that derives from his sociocultural endowment and experience. Spontaneous thought and action are orphans in the home of science. Much of our trouble in dealing with the "center" of organism-environment interaction has arisen from thinking about it in terms of the so-called mind-body problem. The senses of touch and position, of vision and hearing, and other perceptions of immediate and remote boundaries between self and circumstances provide information on zones of interaction. The actual "point of interaction" is thought of as a diffuse area or function within the brain by which intraorganismic and extraorganismic events are interwoven. But this enchanted loom of Sherrington's has been automated; it has become self-propelled and self-guided by conjuring up an entranced weaver who springs into action when it gets in trouble and occupies himself with his own fantasies when things go smoothly. If we are not to repeat old errors by personifying the entranced weaver as a *deus* or *demoniacus ex machina*—an embodiment of the divine or devilish influences which occasionally possess us—we must examine how, when, and why the human brain has dreamed up a personification of the fitting-together capacity of its highest centers and endowed that "self" or "I" with illusions of individuality and initiative in its "own" affairs and launched it in pursuit of relative, if not absolute, omniscience and omnipotence. And in this examination, it will be well to bear in mind that our concepts of the "brain" are only barely more substantial and well founded than our concepts of the "person."

In utmost centers of integration, brain and mind and person flicker in and out of a triune unity and separateness as a brain-mind-person system in the middle of a larger system of physico-chemical transformations, organismic structure, individual action, and sociopersonal intentions. Now opposed, then united, man's nature and nurture coerce and cajole him onward in space and forward in time, while his memory is constantly taking him back to his origins.

And where is this time-space traveler going? We cannot say. We can only say something about how he goes upon his journey. He does it by continually, if intermittently, unraveling his story by analysis and weaving it together again by synthesis. He is guided by a fitting-together capacity which superintends his traveling and formulates a series of myths about the meaning of his journeying. And this fitting together, reflecting his nature and nurture, uses conflict between and unity of patterns of interneuronal relations to chart courses in his highest centers of being and doing. But his course is a thing of fits and starts because, as Patrick Corbett says:

> Man cannot stand still, and cannot, indefinitely, repeat himself. He has to break the crust of every custom that he lays upon the surface of his life, then lay another one instead of it, and then begin again. Why is that so? Why is it that this special system we call "man" can only keep its balance by means of successive innovations? We do not know; we have only glimmerings of insight into the nature of the problem. . . . Meanwhile, taking respectful but cautious note of the speculations we are offered from the first chapter of Genesis to the early works of Marx, we must simply take it as a fact that man is an animal that has to make things new in order to survive. . . . Words are the linguistic instruments of innovation . . . judgments of value . . . are the linguistic forms in which we commit ourselves at one moment in order to be able to challenge that commitment at the next . . . the sagacious man . . . even in the creative moment . . . realizes that consolidation has to follow; and that, even in the thick of success-ful consolidation, or in the depths of failure, he hankers for the novel theme to come.[2]

Man does indeed have to "make things new in order to survive" and go about his journey from the not-here, not-now of his past to that of his future. But beyond all his innovations in the arts and sciences, and in organizing a new relation between him and his environment, perhaps his greatest act of creation was transforming himself into a "thinking reed." For by inventing "I," man gave him-self a mind's eye with which he can look into the inmost secrets of the atom as master, or raise his dusty vision and greet the stars as equal.

But in truth, man did not invent his "I"; it was done for him by the unresting cells in the brain of some remote prehuman ancestor suddenly seeing himself from the viewpoint of another. And thus it is that man's most precious possession other than life itself, his very identity as "I," came, and still comes to him, only when he leapingly transcends his own isolation. He knows himself in actions and awareness that take him out of himself. But he also tires occasionally from the strain of continually creating episodes of knowing, being, and doing. He yearns for tranquil contemplation of what he has done and might yet do. He says, "I want to enjoy myself" because he has a self as well as an "I," and:

> The self is the content of consciousness at all times when one is thoroughly comfortable about one's self-respect, the prestige that one enjoys among one's fellows, and the respect and deference which they pay one. Under these estimable circumstances there is no anxiety; the self is the whole works. . . .[3]

But even in the thick of such successful consolidations of his self, man knows that being troubled will come. For he senses a nonhomeostatic urging on that rises from his basic nature as "a thing of watery salts held in cohesion by unresting cells." For at the very moment that his expansive self tells its self, "I am content," attention fastens upon some aspect of the situation, awareness begins to close around the focus, unconsciousness overspreads the rest, and "I," coming into existence by recognizing contentment, ends it by confronting its now slightly altered self with the eternal question, "What's going on here?"

Whatever our state of inaction or mode of action, this basic question is never far away. For our unresting cells act as if they had a mind of their own because, "Something akin to the mental as we experience it may be a common property of all living things and even of the cosmos as a whole, as some suppose."[4]

And hence, even in the most blissful self-absorption, in the most tranquil circumstance, or in the most smooth-flowing action, perhaps especially in these conditions, the "mind" of the cosmos or of our living cells prods us with the question and stirs us into questioning. And in the same way that we use our mind for our purposes —or our minding uses us for its—the only answer we have for where man is going on his journey, and why, is that man is a creation of nature for putting questions to herself.

One of her eternal questions is, "Can it be done?" For man this question is posed not in terms of whether he can master nature, but whether he can master his own questioning nature, and especially his own strivings for mastery of nature. If he undertakes to find a "yes" for every "can it be done?" he is no longer serving but is contending with nature for primacy in creation. There can be no question about the outcome of that contention. For when man no longer serves nature's main purpose—the facilitation of life—he endangers not nature so much as he does himself. As E. S. Russell notes:

> . . . intelligence is only a means to life, not life itself. Instead of attempting to explain the "teleological" nature of organic activities in terms of concepts derived from man's knowledge of his own purposive activity, as do the mechanists and vitalists, we should take precisely the opposite view, and regard human purposive activities (including machine-making) and modes of thought as being a specialized development of the fundamental "purposiveness," or as I prefer to call it, the directiveness and creativeness of life.[5]

There is much truth in this view of man as a part of and an expression of the directiveness and creativeness of life itself. And there is also much wisdom in the Bhagavad-Gita, which says that action is the product of forces inherent in nature and that only the ignorant and egoistic person can say "I am the doer." But man always has some intelligence, and occasionally to a high degree. And intelligence has something to do with the ability to contemplate contradictions. The great contradiction in man's living is in his relation to life and to nature. And it is in encounters with that contradiction that man develops his intelligence as a matter of necessity.

That contradiction is posed today in terms of conflicts between "Eastern" and "Western," naturalistic and theologic, materialist and idealist points of view. But the contradiction will not be resolved by deciding that one or another view is the true one, nor by any kind of conquest of one by the other. Both are true and both are false. Man is at times united with nature in a unison of organism-environment integration, but at other times he experiences his separateness in organism-environment interactions, and both his absorption and his separateness terrify and exhilarate him.

His natural environment and human culture coerce and cajole him toward adaptation and conformity, but if he integrates too well and too long, his very self may dissolve. But he is also stimulated toward the exercise of his individuality and encouraged to nourish his individuation—to experience his "I" as distinct from his socially-generated "self." If, however, he continually separates himself by either "I, a stranger and afraid in a world I never made" or "I am the master of my fate" operations, he is threatened with isolation, disorientation, and detachment from his own self.

What man—especially generic, collective man as a species—

needs is a suprapersonal, even supranational, fitting-together capacity which is as useful for minding socio-political crises as the individual human brain can be for managing personal contradictions and ambiguities. Mankind has as yet only rudimentary foreshadowings of future fitting-together capacities for dealing with universal problems. In time, one hopes, a hierarchy of individual, group, regional, national, and international fitting-together arrangements will produce a capacity adequate for and suitable to mankind's needs. If so, this universal human fitting-together ability will be characterized, as is the individual's, by an indeterminacy of location of the "highest" or most "central" foci and frames of reference for organizing awareness and action.

Meanwhile, and even then perhaps, the being called man will all his life long continually confront himself with, and be confronted by, his two modes of being and becoming: the social and the personal—the one that makes him a living example of the similarities that unite him with his fellows, the other that makes him an example of living in accord with his differences and an example to his fellows.

The dysjunctive troubles of our proud and angry dust, of our two-sided brain's difficulty with a many-sided world, are from eternity and shall not fail, as Housman said. But human troubles go hand in hand with promises and opportunities. This is not mere optimism; it is the dysjunctive nature of man and his universe. Nor is it whistling in the dark to note that crises involve form as well as content, that the most intense and greatest crises are marked by the equal balance between danger and opportunity, peril and promise. The essence of crisis is a matching of contending forces and the equal probabilities of outcomes.

Human beings are wont, in their various languages, to ask only for "a fair shake," "an equal opportunity," or "a fifty-fifty chance." We feel fairly treated if the odds are not stacked against us. Thus, though we may indeed be in the midst of a great crisis about man's future course, or even his very survival, and though we may feel helpless in the face of the unthinkable, the unimaginable, and the impossible, we may be able to tolerate our mounting apprehension by reminding ourselves that the fact of the crisis guarantees us at least a fifty-fifty chance—and what more do we want?

What we always want, of course, is some relief from the indeterminacy and absolute uncertainty of a fifty-fifty situation. We reassure ourselves by delusional interpretations of history—if a coin has come up heads four times in a row, our concerns with continuity and change, and our bias against indeterminacy, make it seem unreasonable to assert that the chances of heads or tails on the fifth turn of the coin are still only, and exactly, fifty-fifty. Nevertheless, that is the nature of crisis. The chances, in terms of the contradictions and ambiguities that have culminated in and characterize the crisis, are indeed fifty-fifty. The difference, however, is that human beings and human society are not coins passively spinning in the air, tossed there by forces outside themselves. The feeling of giddiness induced at the onset of a crisis heralds the spinning around of the wheels of transpersonal fitting-together, the special modes of thinking in a crisis, by which contradictions and ambiguities are resolved and the odds altered one way or another. What we need is to let the fitting-together capacity of the human brain operate at least occasionally in freedom from the narrow, provincial, egoistic concerns of "I" and "Us." The essence of our contemporary crisis is simple: Most people in the world want to have modestly human food, shelter, and an opportunity to care decently for their children. The technological and material means for satisfaction of these wants exist. Not much of a "dream" is required to get it done. No longer will any conventional evasion or caricatured "solution" suffice. The only possible outcomes now are convulsive or creative. It all depends upon our commitment.

Notes

1. C. Judson Herrick, *George Ellett Coghill*. University of Chicago Press, 1949, p. 8.
2. Patrick Corbett, *Ideologies*. Hutchinson, London, 1965.
3. Harry Stack Sullivan, "The Illusion of Personal Individuality," paper read before the Society on the Theory of Personality, New York Academy of Medicine, May 3, 1944.
4. C. Judson Herrick, *The Brain of the Tiger Salamander*. University of Chicago Press, 1948.
5. E. S. Russell, *The Directiveness of Organic Activities*. Cambridge University Press, 1946.

BIBLIOGRAPHY

A brief list of reference sources cited in support of specific points throughout the text would fall far short of the actual bibliography from which I derived useful ideas and information. But trying to cite, at specific places in the text or in a general bibliography, every tributary source for one's work and thought would be an exercise in compulsive futility. Some compromise is necessary. The papers and books in this bibliography were chosen to provide entries into various relevant lines of work and thought, so that an interested reader pursuing a particular line of investigation could find additional references in the sources cited here.

Thus I found many stimulating ideas in Professor Hadley Cantril's *The "Why" of Man's Experience* and could have cited it, and several other somewhat similar works, at many places in the text. I have also read with interest S. L. Rubinstein's article, "Consciousness in the Light of Dialectical Materialism" (*Science and Society,* X, 252, 1946). This and other discussions of the relation between thought and action are cited in the bibliography to Chapter 5 of Professor Cantril's book. Almost all the sources listed in the following bibliography, therefore, will provide additional references for the interested reader.

Allport, Gordon W. *Becoming* (Terry Lectures). New Haven: Yale University Press, 1955.

Ames, Adelbert. "Architectural Form and Visual Sensations," in *Building for Modern Man,* edited by T. H. Creighton. Princeton, N. J.: Princeton University Press, 1949.

Andrew, Richard "The Situations That Evoke Vocalization in Primates," in *The Relatives of Man,* edited by Harold E. Whipple. *Annals of the New York Academy of Science,* 102: 181, 1962.

Arbib, Michael A. *Brains, Machines, and Mathematics.* New York: McGraw-Hill, 1964.

Arieti, Silvano. *Interpretation of Schizophrenia.* New York: Brunner, 1955.

Barker, Wayne, and Susan Barker. "Experimental Production of Human Convulsive Brain Potentials by Stress-Induced Effects Upon Neural Integrative Function Dynamics of the Convulsive Reaction to Stress." *Proceedings of the Association for Research in Nervous & Mental Disease,* XXIX, 90, 1950.

————, Susan Burgwin, and Donald J. Simons. "The Significance of 'Spontaneous' Abnormalities in Brain Wave Patterns as Observed During Interviews with Epileptic Patients." *Journal of Nervous and Mental Disease, 112:* 187, 1950.

————, and Stewart Wolf. "Experimental Production of *Grand Mal* Seizure During the Hypnoidal State Induced by Sodium Amytal." *American Journal of Medical Science, 214:* 600, 1947.

Beveridge, W. I. B. *The Art of Scientific Investigation.* New York: Random House, Vintage Books, 1961.

Birdwhistell, Ray L. "Paralanguage: 25 Years After Sapir," in *Lectures on Experimental Psychiatry,* edited by Henry W. Brosin. Pittsburgh, Pa.: University of Pittsburgh Press, 1961.

Blackburn, Thomas. *The Price of an Eye.* London: Longmans, 1961.

Bleuler, Eugen. "Autistic Thinking," in *Organization and Pathology of Thought,* edited by David Rapaport. New York: Columbia University Press, 1951.

Bodkin, M. *Archetypal Patterns in Poetry.* New York: Oxford University Press, 1934.

Bromberg, Walter. *The Mind of Man.* New York: Harper Colophon Books, 1963.

Brosin, Henry W., editor. *Lectures on Experimental Psychiatry.* Pittsburgh, Pa.: University of Pittsburgh Press, 1961.

Bruner, Jerome S., Jacqueline J. Goodnow, and George A. Austin. *A Study of Thinking.* New York: Wiley, 1957.

Bull, Nina. *The Attitude Theory of Emotion.* Nervous and Mental Disease Monographs, #81. New York: Coolidge Foundation, 1951.

Burgess, Anthony. *Tremor of Intent.* New York: W. W. Norton, 1966.

Burt, Sir Cyril. "The Structure of Mind." *British Journal of Educational Psychology,* Vol. XIX, 1949.

————. "The Concept of Consciousness." *British Journal of Psychology, 53:* 3, 1962.

Byrne, J. Grandson. *Studies on the Physiology of the Eye: Still Reaction, Sleep, Dreams, Hibernation, Repression, Hypnosis, Narcosis, Coma, and Allied Conditions.* London: H. K. Lewis & Co., 1942.

Cannon, Walter B. *Bodily Changes in Pain, Hunger, Fear and Rage.* New York: Appleton, 1927.

Cantril, Hadley. *The "Why" of Man's Experience.* New York: Macmillan, 1950.

Carpenter, Edward. "The Art of Creation," in *Men Who Have Walked with God.* Edited by Sheldon Cheney. New York: Knopf, 1948.

Cassirer, Ernst. *Language and Myth*, trans. by Susanne K. Langer. New York: Dover Books, 1946.

Cobb, Stanley. *Emotions and Clinical Medicine*. New York: W. W. Norton, 1950.

Coghill, George Ellett. *Anatomy and the Problem of Behavior*. Cambridge, England: Cambridge University Press, 1929.

Cole, Lawrence E. *Human Behavior: Psychology as a Bio-Social Science*. Yonkers, N.Y.: World Book, 1953.

Corbett, Patrick. *Ideologies*. London: Hutchinson & Co., 1965.

Cornelison, Floyd. Paper delivered at the December 1965 Philadelphia meetings of the American Medical Association.

Craig, Albert B., Jr. "Regulation of Respiration in Exercise and Breath Holding," in *Regulation of Respiration. Annals of the New York Academy of Science, 109:* 901, 1963.

Craik, K. W. J. *The Nature of Explanation*. Cambridge, England: Cambridge University Press, 1943.

Dale, H. H. "Accident and Opportunism in Medical Research." *British Medical Journal*, September 4, 1948.

Darwin, Charles R. *The Expression of the Emotions in Man and Animals*. London: J. Murray, 1872; New York: Appleton, 1924.

Davy, Charles. *Words in the Mind*. London: Chatto & Windus, 1965; Cambridge, Mass.: Harvard University Press, 1965.

———. *Towards a Third Culture*. London: Faber, 1961.

Dewey, John. *How We Think*. Boston: D. C. Heath, 1910.

Dickinson, Emily, quoted by Martha Gilbert Dickinson Bianchi in *Life and Letters of Emily Dickinson*. Boston: Houghton, 1924.

Eckermann, John Peter. *Conversations with Goethe*, trans. by John Oxenford. New York: Dutton, Everyman's Library.

Ehrenwald, Jan. *Telepathy and Medical Psychology*. New York: W. W. Norton, 1948.

Erickson, Milton. "Experimental Demonstrations of the Psychopathology of Everyday Life." *Psychoanalytic Quarterly, 8:* 338, 1939.

Farber, S. M. and R. H. L. Wilson, editors. *Control of the Mind*. London: McGraw-Hill, 1961.

Fenichel, Otto. *Problems of Psychoanalytic Technique*. Albany, N.Y.: *Psychoanalytic Quarterly* monograph, 1959.

Fisher, Charles. "Dreams, Images, and Perceptions." *Journal of the American Psychoanalytic Association, 4:* 5, 1956.

Foxe, Arthur N. "Antisocial Aspects of Epilepsy," in *Epilepsy*, edited by Paul H. Hoch and Robert P. Knight. New York: Grune & Stratton, 1947.

Fremont-Smith, Frank. "The Influence of Emotion in Precipitating Convulsions." *American Journal of Psychiatry, 13:* 717, 1934.

———. "The Influence of Emotional Factors upon Physiological and Pathological Process." *Bulletin of the New York Academy of Medicine, 15:* 560, 1939.

Fromm, Erich. *The Forgotten Language*. New York: Rinehart, 1951.

Fulton, John F. "Clifford Allbutt's Description of Psychomotor Seizures." *Journal of the History of Medicine, 12:* 75, 1957.

Galton, Sir Francis. *Inquiries into Human Faculties.* New York: Dutton, 1928.

Gerard, Ralph W. "The Biological Basis of Imagination." *Scientific Monthly,* June 1946.

———. "The Architecture of Knowledge and Neural Functions," in *Lectures on Experimental Psychiatry,* edited by Henry W. Brosin. Pittsburgh, Pa.: University of Pittsburgh Press, 1961.

Ghiselin, Brewster. *The Creative Process.* Berkeley: University of California Press, 1952.

Gibbs, Frederick L., and Erna L. Gibbs. *Atlas of Electroencephalography.* Cambridge, Mass.: Addison-Wesley Press, 1952.

Goffman, Erving. *Interaction Ritual.* New York: Doubleday Anchor Books, 1967.

Gold, H. L. Editorial, "How Now, Gray Cell?" *Galaxy.* December 1955.

Golding, William. *The Hot Gates and Other Occasional Pieces.* New York: Harcourt, Brace & World, 1965.

Goldman-Eisler, Frieda. "Hesitation, Information, and Levels of Speech Production," in *Disorders of Language,* edited by A. V. S. de Reuck and Maeve O'Connor. London: J. A. Churchill, 1964.

Goldwater, Robert, and Marco Treves, editors. *Artists on Art.* New York: Pantheon, 1947.

Gombrich, E. H. "Meditations on a Hobby Horse, or the Roots of Esthetic Form," in *Aspects of Form,* edited by L. L. Whyte. New York: Pellegrini and Cudahy, 1948.

———. *Art and Illusion.* London: Phaidon Press, 1962.

Gowers, W. R. *Epilepsy.* American Academy of Neurology Reprint Series, Vol. I. New York: Dover Books, 1964.

Graves, Robert. *Poetic Unreason.* London: Cecil Palmer, 1925.

Grinker, Roy R. *Psychosomatic Research.* New York: Grove Press, 1961.

Grotjahn, Martin. *Beyond Laughter.* New York: McGraw-Hill, 1957.

Hadamard, Jacques. *The Psychology of Invention in the Mathematical Field.* New York: Dover Books, 1945.

Hall, Edward T. *The Hidden Dimension.* Garden City: Doubleday, 1966.

———. *The Silent Language.* Garden City: Doubleday, 1959.

Halstead, Ward C. *Brain and Intelligence.* Chicago, Ill.: University of Chicago Press, 1947.

Hamill, Ralph C. "*Petit Mal* in Children." *American Journal of Psychiatry, 93:* 303, 1946.

Hanson, N. R. *Patterns of Discovery.* Cambridge, England: Cambridge University Press, 1961.

Harding, Rosamund E. M. *An Anatomy of Inspiration.* Cambridge, England: W. Heffer & Sons, 1942.

Hayes, Capt. M. Horace. *Veterinary Notes for Horse Owners.* 15th ed., revised by J. F. Donald Tutt. London: Stanley Paul, 1964.

Hebb, D. O. *The Organization of Behavior*. New York: J. Wiley & Sons, 1949.

Hendricks, Ives C. "Psychoanalytic Observations on the Aura of Two Cases with Convulsions." *Psychosomatic Medicine*, 2: 43, 1940.

Herrick, C. Judson. *The Brain of the Tiger Salamander*. Chicago Ill.: University of Chicago Press, 1948.

————. *George Ellett Coghill*. Chicago, Ill.: University of Chicago Press, 1949.

Hilgard, E. R. *Theories of Learning*. London: Methuen, 1958.

Hill, Dennis, and Geoffrey Parr, editors. *Electroencephalography*. New York: Macmillan, 1963.

Holt, John. *How Children Fail*. New York: Pitman, 1964.

————. *How Children Learn*, New York: Pitman, 1967.

Horwitz, Murray, David C. Glass, and Agnes M. Niyekawa. "Muscular Tension: Physiological Activation or Psychological Act," in *Psychobiological Approaches to Social Behavior*, edited by P. Herbert Leiderman and David Shapiro. London: Tavistock, 1965.

Housman, A. E. *The Name and Nature of Poetry*. New York: Macmillan, 1933.

Howes, D. H. "Application of the Word-Frequency Concept to Aphasia," in *Disorders of Language*, edited by A. V. S. de Reuck and Maeve O'Connor. London: J. A. Churchill, Ltd., 1964.

Hull, Clark. *Hypnosis and Suggestibility: An Experimental Approach*. New York: Appleton-Century-Crofts, 1933.

Huxley, Aldous. *The Doors of Perception*, and *Heaven and Hell*. New York: Harper Colophon Books, 1963.

Jackson, John Hughlings. *Selected Writings of John Hughlings Jackson*, edited by James Taylor. London: Hodder & Stoughton, 1931; New York: Basic Books, 1958.

James, Henry. "The American," in *John Livingston Lowes*. Boston: Houghton Mifflin, 1927.

James, William. *The Principles of Psychology*. New York: Henry Holt, 1890.

————. *The Energies of Men*. New York: Dodd, Mead, 1926.

Keller, Helen. *The Story of My Life*. New York: Doubleday, 1959.

Kasanin, J. S., editor. *Language and Thought in Schizophrenia: Collected Papers*. Berkley: University of California Press, 1944.

Kiloh, L. G., and J. W. Osselton. *Clinical Electroencephalography*. London: Butterworths, 1961.

Kipling, Rudyard. *Something of Myself*. New York: Doubleday, Doran, 1937.

Koestler, Arthur. *The Act of Creation*. London: Hutchinson, 1964; New York: Macmillan, 1964.

Köhler, Wolfgang. *The Mentality of Apes*. London: Pelican Books, 1957.

Kroger, William S. *Clinical and Experimental Hypnosis*. Philadelphia, Pa.: Lippincott, 1963.

Kubie, Lawrence S. "The Relationship of Symbolic Function in Language Formation and in Neurosis." Transcript of the Seventh Conference on Cybernetics, edited by Heinz von Foerster. New York: Josiah Macy, Jr., Foundation, 1950.

————, and M. H. Erickson. "The Use of Automatic Drawing in the Interpretation and Relief of a State of Acute Obsessional Depression." *Psychoanalytic Quarterly,* 7: 443, 1938.

————. "Neurotic Distortion of the Creative Process." Porter Lecture Series 22. Laurence, Kan.: University of Kansas Press, 1958; New York: Farrar, Strauss and Giroux, 1967.

Laing, R. D. *The Divided Self.* London: Penguin Books, 1965.

Langer, Susanne K. *Philosophy in a New Key.* Cambridge, Mass.: Harvard University Press, 1942.

————. *Feeling and Form.* New York: Scribners, 1953.

Lashley, Karl S. "The Problem of Serial Order in Behavior," in *Cerebral Mechanisms in Behavior,* edited by Lloyd A. Jeffress. New York: John Wiley & Sons, 1951.

————. *The Neuro-Psychology of Lashley.* New York: McGraw-Hill, 1960.

Levitt, Eugene E. *The Psychology of Anxiety.* New York: Bobbs-Merrill, 1967.

Lewis, Cecil Day. *The Poetic Image.* London: Cape, 1947.

Liddell, Howard S. "Contributions of Conditioning in the Sheep and Goat to an Understanding of Stress, Anxiety, and Illness," in *Lectures on Experimental Psychiatry,* edited by Henry W. Brosin. Pittsburgh, Pa.: University of Pittsburgh Press, 1961.

Lilly, John. *Mental Effects of Reduction of Ordinary Levels of Physical Stimuli on Intact, Healthy Persons.* Psychiatric Research Reports #5. American Psychiatric Association, June 1956.

Loeb, Jacques. *Forced Movement, Tropisms, and Animal Conduct.* Philadelphia, Pa.: Lippincott, 1918.

Lorenz, Konrad. *Man Meets Dog.* New York: Houghton Mifflin, 1955.

Lowell, Amy. *Poetry and Poets.* Boston: Houghton Mifflin, 1930.

Lowes, John Livingston. *The Road to Xanadu: A Study in the Ways of the Imagination.* Boston: Houghton Mifflin, 1927.

Luria, A. R. *The Nature of Human Conflicts.* New York: Liveright, 1932.

————. "Factors and Forms of Aphasia," in *Disorders of Language,* edited by A. V. S. de Reuck and Maeve O'Connor. London: J. A. Churchill, Ltd., 1964.

Maslow, A. H. "Self-Actualizing People: A Study of Psychological Health," in *The Self, Explorations in Personal Growth,* edited by Clark E. Moustakas. New York: Harper & Bros., 1956.

May, Rollo. *The Meaning of Anxiety.* New York: Ronald Press, 1950.

McCulloch, Warren S. *Finality and Form.* Springfield, Ill.: Charles C. Thomas, 1952.

————. "Where Is Fancy Bred?" in *Lectures on Experimental Psy-*

chiatry, edited by Henry W. Brosin. Pittsburgh, Pa.: University of Pittsburgh Press, 1961.

——, and Walter Pitts. "How We Know Universals." *Bulletin of Mathematical Biophysics, 9:* 127, 1947.

McKellar, Peter. *Imagination and Thinking.* New York: Basic Books, Inc., 1957.

McLuhan, Marshall. *The Gutenberg Galaxy.* London: Routledge & Kegan Paul, 1962; Toronto: University of Toronto Press, 1962.

Mead, George Herbert. *On Social Psychology.* Selected papers, edited by Anselm Strauss. Chicago, Ill.: University of Chicago Press, 1964.

Meyer, Leonard B. *Emotion and Meaning in Music.* Chicago, Ill.: University of Chicago Press, 1961.

Miller, G. A., E. Galanter, and K. H. Pribram. *Plans and the Structure of Behavior.* New York: Holt, 1960.

Miller, James G. *Unconsciousness.* New York: Wiley, 1942.

Montmasson, J. M. *Invention and the Unconscious.* London: Kegan Paul, 1931.

Mozart, Wolfgang Amadeus. In Jacques Hadamard, *The Psychology of Invention in the Mathematical Field.* New York: Dover Books, 1945.

Murphy, Gardner. *Personality: A Biosocial Approach to Origins and Structure.* New York: Harper & Bros., 1947.

Nkosi, Lewis. *Home and Exile.* London: Longmans, 1964.

Orne, Marvin T. "Implications for Psychotherapy Derived from Current Research on the Nature of Hypnosis." *American Journal of Psychiatry 118:* 1097, 1962.

Pearce, Jane, and Saul Newton. *Conditions of Human Growth.* New York: Citadel, 1963.

Penfield, Wilder, and Theodore Rasmussen. *The Cerebral Cortex of Man.* New York: Macmillan, 1950.

——, and L. Roberts. *Speech and Brain Mechanisms.* Princeton, N.J.: Princeton University Press, 1959.

Pfeiffer, John. *The Human Brain.* New York: Harper & Bros., 1955.

Piéron, Henri. "L'Immobilité Protectrice Chez les Animaux." *Revue Scientifique,* Série 1, 1904.

Poe, Edgar Allen. *Poe's Complete Poetical Works, with Three Essays on Poetry,* edited by R. Brimley Johnson. New York: Oxford University Press, 1909.

Platt, W., and R. A. Baker. "The Relationship of the Scientific Hunch to Research." *Journal of Chemical Education, 8:* 1969, 1931.

Poincaré, Henri. *Science and Method.* New York: Dover Books, 1952.

——. "Mathematical Creation," in *The Foudations of Science,* trans. by George Bruce Halstead. Lancaster, Pa.: The Science Press, 1915. First printed as *Science et Méthode.* Paris: Ernest Flammarion, 1908.

Prince, Morton. *Hypnotherapy, A Survey of the Literature,* edited by Margaret Brenman and Morton Gill. New York: International Universities Press, 1947.

Rapaport, David, editor. *Organization and Pathology of Thought.* New York: Columbia University Press, 1951.

Read, Herbert. *Collected Essays in Literary Criticism.* London: Faber, 1938.

Reik, Theodore. *The Secret Self.* New York: Farrar, Straus & Young, 1953.

————. *Surprise and the Psychoanalyst.* New York: E. P. Dutton, 1937.

Reuck, A. V. S. de, and Maeve O'Connor, editors. *Disorders of Language.* London, J. A. Churchill, Ltd., 1964.

Richards, I. A. *Science and Poetry.* London: Kegan Paul, 1926.

Roedelberger, Franz A., and Vera I. Groschoff. *African Wildlife,* trans. by Nieter O'Leary and Pamela Paulet. London: Constable & Co., 1964. New York: Viking Press, 1965.

Rosenblueth, A., Norbert Wiener, and J. Bigelow. "Behavior, Purpose, and Teleology." *Philosophy of Science, 10:* 8, 1943.

Rugg, Harold. *Imagination.* New York: Harper & Row, 1963.

Russell, E. S. *The Directiveness of Organic Activities.* Cambridge, England: Cambridge University Press, 1946.

Saparina, Yelena. *Cybernetics Within Us.* Hollywood, Calif.: Wilshire, 1967.

Saporta, Sol, editor. *Psycholinguistics.* New York: Holt, Rinehart and Winston, 1961.

Schacter, Stanley. "The Interaction of Cognitive and Physiological Determinants of Emotional State," in *Psychobiological Approaches to Social Behavior,* edited by P. Herbert Leiderman and David Shapiro. London: Tavistock Publications, 1965.

Schilder, Paul. *Image and Appearance of the Human Body.* London: Kegan Paul, Trench, Trubner & Co., Psyche Monographs, 1935.

Schmitt, F. O., editor. *Macromolecular Specificity and Biological Memory.* Cambridge, Mass.: Massachusetts Institute of Technology Press, 1962.

Schulz, Charles M. *But We Love You, Charlie Brown.* New York: Holt, Rinehart & Winston, 1959.

Scott, John Paul. *Animal Behavior.* New York: Doubleday Anchor Books, The Natural History Library, 1963.

Seeley, John. *The Americanization of the Unconscious.* New York: International Science Press, 1967.

Sherrington, Sir Charles. *Man on His Nature.* New York: Doubleday Anchor Books, 1953.

Shumaker, Wayne. *Literature and the Irrational.* Englewood Cliffs, N.J.: Prentice-Hall, Inc., 1960.

Silberer, Hans. "Reports on a Method of Eliciting and Observing Certain Symbolic Hallucination Phenomena," in *Organization and Pathology of Thought,* edited by David Rapaport. New York: Columbia University Press, 1951.

Sinnott, Edmund W. *Cell and Psyche: The Biology of Purpose.* Chapel Hill: University of North Carolina Press, 1950.

Skinner, B. F. *Science and Human Behavior*. New York: Macmillan, 1953.

Sluckin, W. *Minds and Machines*. London: Penguin Books, 1954.

Spearman, C. *Creative Mind*. Cambridge, England: Cambridge University Press, 1930.

Spencer, Herbert. *Principles of Psychology*. London: Williams & Williams, 1871.

Stekel, Wilhelm. "The Polyphony of Thought," in David Rapaport, *Organization and Pathology of Thought*. New York: Columbia University Press, 1951.

Sullivan, Harry Stack. *The Interpersonal Theory of Psychiatry*, edited by Helen Swick Perry and Mabel Blake Cohen. New York: W. W. Norton, 1953.

Sully, J. *An Essay on Laughter*. London: Longmans, Green, 1902.

Suzuki, D. T. *Zen and Japanese Culture*. London: Luzac, 1959.

Taton, R. *Reason and Chance in Scientific Discovery*. London: Hutchinson, 1957.

Temkin, Oswei. *The Falling Sickness*. Baltimore, Md.: Johns Hopkins Press, 1945.

Thorpe, W. H., and O. L. Zangwill. *Current Problems of Animal Behavior*. Cambridge, England: Cambridge University Press, 1961.

Tinbergen, N. *Social Behavior in Animals*. London: Methuen, 1953.

Valéry, Paul. "The Problems of Poetry," in *Paul Valéry: The Art of Poetry*, Vol. VII of *The Collected Works of Paul Valéry*, edited by Jackson Matthews. London: Bollingen Foundation, Routledge, 1958.

Viereck, Peter. "Russia's Conspiracy of Feelings." *Mount Holyoke Alumnae Quarterly*, XLIX (fall 1965).

Wallas, Graham. *The Art of Thought*. New York: Harcourt Brace, 1926.

Walter, W. Grey. "Activity Patterns in the Human Brain," in *Aspects of Form*, edited by L. L. Whyte. New York: Pellegrini and Cudahy, 1951.

————. *The Living Brain*. New York: W. W. Norton, 1953.

————. "Where Vital Things Happen" (Adolph Meyer Research Lecture). *American Journal of Psychiatry*, *116:* 673, 1960.

Warcollier, René. *Mind to Mind*, edited by Emanuel K. Schwartz. New York: Creative Age Press, 1948.

Watts, Alan W. *Psychotherapy East and West*. New York: Pantheon Books, 1961.

Weiss, Paul. *Genetic Neurology*. Chicago, Ill.: University of Chicago Press, 1950.

Weitzenhoffer, André. *Hypnotism*. New York: Wiley, 1953.

Wertham, Fredric. *The Show of Violence*. New York: Bantam Books, 1967.

Wertheimer, Max. *Productive Thinking*. New York: Harper & Bros., 1945.

White, Leslie A. *The Science of Culture*. New York: Grove Press, 1958.

————. "Mind is Minding." *Scientific Monthly*, *48:* 169, 1939.

Whitehead, Alfred North. *Science and the Modern World*. Cambridge, England: Cambridge University Press, 1953.

Whyte, L. L. *The Unconscious Before Freud*. New York: Doubleday Anchor Books, 1962.

————, editor. *Aspects of Form: A Symposium on Form in Nature and Art*. New York: Pellegrini and Cudahy, 1951.

Wiener, Norbert. *Cybernetics, or Control and Communication in the Animal and the Machine*. New York: Wiley, 1948.

————. *The Human Use of Human Beings, Cybernetics and Society*. Boston; Houghton Mifflin, 1950.

Wilson, S. A. Kinnier. *Modern Problems in Neurology*. London: Edward Arnold & Co., 1928.

Wolberg, Louis R. *Hypnoanalysis*. New York: Grune & Stratton, 1945.

Wolff, Harold G. "Protective Reaction Patterns and Disease." *Annals of Internal Medicine*, 27: 944, 1947.

————. "Life Stress and Bodily Disease—a Formulation," in *Life Stress and Bodily Disease*. New York: *Publications of the Association for Research in Nervous & Mental Disease*, Vol. XXIX, 1950.

Wooldridge, Dean E. *The Machinery of the Brain*. New York: McGraw-Hill, 1963.

Yakovlev, Paul I. "Motivity, Behavior, and the Brain." *Journal of Nervous and Mental Disease*, 107: 313, 1948.

Yeats, William Butler. *Essays and Introductions*. New York: Macmillan, 1961.

INDEX

INDEX